Adjust
related

Rubber band

Rod coor

$a = r\theta$

$V + \sigma$

Tue/19, 2-4;30

PLANE TRIGONOMETRY

Plane Trigonometry

E. RICHARD HEINEMAN

Professor of Mathematics
Texas Technological College

SECOND EDITION

McGRAW-HILL BOOK COMPANY, INC.

New York   Toronto   London

1956

PLANE TRIGONOMETRY

Copyright © 1956 by the McGraw-Hill Book Company, Inc.

Library of Congress Catalog Card Number 55–12100

VIII

PREFACE

The principal objective of the author in writing the second edition of PLANE TRIGONOMETRY has been teachability. The book should prove especially beneficial to students who have a weak mathematical background and to those who have not yet acquired the habit of orderly and independent thinking.

Instructors can save time in making problem selections by noticing the first two following features: *

1. The problems in each exercise are so arranged that by assigning numbers 1, 5, 9, etc., or similar sets beginning with 2, 3, or 4, the instructor can obtain balanced coverage of all points involved without undue emphasis on some principles at the expense of others. For example, in the solution of right triangles without logarithms in Exercise 11, each of the four sets of problems includes problems involving the use of the sine, the cosine, and the tangent; each set contains problems involving the angle of elevation, the angle of depression, and the concept of bearing; each set contains approximately the same number of problems in which the unknown is an acute angle (or a leg, or the hypotenuse). This does not mean that the problem lists consist of sets of four problems that are identical except for numerical quantities. Wherever possible, the author has tried to make each problem different in some way, other than numerically, from all other problems in that exercise.

2. Answers to three-fourths of the problems are given in the back of the book. No answers are given, either in the text or in separate pamphlet form, for problems numbered 4, 8, 12, etc.

Completely new problem lists appear in this edition. The number of stated problems has been increased appreciably. Only minor changes have been made in the discussions and illustrative examples. Additional features retained from the first edition (1942) include:

3. Many of the exercises contain true-false questions to test the student's ability to avoid pitfalls and to detect camouflaged truths. An effort has been made to thwart the development of such false notions as "In logarithms, division is replaced by subtraction" and "To find the square root of a number, divide its logarithm by 2." The duty of the

---

* These features also appear in the Alternate Edition (1950), which remains in print.

instructor is, not only to teach correct methods, but also to convince the student of the error in the false methods.

4. The memory work has been reduced to a bare minimum. All unnecessary formulas and concepts have been deliberately omitted. Some of these are cologarithms, confusing reduction formulas, the "fourth" property of logarithms, and formulas for cot $(A + B)$ and cot $(A - B)$.

5. The new characteristic rule for logarithms has been proved by classroom experiment to be effective, especially in finding a number from its logarithm. Instructors who prefer the old rule will find it listed as an alternative.

6. Definite instructions are given for proving identities and solving trigonometric equations. The subject of identities is approached gradually with practice in algebraic operations with the trigonometric functions.

7. A careful explanation of approximations and significant figures is given early in the text. The principle of accuracy in figures is adhered to tenaciously throughout the book. The answers to computation problems are given with no more accuracy than is justified by the given data.

8. All problem sets are carefully graded and contain an abundance of simple problems that involve nothing more than the principles being discussed. The first half of each set of computation problems requires no interpolation. This enables the student to concentrate on the new concepts without being burdened with confusing interpolations.

9. Miscellaneous points include (a) interesting applied problems, (b) problems that are encountered in calculus, (c) a careful explanation of the concept of infinity, (d) memory schemes, (e) the uses of the sine and cosine curves, and (f) a note to the student.

For the convenience of teachers, brief outlines for two-semester-hour and three-semester-hour courses are given.

Two-semester-hour Course of 30 Lessons
(Allowing 3 hours for quizzes)

Chapter	1	2	3	4	5	6	7	8	9	10	11	12
Number of Lessons	3	4	$2\frac{1}{2}$	1	$1\frac{1}{2}$	1	3	1	4	$1\frac{1}{2}$	$3\frac{1}{2}$	1

Three-semester-hour Course of 45 Lessons
(Allowing 5 hours for examinations)

Chapter	1	2	3	4	5	6	7	8	9	10	11	12
Number of Lessons	4	4	4	2	2	2	5	2	6	2	5	2

The author wishes to thank The Macmillan Company for permission to use passages from his *College Algebra* (New York, 1947).

E. Richard Heineman

CONTENTS

NOTE TO THE STUDENT

A mastery of the subject of trigonometry requires (1) a certain amount of memory work and (2) a great deal of practice and drill in order to acquire experience and skill in the application of the memory work. Your instructor is a "trouble-shooter" who attempts to prevent you from going astray, supplies missing links in your mathematical background, and tries to indicate the "common sense" approach to the problem. The memory work in any course is one thing that the student can and should perform by himself. The least you can do for your instructor and yourself is to *commit to memory each definition and theorem as soon as you contact it*. This can be accomplished most rapidly, not by reading, but by writing the definition or theorem until you can reproduce it without the aid of the text.

In working the problems, do not continually refer back to the illustrative examples. Study the examples so thoroughly (by writing them) that you can reproduce them with your text closed. Only after the examples are entirely clear and have been completely mastered should you attempt the unsolved problems. These problems should be worked *without referring to the text*.

GREEK ALPHABET

Alpha	A, α	Nu	N, ν
Beta	B, β	Xi	Ξ, ξ
Gamma	Γ, γ	Omicron	O, o
Delta	Δ, δ	Pi	Π, π
Epsilon	E, ϵ	Rho	P, ρ
Zeta	Z, ζ	Sigma	Σ, σ, s
Eta	H, η	Tau	T, τ
Theta	Θ, θ	Upsilon	Υ, υ
Iota	I, ι	Phi	Φ, ϕ
Kappa	K, κ	Chi	X, χ
Lambda	Λ, λ	Psi	Ψ, ψ
Mu	M, μ	Omega	Ω, ω

REFERENCE MATERIAL FROM PLANE GEOMETRY

1. Two angles are said to be *complementary* if their sum is 90°.

2. Two angles are said to be *supplementary* if their sum is 180°.

3. The sum of the three angles of a triangle is 180°.

4. In a right triangle, the sides that form the right angle are called the *legs*; the side opposite the right angle is called the *hypotenuse*.

5. Pythagorean theorem: *The square of the hypotenuse of a right triangle equals the sum of the squares of its legs.*

6. In a right triangle with angles 30°, 60°, 90°, the hypotenuse is twice the shorter leg.

7. An *isosceles* triangle has two equal sides, and hence two equal angles.

8. An *equilateral* triangle has three equal sides. Each angle is 60°.

9. A tangent line to a circle is perpendicular to the radius drawn to the point of tangency.

10. If two triangles have the three angles of one equal respectively to the three angles of the other, the triangles are similar and their corresponding sides are proportional.

CHAPTER 1

THE TRIGONOMETRIC FUNCTIONS

1. Trigonometry. Trigonometry is that branch of mathematics which deals primarily with six ratios called the trigonometric functions. These ratios are important for two reasons. First, they are the basis of a theory which is used in other branches of mathematics as well as in physics and engineering. Second, they are used in solving triangles. From geometry we recall that two sides and the included angle of a triangle suffice to fix its size and shape. It will be shown later that the length of the third side and the size of the remaining angles can be computed by means of trigonometry.

2. Directed segments. A directed line is a line upon which one direction is considered positive; the other, negative. Thus in Fig. 1 the arrowhead indicates that all segments measured from

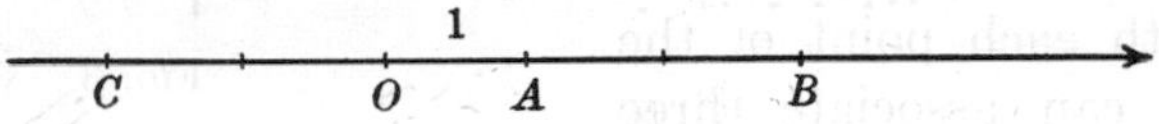

FIG. 1

left to right are positive. Hence if $OA = 1$ unit of length, then $OB = 3$, and $BC = -5$. Observe that since the line is directed, CB is not equal to BC. However, $BC = -CB$; or $CB = -BC$. Also note that $OB + BC + CO = 0$.

3. The rectangular coordinate system. A rectangular (or Cartesian) coordinate system consists of two perpendicular *directed* lines. It is conventional to draw and direct these lines as in Fig. 2. The **x-axis** and the **y-axis** are called the **coordinate axes;** their intersection O is called the **origin.** The position of any point in the plane is fixed by its distances from the axes.

The x-coordinate * (or x) *of point P is the directed segment NP* (or OM) *measured from the y-axis to point P. The y-coordinate* *

* The x-coordinate and y-coordinate are also called the *abscissa* and *ordinate*, respectively.

1

(or y) *of point* P *is the directed segment* MP, *measured from the* x-*axis to point* P. It is necessary to remember that each coordinate is measured *from axis to point*. Thus the x of P is NP (not PN); the y of P is MP (not PM). The point P, with x-coordinate x and y-coordinate y, is denoted by $P(x, y)$. It follows that the x of any point to the right of the y-axis is positive; to the left, negative. Also the y of any point above the x-axis is positive; below, negative.

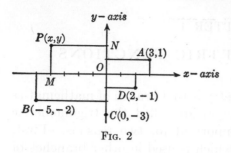

Fig. 2

To **plot** a point means to locate and indicate its position on a coordinate system. Several points are plotted in Fig. 2.

The distance from the origin O to point P is called the **radius vector** (or r) of P. This distance r is not directed and *is always positive* by agreement. Hence with each point of the plane we can associate three

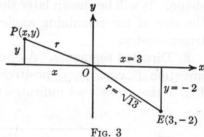

Fig. 3

coordinates: x, y, and r. The radius vector r can be found by using the Pythagorean * relation $x^2 + y^2 = r^2$.

Quadrant II	Quadrant I
$x = -$	$x = +$
$y = +$	$y = +$
Quadrant III	Quadrant IV
$x = -$	$x = +$
$y = -$	$y = -$

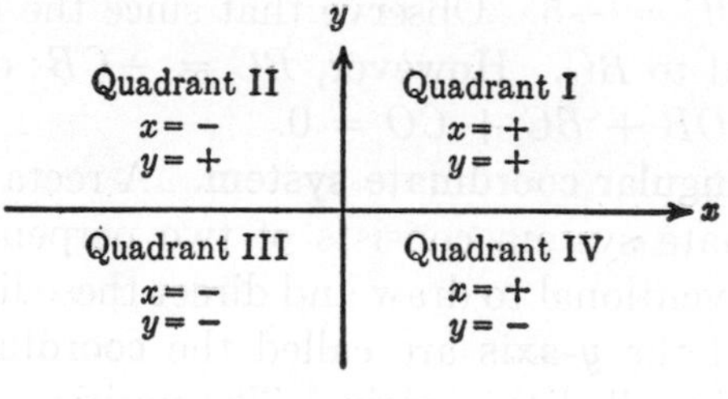

Fig. 4

The coordinate axes divide the plane into four parts called **quadrants** as indicated in Fig. 4.

* Pythagorean theorem: *The square of the hypotenuse of a right triangle equals the sum of the squares of its legs.*

Illustration 1. To find r for the point $(5, -12)$, use

$$r^2 = 5^2 + (-12)^2 = 169, \qquad r = 13.$$

Illustration 2. If $x = 15$ and $r = 17$, we obtain y by using

$$x^2 + y^2 = r^2.$$

Hence $(15)^2 + y^2 = (17)^2$; $225 + y^2 = 289$; $y^2 = 64$; $y = \pm 8$. If the point is in quadrant I, $y = 8$; if the point is in quadrant IV, $y = -8$. (Since x is positive, the point cannot lie in either quadrant II or quadrant III.)

EXERCISE 1

1. Plot on coordinate paper and then find the value of r for each of the following points: $(4, -3)$, $(-8, 0)$, $(-2, -7)$, $(\sqrt{13}, \sqrt{3})$.

2. Plot on coordinate paper and then find the value of r: $(15, 8)$, $(0, -3)$, $(-1, 2)$, $(\sqrt{7}, -\sqrt{2})$.

3. Plot on coordinate paper and then find the value of r: $(-12, 5)$, $(6, 0)$, $(3, 2)$, $(-5, -\sqrt{11})$.

4. Plot on coordinate paper and then find the value of r: $(-8, -6)$, $(0, 2)$, $(5, -6)$, $(-2, \sqrt{21})$.

5. Use the Pythagorean theorem to find the missing coordinate and then plot the point:

    (a) $y = 15$, $r = 17$, point is in Q II.*
    (b) $x = 8$, $r = 9$, point is in Q I.
    (c) $x = 0$, $r = 4$, y is negative.

6. Find the missing coordinate and then plot the point:

    (a) $x = -3$, $r = 5$, point is in Q III.
    (b) $y = -1$, $r = \sqrt{10}$, point is in Q IV.
    (c) $y = 0$, $r = 2$, x is negative.

7. Find the missing coordinate and then plot the point:

    (a) $x = 7$, $r = 25$, point is in Q IV.
    (b) $y = 5$, $r = 7$, point is in Q II.
    (c) $y = -9$, $r = 9$.

8. Find the missing coordinate and then plot the point:

    (a) $y = 12$, $r = 13$, point is in Q I.
    (b) $x = -6$, $r = 7$, point is in Q III.
    (c) $x = -7$, $r = 7$.

9. In which quadrants is the following ratio positive?

    (a) $\dfrac{y}{r}$. (b) $\dfrac{x}{r}$. (c) $\dfrac{y}{x}$.

10. In which quadrants is the following ratio negative?

    (a) $\dfrac{y}{r}$. (b) $\dfrac{x}{r}$. (c) $\dfrac{y}{x}$.

11. What is the x of all points on the y-axis? What is the y of all points on the x-axis?

* Q II means quadrant II.

4. Trigonometric angles. In geometry an angle was thought of as the "opening" between two lines. *A trigonometric angle is an amount of rotation required to move a line from one position to another.* A *positive* angle is generated by *counterclockwise* rota-

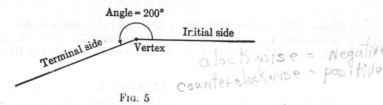

Angle = 200°

Initial side

Terminal side   Vertex

clockwise = Negative
counterclockwise = positive

Fig. 5

tion; a *negative* angle, by *clockwise* rotation. Figure 5 illustrates the terms used and shows an angle of 200°. Figure 6 shows angles of 500° and −420°. The −420° angle may be thought of as the amount of rotation effected by the minute hand of a clock be-

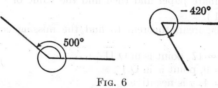

500°   −420°

Fig. 6

between 12:15 and 1:25. *To draw a trigonometric angle, we need, in addition to its sides, a curved arrow extending from its initial side to its terminal side.*

5. Standard position of an angle. *An angle is said to be in standard position if its vertex is at the origin and its initial side coincides with the positive x-axis.* An angle is said to be in a certain quadrant if its terminal side lies in that quadrant *when the angle is in standard position.* For example, 600° is in the third quadrant; or, −70° is a fourth-quadrant angle.

Angles are said to be **coterminal** if their terminal sides coincide when the angles are in standard position. For example, 200°, 560°, −160° are coterminal angles. From a trigonometric viewpoint these angles are not equal; they are merely coterminal.

EXERCISE 2

Place each of the following angles in standard position; draw a curved arrow to indicate the rotation. Draw and find the size of two other angles, one positive and one negative, that are coterminal with the given angle.

1. 405°.   **2.** 260°.   **3.** 100°.   **4.** 340°.
5. 200°.   **6.** 150°.   **7.** 300°.   **8.** 440°.

Each of the following points is on the terminal side of a positive angle in standard position. Plot the point; draw the terminal side of the angle; indicate the angle by a curved arrow; use a protractor to find to the nearest degree the size of the angle.

9. (−3, 5).   **10.** (2, −2).   **11.** (5, 4).   **12.** (−7, −3).
13. (4, −1).   **14.** (1, 7).   **15.** (−2, −3).   **16.** (−9, 4).

17. A flywheel makes 1200 revolutions per minute. Through how many degrees does it move in one second?

6. Definitions of the trigonometric functions of a general angle. The whole subject of trigonometry is based upon the six **trigonometric functions.** The names of these functions, with their abbreviations in parentheses, are: sine **(sin)**, cosine **(cos)**, tangent **(tan)**, cotangent **(cot)**, secant **(sec)**, cosecant **(csc)**. In a certain sense, the following definitions are the most important in this book.

A COMPLETE DEFINITION OF THE TRIGONOMETRIC FUNCTIONS OF ANY ANGLE θ

1. Place the angle θ * in standard position.
2. Choose any point P on the terminal side of θ.
3. Drop a perpendicular from P to the x-axis, thus forming a triangle of reference for θ.
4. The point P has three coordinates x, y, r, in terms of which we define the following trigonometric functions:

$$\sin \theta = \frac{y}{r},$$

$$\cos \theta = \frac{x}{r},$$

$$\tan \theta = \frac{y}{x},$$

$$\cot \theta = \frac{x}{y},$$

$$\sec \theta = \frac{r}{x},$$

$$\csc \theta = \frac{r}{y}.$$

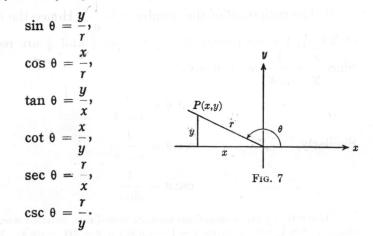

Fig. 7

* See Greek alphabet opposite p. 1.

A function of θ is a quantity whose value can be determined whenever a value is assigned to θ. For example, $3\theta^2 + 1$ is a function of θ. If θ has the value 5, then $3\theta^2 + 1$ has the value 76. If $\theta = -4$, then $3\theta^2 + 1 = 49$. Likewise $\theta^3 + 7$ and 8θ are functions of θ.

In order to prove that $\sin \theta$ is a function of θ, we shall show that the value of $\sin \theta$ is independent of the choice of point P on the terminal side of θ. Let $P'(x', y')$ be any other point on OP.

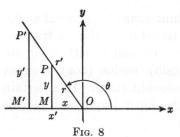

FIG. 8

Then, using the coordinates of P', we have $\sin \theta = y'/r'$. Since triangles $OP'M'$ and OPM are similar, it follows that

$$\frac{y'}{r'} = \frac{y}{r},$$

and the value of $\sin \theta$ is the same whether it is obtained by using P or by using P'. If, however, the value of θ is changed, then the value of y/r is changed, and the value of $\sin \theta$ is changed. Since the value of $\sin \theta$ depends upon the value of θ, and is independent of the choice of P, we can say that $\sin \theta$ is a function of θ. *The values of the trigonometric functions * of θ depend solely upon the value of θ.*

7. Consequences of the definitions.

(a) The **reciprocal** of the number a is $\dfrac{1}{a}$. Hence the reciprocal of 3 is $\frac{1}{3}$; the reciprocal of $-\frac{1}{4}$ is -4; $\frac{2}{5}$ and $\frac{5}{2}$ are reciprocals. Since $\dfrac{x}{y} = \dfrac{1}{y/x}$, we can say

$$\cot \theta = \frac{1}{\tan \theta}.$$

Similarly,
$$\sec \theta = \frac{1}{\cos \theta},$$

$$\csc \theta = \frac{1}{\sin \theta}.$$

* Three other functions sometimes used are versed sine, coversed sine, and haversine: vers $\theta = 1 - \cos \theta$; covers $\theta = 1 - \sin \theta$; hav $\theta = \frac{1}{2}(1 - \cos \theta)$. We shall not use these functions in this book.

Multiplying both sides of the last equation by sin θ, we get

$$\sin \theta \csc \theta = 1.$$

Dividing both sides of this equation by csc θ, we obtain

$$\sin \theta = \frac{1}{\csc \theta}.$$

Hence *sin θ and csc θ are reciprocals; also cos θ and sec θ are reciprocals; and tan θ and cot θ are reciprocals.* The following table indicates the reciprocal functions:

$$
\left.
\begin{array}{c}
\sin \theta \\
\cos \theta \\
\left.\begin{array}{c}\tan \theta \\ \cot \theta\end{array}\right\} \\
\sec \theta \\
\csc \theta
\end{array}
\right\}
\Bigg\}\ \ \text{Reciprocals}
$$

Caution. The symbol *cos* in itself has no meaning. To have interpretation, it must be followed by some angle. Write *cos θ*, not *cos*. Notice that sin θ csc θ = 1 means that the sine of any angle times the cosecant of the *same* angle equals unity.

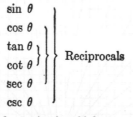

Fig. 9

(b) *Any trigonometric function of an angle is equal to the same function of all angles coterminal with it.* This follows directly from Art. 6. Thus

$$\sin 370° = \sin (370° - 360°) = \sin 10°,$$
$$\cos (-100°) = \cos (-100° + 360°) = \cos 260°,$$
$$\tan 900° = \tan (900° - 720°) = \tan 180°.$$

(c) *The sine is positive for angles in the top quadrants; the cosine is positive for angles in the right-hand quadrants.*

Since r is always positive, sin θ is positive whenever y is positive, *i.e.*, in the upper quadrants, I and II. Similarly sin θ is negative in the lower quadrants, III and IV. Also sin θ is 0 when $y = 0$, which occurs when θ is 0° or 180°.

Likewise, cos θ has the same sign as x. Hence cos θ is positive in the right-hand quadrants, I and IV. Also cos θ is negative in the left-hand quadrants, II and III. And $\cos \theta$ is 0 whenever $x = 0$, which occurs when θ is 90° or 270°.

Moreover, $\tan \theta = y/x$ is positive when y and x have the same sign, namely in quadrants I and III. Also, $\tan \theta$ is negative when y and x have opposite signs, namely in quadrants II and IV.

The sign of each of the three remaining functions is the same as the sign of its reciprocal. Thus $\csc \theta$ is positive in the upper quadrants.

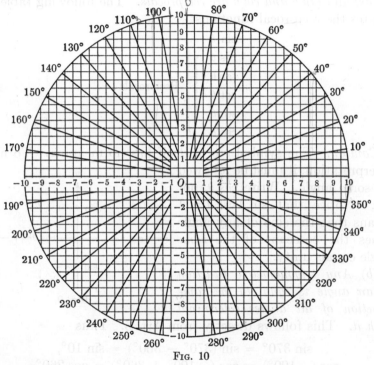

Fig. 10

Example 1. Find the values of sin 160°, cos 160°, tan 160°.

Solution. In Fig. 10 the angle 160° is in standard position. For convenience, on the terminal side of 160° choose point P so that $r = 10$. In forming a triangle of reference we find that $x = -9.4$, $y = 3.4$. Hence

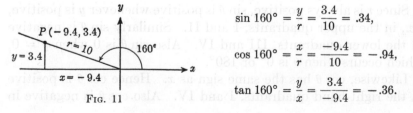

$$\sin 160° = \frac{y}{r} = \frac{3.4}{10} = .34,$$

$$\cos 160° = \frac{x}{r} = \frac{-9.4}{10} = -.94,$$

$$\tan 160° = \frac{y}{x} = \frac{3.4}{-9.4} = -.36.$$

Fig. 11

Example 2. Find the trigonometric functions of 180°.

Solution. Place the angle in standard position. For point P let us choose $(-1, 0)$. Since r is always positive, $r = 1$. The triangle of reference has "collapsed," but P does have the coordinates x, y, r. Then

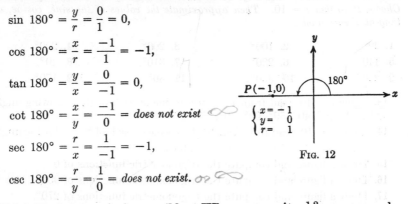

$$\sin 180° = \frac{y}{r} = \frac{0}{1} = 0,$$

$$\cos 180° = \frac{x}{r} = \frac{-1}{1} = -1,$$

$$\tan 180° = \frac{y}{x} = \frac{0}{-1} = 0,$$

$$\cot 180° = \frac{x}{y} = \frac{-1}{0} = \text{does not exist}$$

$$\sec 180° = \frac{r}{x} = \frac{1}{-1} = -1,$$

$$\csc 180° = \frac{r}{y} = \frac{1}{0} = \text{does not exist.}$$

$$\begin{cases} x = -1 \\ y = 0 \\ r = 1 \end{cases}$$

FIG. 12

Division by zero is impossible. When we write $\frac{12}{3}$, we are asking, "How many 3's add up to 12?" Consequently $\frac{1}{0}$ means "How many zeros will add up to 1?" Such a question is obviously absurd . . . Another explanation: $\frac{12}{3} = 4$ because $(3)(4) = 12$. If $\frac{1}{0} = a$, then $(0)(a)$ must equal 1. No such number a exists.

Example 3. Assuming angle θ is in standard position, compute the trigonometric functions of θ if point $P(-2, -3)$ is on its terminal side.

Solution. The Pythagorean theorem gives us $r = \sqrt{13}$. Angle θ and its triangle of reference are shown in Fig. 13. Then

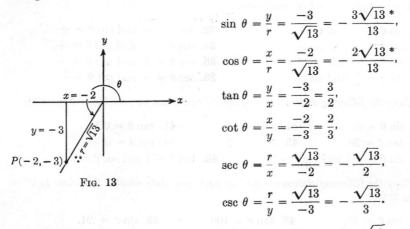

FIG. 13

$$\sin \theta = \frac{y}{r} = \frac{-3}{\sqrt{13}} = -\frac{3\sqrt{13}}{13} *,$$

$$\cos \theta = \frac{x}{r} = \frac{-2}{\sqrt{13}} = -\frac{2\sqrt{13}}{13} *,$$

$$\tan \theta = \frac{y}{x} = \frac{-3}{-2} = \frac{3}{2},$$

$$\cot \theta = \frac{x}{y} = \frac{-2}{-3} = \frac{2}{3},$$

$$\sec \theta = \frac{r}{x} = \frac{\sqrt{13}}{-2} = -\frac{\sqrt{13}}{2},$$

$$\csc \theta = \frac{r}{y} = \frac{\sqrt{13}}{-3} = -\frac{\sqrt{13}}{3}.$$

* Rationalizing the denominator by multiplying top and bottom by $\sqrt{13}$.

EXERCISE 3

Place each of the following angles in standard position, using a curved arrow to indicate the rotation. Use Fig. 10 to label the sides of the triangle of reference. Choose P so that r = 10. Then approximate the values of the sine, cosine, and tangent of each angle.

1. 20°.   2. 100°.   3. 200°.   4. 290°.
5. 140°.   6. 230°.   7. 310°.   8. 40°.
9. 250°.   10. 350°.   11. 80°.   12. 170°.

13. Using $r = 10$, read from Fig. 10 the sine of each of the following angles:
0°, 10°, 20°, 30°, 40°, 50°, 60°, 70°, 80°, 90°.

14. Using $r = 10$, read from Fig. 10 the cosine of each of the following angles:
0°, 10°, 20°, 30°, 40°, 50°, 60°, 70°, 80°, 90°.

15. Draw a figure and compute the trigonometric functions of 0°.

16. Draw a figure and compute the trigonometric functions of 90°.

17. Draw a figure and compute the trigonometric functions of 270°.

18. Draw a figure and compute the trigonometric functions of −180°.

Each of the following points is on the terminal side of an angle θ, in standard position. Use a curved arrow to draw θ. Construct and label the sides of the triangle of reference as in Fig. 13. Find the six trigonometric functions of θ.

19. $(-8, -6)$.   20. $(-8, 15)$.   21. $(5, -12)$.
22. $(24, 7)$.   23. $(2, -1)$.   24. $(1, 3)$.
25. $(-2, -5)$.   26. $(-5, 4)$.   27. $(1, 2\sqrt{2})$.
28. $(3, -\sqrt{7})$. 29. $(-\sqrt{2}, \sqrt{7})$.   30. $(-\sqrt{13}, -\sqrt{3})$.

Copy the following statements and identify the quadrant in which θ must be in order to satisfy each set of conditions.

31. $\sin \theta = -$ and $\cos \theta = -$.   32. $\sin \theta = -$ and $\cos \theta = +$.
33. $\sin \theta = +$ and $\cos \theta = -$.   34. $\cos \theta = -$ and $\tan \theta = +$.
35. $\sin \theta = -$ and $\tan \theta = -$.   36. $\csc \theta = +$ and $\tan \theta = -$.
37. $\csc \theta = -$ and $\cot \theta = +$.   38. $\sec \theta = -$ and $\cot \theta = -$.

Copy the following statements and identify each one as possible or impossible.

39. $\sin \theta = 0$.   40. $\sin \theta = 3$.   41. $\tan \theta = 0.1$.
42. $\tan \theta = 20$.   43. $\cos \theta = 2$.   44. $\cos \theta = 0$.
45. $\sin \theta = -\frac{1}{2}$ and $\csc \theta = 2$.   46. $\tan \theta = 4$ and $\sec \theta = 3$.

Copy the following statements and in each case state whether θ is close to 0° or close to 90°.

47. $\tan \theta = .01$.   48. $\tan \theta = 100$.   49. $\sin \theta = .01$.
50. $\sin \theta = .99$.   51. $\cos \theta = .01$.   52. $\cos \theta = .99$.

8. Given one trigonometric function of an angle, to draw the angle and find the other functions. When we know (1) the quadrant in which an angle lies and (2) the value of one trigonometric function of this angle, it is possible, by using the Pythagorean theorem and the general definition, to draw the angle and find its other five trigonometric functions.

Example. Given $\cos \theta = \frac{2}{5}$ and θ is not in Q I, to draw θ and find its other functions.

Solution. Since $\cos \theta$ is positive in the two right-hand quadrants and since Q I is ruled out, θ must lie in Q IV. Remembering that for all angles $\cos \theta = x/r$ and that in this case $\cos \theta = \frac{2}{5}$, we can use $x = 2$ and $r = 5$.* By means of $x^2 + y^2 = r^2$, we find $y = -\sqrt{21}$, the negative sign being chosen because $P(x, y)$ is in Q IV. Then

$$\sin \theta = \frac{y}{r} = \frac{-\sqrt{21}}{5} = -\frac{\sqrt{21}}{5},$$

$$\tan \theta = \frac{y}{x} = \frac{-\sqrt{21}}{2} = -\frac{\sqrt{21}}{2},$$

$$\cot \theta = \frac{x}{y} = \frac{2}{-\sqrt{21}} = -\frac{2\sqrt{21}}{21},$$

$$\sec \theta = \frac{r}{x} = \frac{5}{2},$$

$$\csc \theta = \frac{r}{y} = \frac{5}{-\sqrt{21}} = -\frac{5\sqrt{21}}{21}.$$

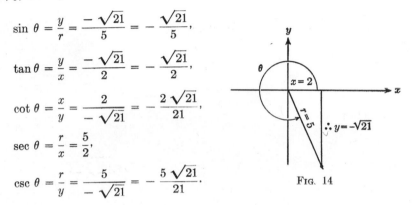

Fig. 14

EXERCISE 4

Construct and label the sides of the triangle of reference. Use a curved arrow to indicate θ. Find the remaining trigonometric functions.

1. $\sin \theta = \frac{2}{3}$, θ not in Q II.
2. $\cos \theta = -\frac{6}{7}$, θ not in Q III.
3. $\tan \theta = -\frac{1}{4}$, θ not in Q II.
4. $\sin \theta = -\frac{5}{8}$, θ not in Q IV.
5. $\cos \theta = \frac{24}{25}$, $\tan \theta = -$.
6. $\tan \theta = \frac{12}{5}$, $\cos \theta = +$.
7. $\sin \theta = \frac{15}{17}$, $\cos \theta = -$.
8. $\cos \theta = \frac{4}{5}$, $\sin \theta = +$.
9. $\tan \theta = \frac{3}{5}$, θ not in Q I. *Hint:* Both x and y must be negative: $\dfrac{3}{5} = \dfrac{-3}{-5}$,

* Equally correct but not so convenient would be $x = 6$, $r = 15$ or $x = 1$, $r = \frac{5}{2}$.

10. $\sin \theta = -\dfrac{2\sqrt{2}}{3}$, θ not in Q III.

11. $\cos \theta = -\dfrac{\sqrt{7}}{4}$, θ not in Q II.

12. $\tan \theta = -5$, θ not in Q IV.   *Hint:* $-5 = \dfrac{5}{-1}$.

13. $\sec \theta = -3$, θ not in Q III.

14. $\cot \theta = \dfrac{2\sqrt{5}}{5}$, θ not in Q I.

15. $\csc \theta = a$, θ *is* in Q I.

16. $\sec \theta = \dfrac{\sqrt{13}}{2}$, θ not in Q I.

CHAPTER 2

TRIGONOMETRIC FUNCTIONS
OF AN ACUTE ANGLE

9. Trigonometric functions of an acute angle. Let θ be an acute angle of a right triangle (Fig. 15). If θ were in standard position, this right triangle would be its triangle of reference. The hypotenuse would be the r of some point P on the terminal side of θ; the side opposite θ would be the y of P; and the side adjacent θ would be the x of P. Then the general definitions (Art. 6) involving x, y, and r would become special definitions involving *opp.*, *adj.*, and *hyp.*

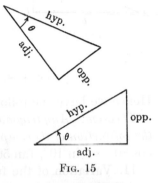

FIG. 15

We conclude that *for any* **acute** *angle θ lying in a right triangle,*

$$\sin \theta = \frac{opp.}{hyp.},$$

$$\cos \theta = \frac{adj.}{hyp.},$$

$$\tan \theta = \frac{opp.}{adj.}.$$

The other three functions can be obtained through their reciprocals.

EXERCISE 5

For each of the following right triangles write the sine, cosine, and tangent of each of the acute angles. Leave results in fractional form.

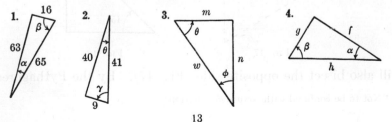

13

10. Cofunctions. The sine and cosine are said to be **cofunctions;** * *i.e.*, the cosine is the cofunction of the sine and the sine is the cofunction of the cosine. Similarly, the tangent and cotangent are cofunctions, and the secant and cosecant are cofunctions.

If A and B are the acute angles in right triangle ABC, then

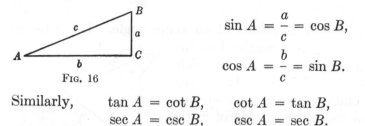

FIG. 16

$$\sin A = \frac{a}{c} = \cos B,$$

$$\cos A = \frac{b}{c} = \sin B.$$

Similarly, $\tan A = \cot B,$ $\cot A = \tan B,$

$\sec A = \csc B,$ $\csc A = \sec B.$

Hence we have the following:

Theorem. Any trigonometric function of an acute angle is equal to the cofunction of its complementary angle. Thus $\sin 70° = \cos 20°$, $\cos 80° = \sin 10°$, $\tan 50° = \cot 40°$.

11. Variation of the functions of an acute angle. If r is fixed and if θ increases from $0°$ to $90°$ (Fig. 10), then y increases and x decreases. It follows that *as an acute angle increases, its sine, tangent, and secant increase* while their cofunctions, the cosine, cotangent, and cosecant, decrease. Since neither leg of a right triangle can equal the hypotenuse, the sine and cosine of an acute angle must always be less than 1.

12. The trigonometric functions of 30°, 45°, 60°. Consider an equilateral triangle of side 2. The bisector of one of the 60° angles

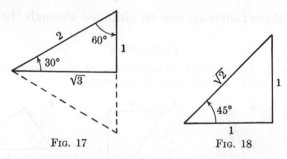

FIG. 17   FIG. 18

will also bisect the opposite side (Fig. 17). By the Pythagorean

* Not to be confused with *reciprocal* functions.

theorem, the length of the bisector is $\sqrt{3}$.   Using Art. 9, we find

$$\sin 30° = \frac{1}{2}, \qquad\qquad \sin 60° = \frac{\sqrt{3}}{2},$$

$$\cos 30° = \frac{\sqrt{3}}{2}, \qquad\qquad \cos 60° = \frac{1}{2},$$

$$\tan 30° = \frac{1}{\sqrt{3}} = \frac{\sqrt{3}}{3}, \qquad \tan 60° = \sqrt{3}.$$

The 30°-60°-90° triangle can be easily remembered if we note that the largest side is twice the shortest side.

To compute the functions of 45°, draw an isosceles right triangle of leg 1 (Fig. 18).   The hypotenuse, by the Pythagorean theorem, must be $\sqrt{2}$.   Then, by Art. 9,

$$\sin 45° = \frac{1}{\sqrt{2}} = \frac{\sqrt{2}}{2},$$

$$\cos 45° = \frac{1}{\sqrt{2}} = \frac{\sqrt{2}}{2},$$

$$\tan 45° = \frac{1}{1} = 1.$$

Because of their frequent occurrence, the following should be memorized:

$$\sin 30° = \cos 60° = \frac{1}{2},$$

$$\sin 45° = \cos 45° = \frac{\sqrt{2}}{2},$$

$$\sin 60° = \cos 30° = \frac{\sqrt{3}}{2}.$$

As we shall see later, the tangent of any angle can be obtained by dividing its sine by its cosine.   The three remaining functions can be obtained through their reciprocals.

The expression $\sin^2 \theta$ is a shorter way of writing $(\sin \theta)^2$. Since sin θ is merely a number (the ratio of two distances), we can

function are merely ratio of two distance

speak of the square of this number and call it $\sin^2 \theta$. Thus

$$\sin^2 60° = \left(\frac{\sqrt{3}}{2}\right)^2 = \frac{3}{4}; \qquad \sin^3 30° = \left(\frac{1}{2}\right)^3 = \frac{1}{8};$$

$$\sec^2 30° = \left(\frac{1}{\cos 30°}\right)^2 = \frac{1}{\cos^2 30°} = \frac{1}{\left(\dfrac{\sqrt{3}}{2}\right)^2} = \frac{1}{\dfrac{3}{4}} = \frac{4}{3}.$$

If we recall (Prob. 15, page 10) that $\sin 0° = 0$, $\cos 0° = 1$, $\sin 90° = 1$, $\cos 90° = 0$, we can easily remember the sine and cosine of special first-quadrant angles by forming a mental picture of Fig. 19.

	0°	30°	45°	60°	90°
sin	$\dfrac{\sqrt{0}}{2}$	$\dfrac{\sqrt{1}}{2}$	$\dfrac{\sqrt{2}}{2}$	$\dfrac{\sqrt{3}}{2}$	$\dfrac{\sqrt{4}}{2}$
cos	$\dfrac{\sqrt{4}}{2}$	$\dfrac{\sqrt{3}}{2}$	$\dfrac{\sqrt{2}}{2}$	$\dfrac{\sqrt{1}}{2}$	$\dfrac{\sqrt{0}}{2}$

FIG. 19

EXERCISE 6

Compute the value of each of the following expressions. <u>*Do not express in decimals.*</u>

1. $3 \cos 60° + \sin^4 45° - \cos 0°.$
2. $\sin^5 30° + \cos^2 60° + \cos 90°.$
3. $\sin 60° + 4 \cos^3 30° + \sin^2 0°.$
4. $\sin 45° \cos^3 45° + \sin 90°.$
5. $\cos^2 45° + 2 \sin 60° \cos 30° + 6 \sin 30°.$
6. $\sin 60° \cos 45° + 7 \sin 45° \cos 30°.$
7. $3 \sin 30° \sin 45° + \cos 60° \cos 45°.$
8. $\sin^2 60° - \sin^4 30° + \cos^4 30° + \cos^2 60°.$

Identify as true or false and give reasons.

9. $\cos 56° < \cos 78°.*$
10. $\tan 31° < \tan 39°.*$
11. $\cos (70° - \theta) = \sin (20° + \theta).$
12. $\sin^2 17° = \cos^2 73°.$
13. $\sin 28° = \dfrac{1}{\sec 62°}.$
14. $\sin 30° + \sin 30° = \sin 60°.$
15. $\csc^6 60° = \frac{64}{27}.$
16. $\dfrac{1}{\cos 34°} = \csc 56°.$

* The symbol $<$ is read "is less than."

13. Tables of trigonometric functions. In Table I (pages 2–6 in the tables) there are listed, to four decimal places, the sine, cosine, tangent, and cotangent for acute angles at intervals of 10'. For angles less than 45°, find the name of the function at the *top* of the column, then read *down* until the angle is found at the *left*. For angles greater than 45°, find the name of the function at the *bottom* of the column, then read *up* until the angle is found at the *right*.

The two problems we shall need to consider are:

1. Given an angle, to find one of its trigonometric functions, and

2. Given a trigonometric function of some angle, to find the angle.

14. Given an angle, to find one of its functions.

Example 1.   Find tan 8° 20'.

Solution.   On page 2 in the column with *tan* at its *head*, come down to the number in line with 8° 20'. Thus tan 8° 20' = .1465.

Example 2.   Find sin 74° 50'.

Solution.   On page 3, in the column with *sin* at its *foot*, move up to the number in line with 74° 50'. Hence sin 74° 50' = .9652.

15. Given a function of an angle, to find the angle.

Example 1.   Find θ if sin θ = .9387.

Solution.   Since sines are found in column three reading *down* and in column six reading *up*, we must search through these two columns until we find the number .9387. It appears in the sixth column which has *sin* at its *foot*. This column contains the sines of the angles in the *right* column. On a line with .9387, we find in the *right* column the angle 69° 50'. Hence,

if   sin θ = .9387,

then θ = 69° 50'.

Example 2.   Find θ if cot θ = 1.288.

Solution.   We search the two cotangent columns, the fourth going up and the fifth going down, and find 1.288 in the fifth column. Since this column has *cot* at its *head*, we associate this number with the angle at the *left*, 37° 50'. Hence,

if   cot θ = 1.288,

then * θ = 37° 50'.

* The student should guard against writing cot θ = 1.288 = 37° 50'. The second equality sign is incorrectly used because 1.288 does *not* equal 37° 50'; and cot θ does *not* equal 37° 50'.

EXERCISE 7

Use a four-place table (Table I) *to find the value of the following.*

1. tan 23° 40′.	**2.** cot 10° 30′.	**3.** cos 77° 10′.
4. sin 85° 50′.	**5.** cot 56° 50′.	**6.** tan 46° 0′.
7. sin 42° 30′.	**8.** cos 29° 40′.	**9.** cos 4° 20′.
10. sin 35° 20′.	**11.** tan 80° 0′.	**12.** cot 64° 10′.

Use a four-place table (Table I) *to find* θ *from the following function of* θ.

13. sin θ = .9563.	**14.** cos θ = .6202.	**15.** cot θ = 2.434.
16. tan θ = .1944.	**17.** cot θ = 1.257.	**18.** tan θ = .9601.
19. sin θ = .9995.	**20.** cos θ = .6967.	**21.** tan θ = 2.414.
22. cot θ = .2095.	**23.** cos θ = .7153.	**24.** sin θ = .3365.

16. Interpolation. When a sports announcer says, "The ball is on the 27-yard line," most football fans realize that the announcer estimates that the ball is $\frac{2}{5}$ of the way from the 25-yard line to the 30-yard line. This process of literally "reading between the lines" is called interpolation. Another example is, "Interpolate to approximate the value of $\sqrt{8}$." Knowing $\sqrt{4} = 2$ and $\sqrt{9} = 3$, we conclude that $\sqrt{8}$ is a number between 2 and 3.* Moreover, 8 is $\frac{4}{5}$ of the way from 4 to 9. Assume that for a small increase in a number N, the change in $\sqrt{N}$ is proportional to the change in N.† Then $\sqrt{8}$ would lie $\frac{4}{5}$ of the way from 2 to 3. Since $\frac{4}{5}$ of 1 is .8, we conclude that $\sqrt{8}$ is approximately 2.8. This result is correct to only one decimal place. The process of interpolation is important in all work involving the use of tables.

We already know that the trigonometric functions do not change uniformly with the change in the angle (if an angle is doubled, its sine does not double). But if the angle is changed by only a few minutes, the change in the function is very nearly proportional to the change in the angle.

Example 1. Find sin 56° 14′.
Solution. Here we must interpolate between 56° 10′ and 56° 20′.

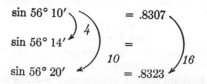

$$\begin{array}{ccc} \sin 56°\,10' & & = .8307 \\ \sin 56°\,14' & 4 \quad\quad & = \\ & 10 & 16 \\ \sin 56°\,20' & & = .8323 \end{array}$$

---

* The square root of a number increases when the number increases.
† Not strictly true, but a good approximation if the change is small.

As the angle increases 10′ (from 56° 10′ to 56° 20′), its sine increases 16 ten-thousandths. Our angle is $\frac{4}{10}$ of the way from 56° 10′ to 56° 20′. Hence the sine of our angle is $\frac{4}{10}$ of the way from .8307 to .8323. But $\frac{4}{10}(16) = 6\frac{2}{5} \to 6$. (Round off to 6 because $6\frac{2}{5}$ is closer to 6 than it is to 7.) Since the sine is increasing, *add* the 6 to .8307 to get

$$\sin 56° 14′ = .8313.$$

Example 2. Find cos 31° 17′.
Solution.

$$
\begin{array}{lll}
\cos 31° 10′ & & = .8557 \\
\cos 31° 17′ & \quad 7 & = \\
& 10 & \qquad -15 \\
\cos 31° 20′ & & = .8542
\end{array}
$$

An *increase* of 10′ in the angle causes a *decrease* of 15 in the cosine. Our angle is $\frac{7}{10}$ of the way from 31° 10′ to 31° 20′. Hence we want $\frac{7}{10}$ of the decrease of 15. But $\frac{7}{10}(15) = 10\frac{1}{2} \to 11.*$ *Subtracting* this number from .8557 gives

$$\cos 31° 17′ = .8546.$$

Example 3. Find θ if tan θ = .4934.
Solution.

$$
\begin{array}{lll}
\tan 26° 10′ & & = .4913 \\
\tan \theta & & = .4934 \qquad 21 \\
& 10′ & \qquad\qquad 37 \\
\tan 26° 20′ & & = .4950
\end{array}
$$

Our number .4934 is $\frac{21}{37}$ of the way from .4913 to .4950. Hence θ should be $\frac{21}{37}$ of the way from 26° 10′ to 26° 20′. But $\frac{21}{37}(10′) = 5\frac{25}{37}′ \to 6′$. Hence

$$\theta = 26° 16′.$$

Example 4. Find θ if cos θ = .2581.
Solution.

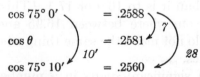

$$
\begin{array}{lll}
\cos 75° 0′ & & = .2588 \\
\cos \theta & & = .2581 \qquad 7 \\
& 10′ & \qquad\qquad 28 \\
\cos 75° 10′ & & = .2560
\end{array}
$$

Our number is $\frac{7}{28}$ of "the way down." Hence θ is $\frac{7}{28}(10′) = \frac{10}{4}′ = 2\frac{1}{2}′ \to 2′$ †
away from 75° 0′. Therefore

$$\theta = 75° 2′.$$

* In "rounding off" a number that is *exactly halfway*, it is conventional to choose the number that makes the *final result even* rather than odd. In this case the final result is written as .8546 rather than .8547. This procedure will be followed throughout this book.

† Number is exactly halfway. Make result even.

It is to be noted that, in this three-line method of interpolation, the small *angle* is always written on top. All differences are measured from the small angle and its function.

EXERCISE 8

Use a four-place table (Table I).
Interpolate to find the value of the following.

1. cos 58° 42′.	**2.** sin 61° 29′.	**3.** tan 20° 41′.
4. cot 7° 52′.	**5.** sin 30° 17′.	**6.** cos 17° 35′.
7. cot 53° 23′.	**8.** tan 70° 13′.	**9.** tan 47° 39′.
10. cot 82° 51′.	**11.** cos 37° 34′.	**12.** sin 16° 27′.
13. cot 24° 24′.	**14.** tan 32° 46′.	**15.** sin 72° 8′.
16. cos 69° 46′.		

Interpolate to find θ.

17. sin θ = .8765.	**18.** cos θ = .6640.	**19.** cot θ = 1.234.
20. tan θ = .7856.	**21.** cos θ = .9586.	**22.** sin θ = .3441.
23. tan θ = 1.317.	**24.** cot θ = .3177.	**25.** cot θ = .4020.
26. tan θ = 3.789.	**27.** sin θ = .0777.	**28.** cos θ = .7574.
29. tan θ = .5929.	**30.** cot θ = 1.113.	**31.** cos θ = .5067.
32. sin θ = .9235.		

17. Approximations and significant figures. If a given distance is *measured* and if its length is expressed in decimal form, it is conventional to write no more digits than are correct (or probably correct). Thus, if we say that the measured distance between points A and B is 17 ft., we mean that the result is given to the nearest foot; *i.e.*, the true distance is closer to 17 ft. than it is to 16 ft. or 18 ft. This is an example of two-figure accuracy. If we say that the measured distance AB is 17.0 ft., we mean that the true distance is given to three significant figures; *i.e.*, it is closer to 17.0 than it is to 16.9 or 17.1. This implies that the true distance is somewhere between 16.95 and 17.05. Notice that 17 and 17.0 do not mean the same thing when they represent approximate values.

The number of significant digits in a number is obtained by counting the digits from left to right, beginning with the first nonzero digit and ending with the rightmost digit.* Thus, 0.078060 has five significant digits, 70.00 has four, and 0.790 has

---

* Ambiguity may result if the number in question is an integer ending in one or more 0's. For example, if the radius of the earth is given as 4000 miles, we may not know how many 0's are significant. If, however, the number 4000 was obtained from 3960 by rounding it off to the nearest multiple of 100 miles, then the first 0 is

only three. Notice that the number of significant digits does not depend on the position of the decimal point.

Results computed by multiplication or division from approximate data will usually have no higher degree of accuracy than that of the data used. *We agree to round off the result so that it will have as many significant figures as there are in the least accurate number in the data.* If a field is measured and found to be 11.3 rods long and 10.7 rods wide, we would be tempted to say that its area is (11.3)(10.7) = 120.91 square rods. To do so would be to claim false accuracy. The result should be rounded off to three significant figures (the same as in the given data) to obtain 121 square rods. The first two figures in this result are correct, but the third is only a good approximation because the true area is somewhere between (11.25)(10.65) = 119.8125 square rods and (11.35)(10.75) = 122.0125 square rods.

Since nearly all the angles listed in Table I have trigonometric functions that are nonending decimals, the numbers appearing in the body of this table are merely four-figure approximations. Hence most of the results obtained by the use of this table will be approximations and should be considered as such.

Recall that, in rounding off a number that is exactly halfway, it is conventional to choose the number that makes the final result even rather than odd.

In solving triangles, we agree to set up the following correspondence between accuracy in sides and angles.

Accuracy in Sides	Accuracy in Angles
2-figure..........	Nearest degree
3-figure..........	Nearest multiple of 10 minutes
4-figure..........	Nearest minute
5-figure..........	Nearest tenth of a minute

Hence within each of the following sets of data the same degree of accuracy prevails:

23, 42, 62°;
.461, 61° 10′, 44° 50′, 74° 0′;
8.624, 82° 33′, 64° 00′;
.078247, 23° 19.7′, 48° 0.0′.

significant; the other two are not. In a case of this kind, computers sometimes underscore the digits that are significant: 4000. Another way of indicating that 4000 represents two-figure accuracy is to express it as 4.0(10³).

If the data include a side with two-figure accuracy and another side with three-figure accuracy, then the computed parts should be written with only two-figure accuracy. The computed angles should be taken to the nearest degree. If the given data include a number whose degree of accuracy is doubtful, we shall (in this book) *assume the maximum degree of accuracy*. For example, with no information to the contrary, the side 700 ft. will be treated as a three-figure number; the angle 46° 20′ will be considered as having four-figure accuracy.

EXERCISE 9

Round off the following numbers and angles to (a) four-figure accuracy, (b) three-figure accuracy, and (c) two-figure accuracy.

1. .78346.   **2.** .081765.   **3.** 19.275.   **4.** 9.1748.
5. 18° 43.5′.   **6.** 42° 34.6′.   **7.** 7° 28.4′.   **8.** 66° 17.5′.

The number 77.4 is the best three-figure approximation for all numbers from 77.35 to 77.45 *inclusive.** *What range of numbers is covered by each of the following approximations?*

9. 4.28.   **10.** 91.3.   **11.** 69.1.   **12.** 2.04.
13. 82.35.   **14.** 1.876.   **15.** 3.080.   **16.** 56.47.

18. The solution of right triangles. To solve a triangle means to find from the given parts the values of the remaining parts. A right triangle is determined by

(a) Two of its sides, or

(b) One side and an acute angle.

In either case it is possible to find the remaining parts by using the special definitions in Art. 9 together with the fact that the acute angles of a right triangle are complementary. For convenience we list here again these special definitions.

For any **acute** *angle θ lying in a right triangle:*

$$\sin \theta = \frac{\text{opp.}}{\text{hyp.}},$$

$$\cos \theta = \frac{\text{adj.}}{\text{hyp.}},$$

$$\tan \theta = \frac{\text{opp.}}{\text{adj.}}.$$

* See footnote on p. 19.

For any triangle we shall use the small letters a, b, and c to denote the lengths of the sides that are opposite the angles A, B, and C, respectively. In a right triangle we shall always reserve the letter c for the hypotenuse.

Example 1. Solve the right triangle having an acute angle of 38° 50′, the side adjacent to this angle being 311.

Solution. We first draw the triangle to scale and label numerically the parts that are known. Then

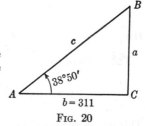

FIG. 20

(1) $B = 90° - 38° 50′$
                $= 51° 10′.$

(2) To find a, we observe that the given side and the required side are related to the given angle by the equation

$$\tan 38° 50′ = \frac{a}{311}.$$

Multiply both sides of the equation by 311:

$$311 \tan 38° 50′ = a.$$

Hence $a = 311(.8050) = 250.$

(3) To find c, we notice that the given parts, 38° 50′ and 311, are related to the required part through the cosine of the angle:

$$\cos 38° 50′ = \frac{311}{c}.$$

Multiply both sides by c:

$$c \cos 38° 50′ = 311.$$

Divide both sides by cos 38° 50′:

$$c = \frac{311}{\cos 38° 50′} = \frac{311}{.7790} = 399.$$

This problem illustrates three-figure accuracy in the data and the computed results.

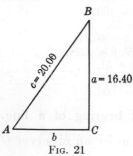

FIG. 21

Example 2. Solve the right triangle whose hypotenuse is 20.00 and one of whose legs is 16.40.

Solution. Draw the triangle and label numerically the given parts.

(1) Since the hypotenuse and the side opposite A are given,

$$\sin A = \frac{16.40}{20.00} = .8200.$$

Four-place accuracy in the given sides means that the angles should be found to the nearest minute.

Interpolating, we find

$$A = 55° 5'.$$

(2) $$B = 90° - 55° 5'$$

$$= 34° 55'.$$

(3) To find b, use

$$\cos A = \frac{b}{20.00}.$$

Multiply both sides by 20.00:

$$20.00 \cos A = b.$$

Hence $$b = (20.00) \cos 55° 5' = (20.00)(.5724) = 11.45.$$

The value of b could have been found by using

$$\tan A = \frac{16.40}{b} ; \qquad b = \frac{16.40}{\tan 55° 5'} = \frac{16.40}{1.432} = 11.45.$$

This serves as a partial check on the solution.
It may be easier to use

$$b = \frac{16.40}{\tan 55° 5'} = 16.40 \cot 55° 5' = (16.40)(.6980)$$

$$= 11.4472 \rightarrow 11.45.$$

This problem illustrates four-figure accuracy in the data and the results.

In solving a right triangle by use of trigonometric functions it is desirable to find as many as possible of the required parts directly from the given parts.   Why?

EXERCISE 10

Use a four-place table (Table I) to solve the following right triangles.

1. $A = 66° 30'$, $c = 700$.
2. $B = 43° 40'$, $c = 60.0$.
3. $A = 20° 0'$, $a = 1.71$.
4. $B = 77° 10'$, $b = 585$.
5. $b = 0.440$, $c = 0.600$.
6. $a = 314$, $b = 200$.
7. $a = 132$, $b = 250$.
8. $a = 258$, $c = 400$.
9. $a = 41$, $b = 20$.
10. $b = 49$, $c = 55$.
11. $a = 3872$, $c = 4105$.
12. $a = 76.54$, $b = 60.81$.
13. $B = 11° 28'$, $a = 7014$.
14. $A = 55° 15'$, $b = 4228$.
15. $B = 81°$, $c = 90$.
16. $A = 33°$, $c = 51$.
17. $A = 65° 30'$, $a = 742$.
18. $a = 304$, $c = 800$.
19. $A = 38° 40'$, $b = 555$.
20. $b = 120$, $c = 900$.

19. Angles of elevation and depression; bearing of a line.

The *angle of* $\begin{Bmatrix} elevation \\ depression \end{Bmatrix}$ of a point P as seen by an observer O

is the vertical angle measured from the horizontal line through $O \begin{Bmatrix} upward \\ downward \end{Bmatrix}$ to the line of sight OP.

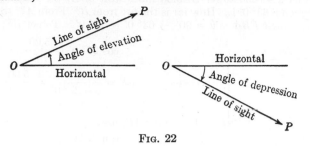

FIG. 22

The *bearing* of a line in a horizontal plane is the *acute* angle made by this line with a north-south line. In giving the bearing of a line, write first the letter N or S, then the angle of deviation from north or south, then the letter E or W. Thus, in Fig. 23 the bearing of line OA is N 70° E; or the bearing of point A from point O is N 70° E.

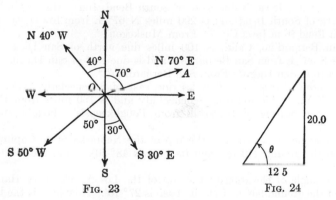

FIG. 23   FIG. 24

Example 1. A vertical stake 20.0 in. high casts a horizontal shadow 12.5 in. long. What time is it if the sun rose at 6:00 A.M. and will be directly overhead at noon?

Solution. The angle of elevation of the sun (Fig. 24) is found by

$$\tan \theta = \frac{20.0}{12.5} = 1.600,$$

$$\theta = 58° 0'.$$

It takes the earth 6 hr. to rotate through 90°. Since this rotation is uniform, each degree of elevation of the sun will correspond to $\frac{6}{90}$ of an hour or 4 min,

Consequently a rotation through 58° 0′ will require (58)(4 min.) = 232 min. = 3 hr. and 52 min. Hence the time is 9:52 A.M.

Example 2. From a lookout tower A a column of smoke is sighted due south. From a second tower B, 5.00 miles west of A, the smoke is observed in the direction S 63° 0′ E. How far is the fire from B? From A? (See Fig. 25.)

Solution. Angle $FBA = \theta = 90° - 63° 0′ = 27° 0′$. To get BF, use

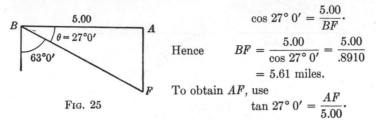

FIG. 25

$$\cos 27° 0′ = \frac{5.00}{BF}.$$

Hence $\qquad BF = \dfrac{5.00}{\cos 27° 0′} = \dfrac{5.00}{.8910}$

$$= 5.61 \text{ miles.}$$

To obtain AF, use

$$\tan 27° 0′ = \frac{AF}{5.00}.$$

Hence $\qquad AF = 5.00 \tan 27° 0′ = (5.00)(.5095)$

$$= 2.55 \text{ miles.}$$

EXERCISE 11

1. New Orleans, La., is 360 miles due south of Memphis, Tenn. Norman, Okla., is 420 miles west of Memphis. What is the bearing of Norman from New Orleans? New Orleans from Norman? *

2. Iowa City, Iowa, is due west of South Bend, Ind. Muskegon, Mich., is due north of South Bend and is 290 miles N 67° E from Iowa City. How far is South Bend from Iowa City? From Muskegon? *

3. San Bernardino, Calif., is 100 miles due north of San Diego. Yuma, Ariz., is S 56° E from San Bernardino and is due east of San Diego. How far is Yuma from San Diego? From San Bernardino? *

4. Haverhill, Mass., is 150 miles due east of Schenectady, N.Y. Poughkeepsie, N.Y., is due south of Schenectady and is 160 miles from Haverhill. What is the bearing of Haverhill from Poughkeepsie? Poughkeepsie from Haverhill? *

5. The angle of elevation of the top of the Nebraska State Capitol from a point on the ground 410 ft. from its base is 48° 50′. Find the height of the building.

6. The angle of elevation of the top of the Los Angeles City Hall from a point on the ground 904 ft. from its base is 27° 10′. How high is the building?

7. From a point 702 ft. from, and in the same horizontal plane with, the top of the Lower Falls of the Yellowstone River, the angle of depression of the foot of the falls is 23° 40′. Find the height of the Lower Falls.

8. A balloon is 552 ft. above one end of a bridge that spans the Mississippi River at Dubuque, Iowa. The angle of depression of the other end of the bridge from the balloon is 33° 10′. How long is the bridge?

9. A love-sick swain looks out of his office window, 50 ft. above the ground, and sees, with an angle of depression of 40°, his girl friend standing on the sidewalk, talking to another suitor. How far are the lovers apart?

* Ignore the curvature of the earth and assume only two-place accuracy. Get angles to the nearest degree. Get distances to the nearest multiple of 10 miles.

10. From a point A on the top of a cliff that is 160 ft. above sea level, the angle of depression of an anchored rowboat B is 14° 50′. Find the length of the airline distance AB from the cliff to the boat.

11. A vertical stake 40.0 in. high casts a horizontal shadow 36.0 in. long. What time is it if the sun rose at 6:05 A.M. and will be directly overhead at 12:05 P.M.?

12. A vertical stake 52.1 in. high casts a horizontal shadow 20.0 in. long. What time is it if the sun was directly overhead at 11:55 A.M. and will set at 5:55 P.M.?

13. Let θ be the angle between two lines, l and m. Let AB be any segment of line l. If AC and BD are perpendiculars drawn to line m, then CD is called the **projection** of AB on line m. Show that $CD = AB \cos \theta$. Investigate this relationship for values of θ close to 0°. For θ close to 90°.

14. Detroit is 240 miles east and 50 miles south of Milwaukee. In what direction should a plane travel in flying from Milwaukee to Detroit? *

15. Fargo, N.Dak., is 230 miles due north of Sioux Falls, S.Dak. An airplane leaves Sioux Falls at 1:00 P.M. and flies 300 mph in the direction N 16° 10′ E. When will the plane be due east of Fargo? *

16. The angle of elevation of a ladder leaning against a wall is 77°. The foot of the ladder is 1.8 ft. from the wall. Find the length of the ladder.

17. Find the perimeter of a regular polygon of 90 sides inscribed in a circle of radius 1.000. Compare this number with the circumference of the circle.

18. A passenger on a ship sailing north at 5.0 mph noticed that at noon a radio tower on land was due east of the ship. At 1:30 P.M., the bearing of the tower from the ship was S 35° E. How far was the ship from the tower at 1:30 P.M.?

19. A locomotive traveling on a straight stretch of track rises 10.6 ft. while moving 90.0 ft. on the track. Find the angle of elevation of the track.

20. The diagonal of a rectangle is exactly three times the shorter side. Find to four-figure accuracy the angle made by the diagonal with the longer side.

21. The pilot of an airplane left A and flew 200 miles in the direction S 20° 20′ W. He then turned and flew 148 miles in the direction S 69° 40′ E. If he now heads back to A, in what direction should he fly?

22. What is the angle made by a diagonal of a cube and a touching diagonal of a face of the cube?

23. Each of the equal sides of an isosceles triangle is 40.4 in. Each of the equal angles is 75° 0′. Find the altitude and the base of the triangle.

24. A surveyor, running a line due north, discovered that he had to change his course to bypass a thicket. From point A he measured 500.0 ft. in the direction N 29° 10′ W to point B. (a) How many feet should he measure from B in the direction N 54° 0′ E to arrive at a point C which is due north of A? (b) Find the distance from A to C.

25. An observer at A looks due north and sees a meteor with an angle of elevation of 70°. At the same instant, another observer, 30 miles east of A, sees the same meteor and approximates its position as N 50° W but fails to note its angle of elevation. Find the height of the meteor and its distance from A.

* Ignore the curvature of the earth and assume only two-place accuracy. Get angles to the nearest degree. Get distances to the nearest multiple of 10 miles.

26. From the top of a 100-ft. building, on level ground, the angle of depression of the bottom of a television tower is 16° 40'. From the bottom of the building, the angle of elevation of the top of the tower is 64° 10'. Find the height of the tower.

27. From the top of a lighthouse a ft. above sea level at high tide, the angle of depression of a buoy is θ at high tide and ϕ at low tide. Show that the height of the tide is $a(\cot \theta \tan \phi - 1)$.

28. From point A, the elevation of a mountain peak is θ. From point B, in the same horizontal plane with A and a feet closer to the base of the mountain, the angle of elevation of the peak is ϕ. Show that the height of the peak above the level of A and B is $\dfrac{a}{\cot \theta - \cot \phi}$ ft.

CHAPTER 3

TRIGONOMETRIC IDENTITIES

20. The fundamental relations. In Art. 8 we discussed the problem of determining all the trigonometric functions of an angle if one of them is given. This was a geometric process involving the construction of a triangle of reference for the angle. We shall now consider purely analytic relations among the functions themselves. These relations are of considerable importance in other branches of mathematics as well as in engineering and physics.

For any * angle θ, the following eight fundamental relations are true:

[1]
$$\csc \theta = \frac{1}{\sin \theta},$$

[2]
$$\sec \theta = \frac{1}{\cos \theta},$$

[3]
$$\cot \theta = \frac{1}{\tan \theta},$$

[4]
$$\tan \theta = \frac{\sin \theta}{\cos \theta},$$

[5]
$$\cot \theta = \frac{\cos \theta}{\sin \theta},$$

[6]
$$\sin^2 \theta + \cos^2 \theta = 1,$$

[7]
$$1 + \tan^2 \theta = \sec^2 \theta,$$

[8]
$$1 + \cot^2 \theta = \csc^2 \theta.$$

* Strictly speaking, for every angle for which the functions actually exist. For example, [4] has no meaning when $\theta = 90°$ because $\cos 90° = 0$; hence $\tan 90°$ $= \frac{\sin 90°}{\cos 90°} = \frac{1}{0} =$ does not exist. Likewise [8] has no meaning for $\theta = 180°$ because $\cot 180°$ and $\csc 180°$ do not exist (see Art. 7). Exceptions like these *can* occur only for $\theta = 0°, 90°, 180°, 270°$, and angles coterminal with them. Notice, however, that [6] does hold for $\theta = 180°$: $\sin^2 180° + \cos^2 180° = 0^2 + (-1)^2 = 1$.

29

These relations are invaluable for many considerations that follow in this book and should be memorized immediately. The first three relations have already been discussed (Art. 7) and used. We shall prove only [1]:

$$\frac{1}{\sin \theta} = \frac{1}{y/r} = \frac{r}{y} = \csc \theta.$$

The proofs of [4] and [5] are similar. To prove [4]:

$$\frac{\sin \theta}{\cos \theta} = \frac{y/r}{x/r} = \frac{y}{x} = \tan \theta.$$

In order to prove [6], [7], [8], we recall that for any angle θ in standard position, the coordinates of point P on its terminal side are related by the equation

(9) $$x^2 + y^2 = r^2.$$

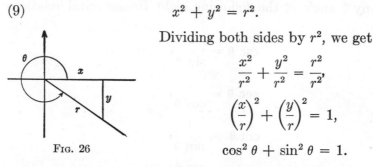

FIG. 26

Dividing both sides by r^2, we get

$$\frac{x^2}{r^2} + \frac{y^2}{r^2} = \frac{r^2}{r^2},$$

$$\left(\frac{x}{r}\right)^2 + \left(\frac{y}{r}\right)^2 = 1,$$

$$\cos^2 \theta + \sin^2 \theta = 1.$$

Dividing equation (9) in turn by x^2 and y^2, we get [7] and [8], respectively.

The student should be able to recognize these eight fundamental relations in other forms. For example,

[1] may be reduced to $\sin \theta \csc \theta = 1,$

[2] may be reduced to $\cos \theta = \dfrac{1}{\sec \theta},$

[6] may be reduced to $\sin \theta = \pm \sqrt{1 - \cos^2 \theta},$

[6] may be reduced to $\cos \theta = \pm \sqrt{1 - \sin^2 \theta},$

[7] may be reduced to $\sec \theta = \pm \sqrt{1 + \tan^2 \theta}.$*

---

* The student should realize from his study of algebra that $\sqrt{1 + \tan^2 \theta}$ is not equal to $1 + \tan \theta$.

The sign that should be chosen in the last three equations is determined by the quadrant in which θ lies. In Q I and Q IV, $\cos \theta = \sqrt{1 - \sin^2 \theta}$; but in Q II and Q III, $\cos \theta = -\sqrt{1 - \sin^2 \theta}$.

Again the student is warned against the careless habit of writing *sin* instead of *sin θ*. Equation [6] says that the square of the sine of any angle plus the square of the cosine of *that same angle* is equal to 1. It could just as well have been written

$$\sin^2 A + \cos^2 A = 1,$$

or
$$\sin^2 7B + \cos^2 7B = 1.$$

Example 1. Prove or disprove:

$$\sin^4 5A + 2 \sin^2 5A \cos^2 5A + \cos^4 5A = 1.$$

Solution. Since the given equation involves only sines and cosines, we shall attempt to derive it from [6], which says that for all values of θ

$$\sin^2 \theta + \cos^2 \theta = 1.$$

Square both sides of the equation:

$$(\sin^2 \theta + \cos^2 \theta)^2 = 1^2,$$
$$\sin^4 \theta + 2 \sin^2 \theta \cos^2 \theta + \cos^4 \theta = 1.$$

Now let $\theta = 5A$:

$$\sin^4 5A + 2 \sin^2 5A \cos^2 5A + \cos^4 5A = 1.$$

This proves the statement is true for all values of A.

Example 2. Prove or disprove:

$$\sin A + \cos A = 1.$$

Solution. We can demonstrate that this equation is not generally true by setting A equal to some specific angle and then showing that the two sides of the equation are not numerically equal. Choosing $A = 30°$, we have

$$\sin 30° + \cos 30° = 1$$
$$0.5 + 0.866 = 1$$
$$1.366 = 1. \quad \text{False.}$$

This proves conclusively that the given equation is not true for all values of A. It is, however, true for some values of A; *e.g.*, if $A = 90°$, we have

$$\sin 90° + \cos 90° = 1$$
$$1 + 0 = 1. \quad \text{True.}$$

The student should note carefully that a general statement can be *disproved* by citing one instance in which it is not true. But a general statement cannot be proved by merely showing that it is true for one special case. It must be proved for all cases.

EXERCISE 12

Use the eight fundamental relations * *to write each of the following expressions as a single trigonometric function of some angle.*

1. $\dfrac{\sin 200°}{\cos 200°}.$

2. $\dfrac{1}{\cot B}.$

3. $\dfrac{1}{\sin \dfrac{B}{2}}.$ $\to \csc \frac{B}{2}$

4. $\dfrac{\cos 7A}{\sin 7A}.$ $\cot 7A$

5. $\sqrt{\csc^2 25° - 1}.$ $+\cot 25$

6. $-\sqrt{1 - \sin^2 130°}.$ $-\cos 130$ Q II

7. $\sqrt{1 - \cos^2 40°}.$ $+\sin 40°$

8. $\sqrt{1 + \cot^2 16°}.$ $\cos 16°$

9. $-\sqrt{\sec^2 170° - 1}.$

10. $\cos 400° \tan 400°.$ $\sin 400°$

Decide which of the following statements are valid consequences of the eight fundamental relations. If the statement is true, cite proof; if false, correct it.

cont cancel 9b

11. $\dfrac{\cos 9A}{\sin 9A} = \cot A.$ *false*

12. $\cot \phi \tan \phi = 1.$

13. $\dfrac{1}{\tan A} = \cot A.$ *false*

14. $\sin \theta = \dfrac{1}{\cos \theta}.$

15. $\sec A \cos \theta = 1.$

16. $\sin \theta + \cos \theta = 1.$

17. $4 \csc^2 \theta = \dfrac{4}{\sin^2 \theta}.$

18. $(6 \cot \theta)^2 = \dfrac{36 \cos^2 \theta}{\sin^2 \theta}.$

19. $\tan^2 \theta = \dfrac{\sin^2 \theta}{\cos^2 \theta}.$

20. $\cos^3 \theta \sec^3 \theta = 1.$

21. $7 \sin^2 3B + 7 \cos^2 3B = 7.$

22. $\cot^2 \theta - \csc^2 \theta = -1.$

23. $1 + 2 \tan^2 \theta + \tan^4 \theta = \sec^4 \theta.$

24. $9 \sec^2 5B - 9 \tan^2 5B = 9.$

$\left(\tan - \sec \right) = -1$

25. $\sin \theta = \sqrt{1 - \cos^2 \theta}$ holds for θ in Q I and Q IV.

26. $\tan \theta = -\sqrt{\sec^2 \theta - 1}$ holds for θ in Q I and Q IV.

27. $\csc \theta = -\sqrt{1 + \cot^2 \theta}$ holds for θ in Q II and Q III.

28. $\sec \theta = \sqrt{1 + \tan^2 \theta}$ holds for θ in Q I and Q III.

29. $\sqrt{\sin^2 260°} = \sin 260°.$ *false*   because III Q

30. $\sqrt{\sin^2 160°} = \sin 160°.$ II Q

31. $\tan 60° = \dfrac{\sin 60°}{\cos 60°} = \dfrac{\frac{1}{2}\sqrt{3}}{\frac{1}{2}} = \sqrt{3}$

32. $\sec 45° = \dfrac{1}{\cos 45°} = \dfrac{1}{\frac{1}{2}\sqrt{2}} = \dfrac{2}{\sqrt{2}} = \sqrt{2}.$

* Do not express in terms of x, y, r.

21. Algebraic operations with the trigonometric functions. The expression $\sin \theta$, meaning the sine of angle θ, is an abstract number. It is the ratio of two distances such as

$$\frac{2 \text{ ft.}}{3 \text{ ft.}} = \frac{2}{3} \quad \text{or} \quad \frac{2 \text{ in.}}{3 \text{ in.}} = \frac{2}{3}.$$

For this reason it can be treated in the same way that we deal with numbers and letters in algebra. For example, $\sin^3 \theta + \cos^3 \theta$ may be expressed as the sum of two cubes.* Since

$$a^3 + b^3 = (a + b)(a^2 - ab + b^2),$$
$$\sin^3 \theta + \cos^3 \theta = (\sin \theta + \cos \theta)(\sin^2 \theta - \sin \theta \cos \theta + \cos^2 \theta)$$
$$= (\sin \theta + \cos \theta)(1 - \sin \theta \cos \theta).$$

Also $(\sec \theta + \tan \theta)^2$ may be expanded as the square of a binomial to equal "the square of the first plus twice the product plus the square of the last":

$$(\sec \theta + \tan \theta)^2 = \sec^2 \theta + 2 \sec \theta \tan \theta + \tan^2 \theta.$$

A glance at the fundamental relations reveals that the functions occurring most often are $\sin \theta$ and $\cos \theta$. Equations [1], [2], [4], [5] express each of the other functions directly in terms of $\sin \theta$ and $\cos \theta$. For this reason it is advantageous in many problems to reduce an expression to sines and cosines.

Example 1. Express $\dfrac{3 \csc \theta}{5 \csc \theta - 6 \cot^2 \theta}$ in terms of $\sin \theta$ and $\cos \theta$.

Solution. $\dfrac{3 \csc \theta}{5 \csc \theta - 6 \cot^2 \theta}$

$$= \frac{3\left(\dfrac{1}{\sin \theta}\right)}{5\left(\dfrac{1}{\sin \theta}\right) - 6\left(\dfrac{\cos^2 \theta}{\sin^2 \theta}\right)}$$

$$= \frac{\dfrac{3}{\sin \theta}}{\dfrac{5 \sin \theta - 6 \cos^2 \theta}{\sin^2 \theta}} \qquad \text{Getting a common denominator for the bottom.}$$

$$= \frac{3}{\sin \theta} \cdot \frac{\sin^2 \theta}{5 \sin \theta - 6 \cos^2 \theta} \qquad \text{Inverting the denominator and multiplying.}$$

$$= \frac{3 \sin \theta}{5 \sin \theta - 6 \cos^2 \theta}. \qquad \text{Reducing the fraction.}$$

* Recall that $\sin^3 \theta$ is a short way of writing $(\sin \theta)^3$.

In order to express this quantity in terms of just $\sin \theta$, replace $\cos^2 \theta$ with $(1 - \sin^2 \theta)$ to obtain $\dfrac{3 \sin \theta}{5 \sin \theta - 6 + 6 \sin^2 \theta}$.

Example 2. Express each of the other trigonometric functions of θ in terms of $\sin \theta$.

First solution.

$$\cos \theta = \pm \sqrt{1 - \sin^2 \theta}, \qquad\qquad \text{using [6];}$$

$$\tan \theta = \frac{\sin \theta}{\cos \theta} = \frac{\sin \theta}{\pm \sqrt{1 - \sin^2 \theta}}, \qquad \text{using [4], [6];}$$

$$\cot \theta = \frac{\cos \theta}{\sin \theta} = \frac{\pm \sqrt{1 - \sin^2 \theta}}{\sin \theta}, \qquad \text{using [5], [6];}$$

$$\sec \theta = \frac{1}{\cos \theta} = \frac{\pm 1}{\sqrt{1 - \sin^2 \theta}}, \qquad \text{using [2], [6];}$$

$$\csc \theta = \frac{1}{\sin \theta}, \qquad\qquad\qquad \text{using [1].}$$

Second solution. Place θ in standard position. In order to make $y/r = \sin \theta$, let $y = \sin \theta$ and $r = 1$. The Pythagorean theorem gives $x = \pm \sqrt{1 - \sin^2 \theta}$. Then

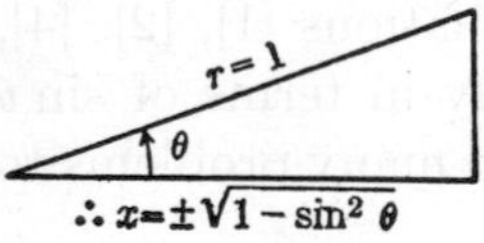

$$\cos \theta = \frac{x}{r} = \pm \sqrt{1 - \sin^2 \theta},$$

$$\tan \theta = \frac{y}{x} = \frac{\sin \theta}{\pm \sqrt{1 - \sin^2 \theta}}, \text{ etc.}$$

FIG. 27

EXERCISE 13

Simplify each of the following.

1. $\dfrac{\sec^3 \theta - \tan^3 \theta}{\sec \theta - \tan \theta}$.

2. $\dfrac{\sin^4 \theta - \cos^4 \theta}{\sin^2 \theta - \cos^2 \theta}$.

3. $\dfrac{\dfrac{1}{3 \tan \theta} - \dfrac{3}{2 \tan^2 \theta}}{\dfrac{2}{\tan^3 \theta} - \dfrac{9}{\tan^4 \theta}}$.

4. $\dfrac{\csc^2 \theta - 5 \csc \theta + 6}{\csc^2 \theta - 3 \csc \theta + 2}$.

Reduce each of the following to an expression that involves no function except $\sin \theta$ and $\cos \theta$. Simplify.

5. $\dfrac{\cot \theta \cos \theta}{\csc \theta - \sin \theta}$.

6. $\dfrac{3 \sec^2 \theta \csc^2 \theta}{\sec^2 \theta + \csc^2 \theta}$.

7. $\dfrac{2 - \tan \theta}{2 \csc \theta - \sec \theta}$.

8. $\dfrac{\cos \theta - \sec \theta}{\tan \theta} + \dfrac{\tan \theta}{\sec \theta}$.

9. Express each of the other trigonometric functions in terms of cos θ.
10. Express each of the other trigonometric functions in terms of tan θ.
11. Express cos 111° in terms of sin 111°.
12. Express sin 190° in terms of cos 190°.
13. Express cot 234° in terms of csc 234°.
14. Express tan 25° in terms of sec 25°.
15. Express sec 4θ in terms of tan 4θ.
16. Express csc 2θ in terms of sin 2θ.

22. Identities and conditional equations.

An **identity** * is an equation that holds true for all permissible † values of the letters involved.

Illustration 1. $x^2 - 9 = (x + 3)(x - 3)$ holds true for all values of x.

Illustration 2. $x^2 + xy - 2y^2 = (x + 2y)(x - y)$ holds true for all values of x and y.

Illustration 3. $x - \dfrac{x^2 - 7x}{x - 5} = \dfrac{2x}{x - 5}$ holds true for all permissible values of x, i.e., for all values of x except $x = 5$. When $x = 5$, each side of the equation involves a fraction whose denominator is zero. Such fractions have no meaning, and we say their value does not exist.

Illustration 4. $\sin^2 \theta + \cos^2 \theta = 1$ holds true for all values of θ.

Illustration 5. $1 + \tan^2 \theta = \sec^2 \theta$ holds true for all permissible values of θ, i.e., for all values of θ except 90°, 270°, and angles coterminal with them.

Illustration 6.   The following "trick with numbers" illustrates a simple identity.

> Choose any number except 0.
> Multiply your number by 5.
> To this number add the square of your original number.
> Multiply your result by 2.
> Divide the number you now have by the original number.
> Subtract 10.
> Divide by your original number.

If you have followed instructions, your result should be 2 regardless of your choice of the original number. To prove this, let x be the original number. Then the numbers that follow are $5x$, $5x + x^2$, $2(5x + x^2)$ or $x(10 + 2x)$, $10 + 2x$, $2x$, and 2. The identity used is

$$\dfrac{\dfrac{2(5x + x^2)}{x} - 10}{x} = 2.$$

It holds for all values of x except 0. Try it for a fraction. For a negative number.

---

* Also called an *identical equation*.

† The *permissible* values of the letters involved are all those values for which each side of the equation has meaning.

A **conditional equation** is an equation that *does not* hold true for all permissible values of the letters involved.

Illustration 7. $2x - 7 = 3$ holds true for only one value of x, namely $x = 5$.

Illustration 8. $x^2 - 8x + 15 = 0$ holds true for only two values of x, namely $x = 3$ and $x = 5$.

Illustration 9. $x(x - 7)(x + 4) = 0$ holds true for only three values of x, namely $x = 0$, $x = 7$, and $x = -4$.

Illustration 10. $\sin \theta = \cos \theta$ holds true for only two values of θ between $0°$ and $360°$. They are $\theta = 45°$ and $\theta = 225°$.

Illustration 11. $\sin \theta = 5 + \cos \theta$ holds true for no value of θ.

The difference between an identity and a conditional equation can easily be seen from the contrasting definitions:

$$\left.\begin{cases} An\ identity \\ A\ conditional\ equation \end{cases}\right\} \text{ is an equation that } \begin{cases} holds\ true \\ does\ not\ hold\ true \end{cases}$$

for all permissible values of the letters involved.

An identity *says* that both sides of an equation are equal for all permissible values. The process by which we demonstrate that the two sides are identical is called "proving the identity." A conditional equation *asks*, "For what values of the unknowns is the left side of this equation equal to the right side?" The process by which these values are found is called "solving the equation."

23. Trigonometric identities. The eight fundamental relations are identities. By using them, we can prove other identities. For one who goes further in mathematics, or in subjects involving mathematics, it is highly important to gain a certain amount of experience in proving identities. For this reason we place considerable emphasis on the following examples and problems.

It is most desirable to prove an identity by *transforming one side* of the equation *to the other side, which should be left unaltered.** The side with which we work is usually the more complicated one. There is no set rule for making these transformations. The following suggestions will, however, indicate the first step in most cases.

---

* The instructor may wish to permit the student to reduce each side of the equation independently to a common third expression. This method is sometimes desirable when both sides are quite complicated.

1. If one side involves only one function of the angle, express the other side in terms of this function.

2. If one side is factorable, factor it.

3. If one side has only one term in its denominator (and several terms in its numerator), break up the fraction.

4. If one side contains one or more indicated operations (such as squaring an expression, adding fractions, or multiplying two expressions), begin by performing these operations. This is especially helpful if this side involves only sines and cosines.

5. When working with one side, keep an eye on the other side to see which transformation will most easily reduce it to the other side. It is frequently helpful to multiply the numerator and denominator of a fraction by the same expression. If possible, avoid introducing radicals.

6. When in doubt, express the more complicated side in terms of sines and cosines and then simplify. *or when complicated*

At each step, look for some combination that can be replaced by a more simple expression.

The following examples illustrate the suggestions.

Example 1. Prove the identity

$$3 \cos^4 \theta + 6 \sin^2 \theta = 3 + 3 \sin^4 \theta.$$

Proof.

$3 \cos^4 \theta + 6 \sin^2 \theta$	$3 + 3 \sin^4 \theta$
$= 3(1 - \sin^2 \theta)^2 + 6 \sin^2 \theta$	
$= 3 - 6 \sin^2 \theta + 3 \sin^4 \theta + 6 \sin^2 \theta$	
$= 3 + 3 \sin^4 \theta.$	

Example 2. Prove the identity

$$\sec^2 \theta + \tan^2 \theta = \sec^4 \theta - \tan^4 \theta.$$

Proof.

$\sec^2 \theta + \tan^2 \theta$	$\sec^4 \theta - \tan^4 \theta$
	$= (\sec^2 \theta + \tan^2 \theta)(\sec^2 \theta - \tan^2 \theta)$
	$= (\sec^2 \theta + \tan^2 \theta) \cdot 1$
	$= (\sec^2 \theta + \tan^2 \theta).$

Example 3. Prove the identity

$$\frac{\sin \theta + \cot \theta}{\cos \theta} = \tan \theta + \csc \theta.$$

Proof.

$$\frac{\sin \theta + \cot \theta}{\cos \theta} \qquad\qquad \tan \theta + \csc \theta$$

$$= \frac{\sin \theta}{\cos \theta} + \frac{\cot \theta}{\cos \theta}$$

$$= \tan \theta + \frac{\dfrac{\cos \theta}{\sin \theta}}{\cos \theta}$$

$$= \tan \theta + \frac{1}{\sin \theta}$$

$$= \tan \theta + \csc \theta$$

(handwritten: $\csc \theta = \dfrac{\cot \theta}{\cos \theta}$)

Example 4. Prove the identity

$$\frac{\sin \theta}{1 + \cos \theta} + \frac{1 + \cos \theta}{\sin \theta} = 2 \csc \theta.$$

Proof. The left side indicates the addition of two fractions that involve only sines and cosines of θ. We begin by adding these fractions.

$$\frac{\sin \theta}{1 + \cos \theta} + \frac{1 + \cos \theta}{\sin \theta} \qquad\qquad 2 \csc \theta$$

$$= \frac{\sin^2 \theta + 1 + 2 \cos \theta + \cos^2 \theta}{(1 + \cos \theta) \sin \theta}$$

$$= \frac{2 + 2 \cos \theta}{(1 + \cos \theta) \sin \theta}$$

$$= \frac{2(1 + \cos \theta)}{(1 + \cos \theta) \sin \theta}$$

$$= \frac{2}{\sin \theta}$$

$$= 2 \csc \theta.$$

Example 5. Prove the identity $\dfrac{\cot \theta}{\csc \theta - 1} = \dfrac{\csc \theta + 1}{\cot \theta}$.

Proof. Since the numerator of the right side is $\csc \theta + 1$, let us multiply top and bottom of the left side by $\csc \theta + 1$.

$$\frac{\cot \theta(\csc \theta + 1)}{(\csc \theta - 1)(\csc \theta + 1)}$$

$$= \frac{\cot \theta(\csc \theta + 1)}{\csc^2 \theta - 1}$$

$$= \frac{\cot \theta(\csc \theta + 1)}{\cot^2 \theta}$$

$$= \frac{\csc \theta + 1}{\cot \theta}.$$

Example 6.   Prove the identity

$$\frac{\cot A + \csc B}{\tan B + \tan A \sec B} = \cot A \cot B.$$

Proof.

$$\frac{\cot A + \csc B}{\tan B + \tan A \sec B}$$

$$= \frac{\dfrac{\cos A}{\sin A} + \dfrac{1}{\sin B}}{\dfrac{\sin B}{\cos B} + \dfrac{\sin A}{\cos A \cos B}}$$

$$= \frac{\dfrac{\sin B \cos A + \sin A}{\sin A \sin B}}{\dfrac{\sin B \cos A + \sin A}{\cos A \cos B}}$$

$$= \frac{\cos A \cos B}{\sin A \sin B}$$

$$= \cot A \cot B.$$

$\cot A \cot B$

(margin note: when get complicated change to sin & cos)

EXERCISE 14

Prove each of the following identities by reducing one side to the other.

1. $\dfrac{\dfrac{5}{3} - \dfrac{x-8}{x-4}}{\dfrac{2}{3} - \dfrac{x-6}{2x-8}} = 4$

2. $\dfrac{x+8 - \dfrac{4x+18}{x+3}}{x+9 - \dfrac{x-6}{x+2}} = \dfrac{(x+1)(x+2)}{(x+3)(x+4)}.$

3. $\dfrac{2 - \dfrac{x+7}{x+5}}{1 - \dfrac{x-13}{x^2-25}} = \dfrac{x-5}{x-4}.$

4. $\dfrac{\dfrac{x^2+12x}{x^2-36} - 1}{4 - \dfrac{3(x+7)}{x+6}} = \dfrac{12}{x-6}.$

5. $\dfrac{\sec \theta}{\csc \theta} = \tan \theta.$

6. $\dfrac{\sin \theta}{\csc \theta} + \dfrac{\cos \theta}{\sec \theta} = 1.$

7. $(\tan \theta + 1)(\tan \theta - 1) = \sec^2 \theta - 2.$
8. $\sin^2 3B + \cos^2 3B + \cot^2 4B = \csc^2 4B.$
9. $3 \tan^2 \theta + 4 \sec^2 \theta = 7 \sec^2 \theta - 3.$
10. $\csc^4 \theta + \cot^4 \theta = 2 \csc^4 \theta - 2 \csc^2 \theta + 1.$
11. $\sin^4 \theta + 3 \cos^2 \theta = 1 + \cos^2 \theta + \cos^4 \theta.$
12. $\tan^4 \theta + \sec^4 \theta = 2 \tan^4 \theta + 2 \tan^2 \theta + 1.$

13. $\dfrac{\sin \theta + 8 \csc \theta}{\sin \theta + 4 \csc \theta} = \dfrac{\sin^2 \theta + 8}{\sin^2 \theta + 4}.$

14. $\dfrac{\tan \theta - 1}{1 - \cot \theta} = \tan \theta.$

15. $\dfrac{1}{\sec \theta + 1 + \cos \theta} = \dfrac{\cos \theta}{1 + \cos \theta + \cos^2 \theta}.$

16. $\dfrac{\csc \theta}{1 - \sin \theta} = \dfrac{1}{\sin \theta - \sin^2 \theta}.$

17. $\dfrac{\csc^3 \theta - 8}{\csc^2 \theta - 3 \csc \theta + 2} = \dfrac{\csc^2 \theta + 2 \csc \theta + 4}{\csc \theta - 1}.$

18. $\tan^4 \theta + 2 \tan^2 \theta + 1 = \sec^4 \theta.$

19. $\dfrac{\sin^3 \theta + \tan^3 \theta}{\sin \theta + \tan \theta} = \sin^2 \theta - \sin \theta \tan \theta + \tan^2 \theta.$

20. $\dfrac{\sec^3 \theta - \cos^3 \theta}{\sec \theta - \cos \theta} = \sec^2 \theta + 1 + \cos^2 \theta.$

21. $\dfrac{2 \cos \theta + 3 \sin \theta \cot \theta}{\sin \theta} = 5 \cot \theta.$

22. $\dfrac{\cot \theta + 4 \sec \theta}{\cot \theta \csc \theta} = \sin \theta + 4 \tan^2 \theta.$

23. $\dfrac{1 + \cot B + \sec B}{\csc B} = \sin B + \cos B + \tan B.$

24. $\dfrac{\sec A + \sin A + \cot A}{\cos A} = \sec^2 A + \tan A + \csc A.$

25. $\dfrac{1}{\sec \theta - 1} - \dfrac{1}{\sec \theta + 1} = 2 \cot^2 \theta.$

26. $\dfrac{\sin \theta}{1 - \cos \theta} + \dfrac{1 - \cos \theta}{\sin \theta} = 2 \csc \theta.$

27. $\dfrac{\tan \theta}{\csc \theta - \cot \theta} - \dfrac{\sin \theta}{\csc \theta + \cot \theta} = \sec \theta + \cos \theta.$

28. $\dfrac{1 - \sin \theta}{\cos \theta} - \dfrac{\cos \theta}{1 + \sin \theta} = 0.$

29. $(1 + \sin \theta)(\sec \theta - \tan \theta) = \cos \theta.$
30. $(2 \sin A + 3 \cos A)^2 + (3 \sin A - 2 \cos A)^2 = 13.$
31. $(\sec B + 3 \cos B)^2 - (\sec B - 3 \cos B)^2 = 12.$
32. $(1 + \tan A)(1 + \cot A) = 2 + \tan A + \cot A.$

33. $\dfrac{5}{1 + 4 \cos^2 \theta} = \dfrac{5 \sec^2 \theta}{\tan^2 \theta + 5}.$ **34.** $\dfrac{\csc \theta}{6 \csc \theta + \cot \theta} = \dfrac{1}{6 + \cos \theta}.$

35. $\dfrac{\tan \theta}{\sec \theta - \cos \theta} = \dfrac{1}{\sin \theta}.$ **36.** $\dfrac{3 \sin \theta + \cos \theta}{3 \tan \theta + 1} = \cos \theta.$

37. $\dfrac{\cot^2 \theta}{\csc^2 \theta - 2 \csc \theta - 3} = \dfrac{\csc \theta - 1}{\csc \theta - 3}.$

38. $\dfrac{\sec^2 \theta - 5}{\sec^2 \theta - 6 \tan \theta + 7} = \dfrac{\tan \theta + 2}{\tan \theta - 4}.$

39. $\dfrac{\sec^3 \theta + 3 \sec \theta - 4 \tan^2 \theta - 4}{\tan^2 \theta - 4 \sec \theta + 4} = \sec \theta.$

40. $\dfrac{\cos^2 \theta}{1 + \cos^2 \theta - \sin \theta} = \dfrac{1 + \sin \theta}{2 + \sin \theta}.$

41. $\dfrac{\cot A \cot B}{1 + \cot B} = \dfrac{\cos A \cos B}{\sin A (\sin B + \cos B)}.$

42. $\dfrac{\sec A \sec B}{\cos A + \sec B} = \dfrac{1}{\cos A(\cos A \cos B + 1)}.$

43. $\dfrac{\sin A + \sin B}{\csc A + \csc B} = \sin A \sin B.$

44. $\dfrac{\tan A + \sec B}{\sec A + \tan B} = \dfrac{\sin A \cos B + \cos A}{\cos B + \cos A \sin B}.$

In Probs. 45 to 48, assume the angle is in Q I.

45. $\sqrt{\dfrac{1 - \sin \theta}{1 + \sin \theta}} = \dfrac{\cos \theta}{1 + \sin \theta}.$ *Hint:* Rationalize the left side by multiplying

under the radical by $\dfrac{1 + \sin \theta}{1 + \sin \theta}.$

46.* $\sqrt{\dfrac{\csc A - 1}{\csc A + 1}} = \dfrac{\cot A}{\csc A + 1}.$

47.* $\sqrt{\dfrac{\sec B + \tan B}{\sec B - \tan B}} = \sec B + \tan B.$

48.* $\sqrt{\dfrac{1 + \cos \theta}{1 - \cos \theta}} = \csc \theta + \cot \theta.$

49. Verify identity 41 for $A = 45°$, $B = 30°$.

50. Verify identity 42 for $\sec A = 2$, $\sec B = 3$.

51. Verify identity 35 for $\theta = 60°$.

52. Verify identity 48 for $\sin \theta = \frac{3}{5}$ with θ in Q I.

53. State a nonpermissible value of θ for which identity 45 does not hold true.

Prove each of the following identities.

54. $\dfrac{\sin A \cos B + \cos A \sin B}{\cos A \cos B - \sin A \sin B} = \dfrac{\tan A + \tan B}{1 - \tan A \tan B}.$

55. $\theta \cos^2 \theta + \csc \theta - \cot \theta \cos \theta + \theta \sin^2 \theta = \theta + \sin \theta.$

56. $(\sin A - \cos A)(1 + \tan A + \cot A) = \sin A \tan A - \cos A \cot A.$

57. $(\sin A \cos B + \cos A \sin B)^2 + (\cos A \cos B - \sin A \sin B)^2 = 1.$

58. $\sin \theta \cos \theta(\cos \theta + \sin^2 \theta \sec \theta + \sec \theta) = 2 \sin \theta.$

59. $\csc^6 \theta - \cot^6 \theta = 1 + 3 \csc^2 \theta \cot^2 \theta.$

60. $(1 + \tan \theta + \cot \theta)^2 = 1 + \sec^2 \theta + \csc^2 \theta + 2 \sec \theta \csc \theta.$

61. $(1 + \cot \theta + \csc \theta)^2 = 2(\cot \theta + \csc \theta)(\csc \theta + 1).$

62. $\dfrac{\cot^2 A}{\sin^2 B} - \dfrac{\cot^2 B}{\sin^2 A} = \cot^2 A - \cot^2 B$

63. $\dfrac{1 + \sin \theta + \cos \theta}{1 + \sin \theta - \cos \theta} = \dfrac{1 + \cos \theta}{\sin \theta}.$

64. $\dfrac{2 \csc \theta + \cot \theta}{2 \csc \theta - \cot \theta} + \dfrac{2 \sec \theta - 1}{2 \sec \theta + 1} = \dfrac{10 - 2 \sin^2 \theta}{3 + \sin^2 \theta}.$

* See hint for Prob. 45.

CHAPTER 4

RELATED ANGLES

24. Related angles. The fact that the table of trigonometric functions deals with only acute angles should have implied that functions of larger angles are expressible in terms of functions of acute angles. Such is really the case. In order to determine the functions of angles larger than 90°, we introduce the concept of the related angle.

The related angle of a given angle θ is the positive acute angle be-

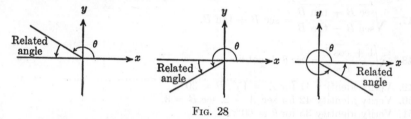

Fig. 28

tween the x-axis and the terminal side of θ. Hence, *to find the related angle of θ* *

(a) *If θ is in Q II, subtract θ from 180°.*

(b) *If θ is in Q III, subtract 180° from θ.*

(c) *If θ is in Q IV, subtract θ from 360°.*

It is to be noted that, in finding the related angle, we always work to or from 180° or 360°, never 90° or 270°. Thus

The related angle of 160° is 20°.

The related angle of 260° is 80°.

The related angle of 310° is 50°.

The related angle of 500° is the related angle of (500° − 360°) = 140°, which is 40°.

EXERCISE 15

Find the related angle of each of the following angles.

1. 290°	**2.** 97°.	**3.** 220°.	**4.** 275°.
5. 106°.	**6.** 268° 45′.	**7.** 306° 50′.	**8.** 895°.
9. 615°.	**10.** −20°.	**11.** −355°.	**12.** −105°.

* Since coterminal angles have the same trigonometric functions, we shall consider only those angles between 0° and 360°.

25. Reduction to functions of an acute angle. Two numbers are said to be numerically equal if they are equal, except perhaps for sign. If a and b are numerically equal, then $a = \pm b$.

Theorem. Any trigonometric function of an angle is numerically equal to the same function of its related angle.

To prove this, let θ_1 be any positive acute angle, and let θ_2, θ_3, θ_4 be positive angles, one in each of the other three quadrants,

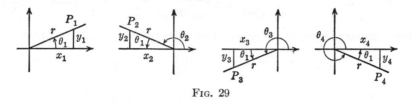

FIG. 29

such that their common related angle is θ_1. Choose points P_1, P_2, P_3, P_4 on the terminal sides of these angles so that all four points have the same radius vector r. The four triangles of reference are congruent. Therefore, the corresponding sides are numerically equal. Hence

$$x_2 = -x_1, \qquad x_3 = -x_1, \qquad x_4 = x_1;$$

and

$$y_2 = y_1, \qquad y_3 = -y_1, \qquad y_4 = -y_1.$$

Then

$$\sin \theta_2 = \frac{y_2}{r} = \frac{y_1}{r} = \sin \theta_1,$$

$$\sin \theta_3 = \frac{y_3}{r} = \frac{-y_1}{r} = -\sin \theta_1,$$

$$\sin \theta_4 = \frac{y_4}{r} = \frac{-y_1}{r} = -\sin \theta_1,$$

and

$$\cos \theta_2 = \frac{x_2}{r} = \frac{-x_1}{r} = -\cos \theta_1,$$

$$\cos \theta_3 = \frac{x_3}{r} = \frac{-x_1}{r} = -\cos \theta_1,$$

$$\cos \theta_4 = \frac{x_4}{r} = \frac{x_1}{r} = \cos \theta_1.$$

Similarly, each of the other functions of θ_2, θ_3, θ_4 is numerically equal to the same function of θ_1, the common related angle. The proper sign, $+$ or $-$, is determined by the quadrant in which the given angle lies.

Example 1. Use the related-angle theorem to find sin 120°, cos 120° without tables.

Solution. The related angle of 120° is 180° $-$ 120° $=$ 60°. Since 120° is in Q II, its sine is positive and its cosine is negative. Hence

$$\sin 120° = + \sin 60° = \frac{\sqrt{3}}{2},$$

$$\cos 120° = - \cos 60° = -\tfrac{1}{2}.$$

The remaining functions can be found by using the fundamental identities:

$$\tan 120° = \frac{\sin 120°}{\cos 120°} = \frac{\sqrt{3}/2}{-\tfrac{1}{2}} = -\sqrt{3},$$

$$\cot 120° = \frac{1}{\tan 120°} = -\frac{1}{\sqrt{3}} = \frac{-\sqrt{3}}{3}, \text{ etc.}$$

Example 2. Use the related-angle theorem to find sin 255° and tan 255°.

Solution. The related angle of 255° is 255° $-$ 180° $=$ 75°. Hence

$$\sin 255° = - \sin 75° = -.9659,$$
$$\tan 255° = + \tan 75° = 3.732.$$

EXERCISE 16

Use the related-angle theorem to find the sine and cosine of each of the following angles without the use of tables.

1. 225°.	**2.** 315°.	**3.** 135°.	**4.** 210°.
5. 330°.	**6.** 150°.	**7.** 240°.	**8.** 300°.
9. 1200°.	**10.** 600°.	**11.** 1050°.	**12.** 855°.

Use the related-angle theorem and tables to find the values of the following functions.

13. tan 318°.	**14.** cos 167°.	**15.** cot 108°.	**16.** sin 202°.
17. cos 254°.	**18.** sin 283°.	**19.** tan 215° 10′.	**20.** cos 326° 30′.
21. sin 99° 50′.	**22.** cot 230° 25′.	**23.** cos 352° 7′.	**24.** tan 169° 42′.

Prove or disprove the following statements without using tables.

25. sin 190° $>$ sin 185°.   **26.** cos 20° $<$ cos 335°.

27. tan 95° $=$ tan 85°.   **28.** sin 170° $= -$ cos 80°.

29. $1 + \tan^2 137° = \sec^2 43°$.   **30.** $\cos^2 39° + \sin^2 321° = 1$.

31. $\dfrac{\cos 112°}{\cos 202°} = \tan 22°$.   **32.** $\dfrac{\sin 343°}{\cos 197°} = \tan 17°$.

Name one angle in each of the other three quadrants whose trigonometric functions are numerically equal to those of the given angle.

33. 252°.   **34.** 345°.   **35.** 26°.   **36.** 161°.

26. Trigonometric functions of $(-\theta)$. Let θ be any angle. Then $(-\theta)$ indicates the same amount of rotation but in the *opposite* direction. Place both angles in standard position on the same

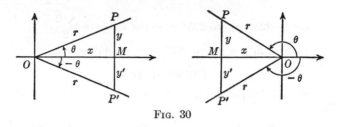

FIG. 30

coordinate system. Choose any point $P(x, y)$ on the terminal side of θ. Drop a perpendicular from P to the x-axis and extend it until it strikes the terminal side of $(-\theta)$ at $P'(x, y')$. The triangles of reference, OPM and $OP'M$, are congruent. Hence $OP = OP' = r$. But y and y' are only numerically equal. Since $y' = -y$, we conclude that

$$\sin(-\theta) = \frac{y'}{r} = \frac{-y}{r} = -\sin\theta,$$

$$\cos(-\theta) = \frac{x}{r} = \cos\theta,$$

$$\tan(-\theta) = \frac{y'}{x} = \frac{-y}{x} = -\tan\theta.$$

Similarly,

$$\cot(-\theta) = -\cot\theta, \; \sec(-\theta) = \sec\theta, \; \csc(-\theta) = -\csc\theta.$$

The student should draw figures for θ in the other quadrants and also for θ a negative angle. For all possible positions of θ the following is true.

Theorem. *For any angle θ,*

$$\sin(-\theta) = -\sin\theta,$$
$$\cos(-\theta) = \cos\theta,$$
$$\tan(-\theta) = -\tan\theta.$$

The other three functions behave as do their reciprocals.

Example. Compute $\sin(-225°)$, $\cos(-225°)$, $\tan(-225°)$.

Solution. Using the preceding theorem and the related-angle theorem,

$$\sin(-225°) = -\sin 225° = -(-\sin 45°) = \frac{\sqrt{2}}{2},$$

$$\cos(-225°) = \cos 225° = -\cos 45° = -\frac{\sqrt{2}}{2},$$

$$\tan(-225°) = -\tan 225° = -\tan 45° = -1.$$

EXERCISE 17

Use the theorem in Art. 26 to compute the sine, cosine, and tangent of the following angles.

1. $-45°$.   **2.** $-30°$.   **3.** $-60°$.   **4.** $-90°$.

Prove or disprove the following without using tables.

5. $\cos(-123°)\sec 123° = -1$.   **6.** $\csc 69° \sin(-69°) = -1$.

7. $\dfrac{\sin(-\theta)}{\cos\theta} = \tan(-\theta)$.   **8.** $\dfrac{\sin(-57°)}{\sin(-33°)} = \cot 33°$.

9. $\sin^2(-\theta) - \cos^2\theta = -1$.   **10.** $\tan^2(-\theta) = \sec^2\theta - 1$.

11. $\cos(-240°) = \cos 60°$.   **12.** $\tan(-175°) = -\tan 5°$.

13. $\tan(-987°)$ is a negative number.   **14.** $\cos(-190°)$ is a positive number.

15. Draw a figure and prove that, if θ is a positive angle in Q IV, then (a) $\sin(-\theta) = -\sin\theta$, (b) $\cos(-\theta) = \cos\theta$.

16. Draw a figure and prove that, if θ is a negative angle in Q II, then (a) $\sin(-\theta) = -\sin\theta$, (b) $\cos(-\theta) = \cos\theta$.

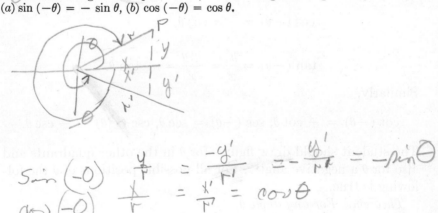

$\sin(-\theta) \quad \dfrac{y}{r} = \dfrac{-y'}{r'} = -\dfrac{y'}{r'} = -\sin\theta$

$\cos(-\theta) \quad \dfrac{x}{r} = \dfrac{x'}{r'} = \cos\theta$

$y = -y'$ just denotes them being different in sign not nec-ey is actual neg

CHAPTER 5

RADIAN MEASURE

27. The radian. Thus far we have employed the *degree* as the unit of measure for angles. It may be thought of as $\frac{1}{360}$ of the angular magnitude about a point. For practical purposes the degree is a convenient unit, but many results in higher mathematics, particularly in calculus, are simplified if another unit, the radian, is used.

A **radian** *is an angle which, if its vertex is placed at the center of a circle, subtends an arc equal in length to the radius of the circle.*

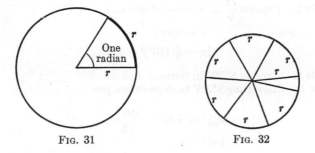

FIG. 31   FIG. 32

28. Radians and degrees. According to the definition of a radian, the number of radians in a circle is equal to the number of times the radius can be laid off along the circumference (Fig. 32). Since $c = 2\pi r$, the number of radians in a circle is 2π. But the number of degrees in a circle is $360°$. Hence

$$2\pi \text{ radians} = 360°,$$

or

(1) $$\pi \textbf{ radians} = \textbf{180}°.$$

Hence

(2) $$1 \text{ radian} = \frac{180°}{\pi} = \frac{180°}{3.14159}$$

$$= 57.2958° = 57° \, 17.75',$$

47

and

(3) $1° = \dfrac{\pi}{180}$ radians $= 0.017453$ radian,

(4) $1' = \dfrac{1°}{60} = \dfrac{0.017453}{60}$ radian $= 0.00029$ radian.

It is better not to try to learn equations (2), (3), (4). Memorize (1) and derive your results from it. In expressing the more common angles in terms of radians, we usually leave the result in terms of π. Thus $90° = \pi/2$. When no unit of measure is indicated, it is understood that an angle is expressed in radians. Thus if we read $\theta = \pi/6$, we understand that $\theta = \pi/6$ radians $= 30°$.

The student should become quite familiar with the radian measure of $30°$, $45°$, $60°$, $90°$, and the angles that are related to them, namely $120°$, $135°$, $150°$, $180°$, $210°$, $225°$, $240°$, $270°$, $300°$, $315°$, $330°$.

Example 1. Express $\dfrac{7\pi}{9}$ in terms of degrees.

Solution. Since $\pi = 180°$,

$$\tfrac{7}{9}\pi = \tfrac{7}{9}(180°) = 140°.$$

Example 2. Express $8°\ 25'$ in terms of radians.
Solution 1. Converting $8°\ 25'$ to degrees, we get

$$8\tfrac{25}{60}° = 8\tfrac{5}{12}° = \frac{101°}{12}.$$

Since $180° = \pi$,

$$1° = \frac{\pi}{180},$$

$$\frac{101°}{12} = \frac{101}{12} \cdot \frac{\pi}{180} = \frac{101\pi}{2160}.$$

This is the accurate result. If π is replaced by 3.1416, we get

$$8°\ 25' = .1469,$$

correct to four decimal places.

Solution 2. Use Table I, page 2 in the tables, and interpolate:

$$8°\ 20' = .1454,$$
$$8°\ 25' = \qquad ,$$
$$8°\ 30' = .1484.$$

Hence $8°\ 25' = .1469.$

Example 3.　Express 2 radians in terms of degrees.
Solution 1.　Since

$$\pi \text{ radians} = 180°,$$

$$1 \text{ radian} = \frac{180°}{\pi},$$

$$2 \text{ radians} = \frac{360°}{\pi}.$$

This exact result may be approximated by the decimal form $\dfrac{360°}{3.1416} = 114.591°$
$= 114° \, 35.5'$, which is correct to tenths of minutes.

Solution 2.　Since

$$1 \text{ radian} = 57° \, 17.75',$$

$$2 \text{ radians} = 2(57° \, 17.75'),$$

$$= 114° \, 35.5'.$$

Example 4.　Evaluate $\csc \dfrac{7\pi}{6}$.

Solution.

$$\csc \frac{7\pi}{6} = \csc \frac{7(\overset{30°}{\cancel{180°}})}{\cancel{6}} = \csc 210° = \frac{1}{\sin 210°} = \frac{1}{-\sin 30°} = \frac{1}{-\frac{1}{2}} = -2.$$

EXERCISE 18

Express in degrees.

1. $\dfrac{\pi}{5}$.　　　　2. $\dfrac{3\pi}{10}$.　　　　3. $\dfrac{5\pi}{6}$.　　　　4. $\dfrac{5\pi}{4}$.

5. $\dfrac{7\pi}{4}$.　　　　6. $\dfrac{5\pi}{3}$.　　　　7. $\dfrac{7\pi}{20}$.　　　　8. 10π.

9. $-\dfrac{11\pi}{18}$.　　10. $\dfrac{7\pi}{6}$.　　11. $\dfrac{50\pi}{9}$.　　12. $-\dfrac{\pi}{6}$.

13. 6.　　　　　14. 3.1.　　　　　15. 1.5.　　　　16. 0.7.

Express in radians, leaving the result in terms of π.

17. 60°.　　　18. 45°.　　　19. 135°.　　　20. 120°.
21. 270°.　　22. 330°.　　23. 240°.　　24. 90°.
25. 22½°.　　26. 40°.　　27. 108°.　　28. 405°.
29. 510°.　　30. 130°.　　31. 900°.　　32. 15°.

Convert to radian measure, obtaining the result to four decimal places.

33. 34° 35'.　　34. 61° 55'.　　35. 83° 26'.　　36. 29° 14'.

Evaluate without using tables.

37. $\sin \dfrac{5\pi}{3}$.　　38. $\cos \dfrac{3\pi}{4}$.　　39. $\cos \dfrac{\pi}{4}$.　　40. $\sin \dfrac{5\pi}{6}$.

41. $\cos 4\pi$.　　42. $\sin \dfrac{\pi}{6}$.　　43. $\sin \dfrac{19\pi}{6}$.　　44. $\cos \dfrac{4\pi}{3}$.

45. $\sec \dfrac{2\pi}{3}$.   **46.** $\tan \dfrac{3\pi}{2}$.   **47.** $\cot \dfrac{\pi}{2}$.   **48.** $\cot \dfrac{7\pi}{4}$.

49. $\tan \left(-\dfrac{11\pi}{6} \right)$.   **50.** $\sin \left(-\dfrac{\pi}{3} \right)$.   **51.** $\cos \left(-\dfrac{5\pi}{4} \right)$.   **52.** $\csc \pi$.

Use Table I *to evaluate the following.* (The angle is understood to be in radians.)

53. $\sin 1.0007$.   **54.** $\cos 0.6021$.   **55.** $\tan 0.1513$.   **56.** $\cos 1.2421$.

57. Express in radians the angle made by the hands of a clock at 4:00. At 1:30.

58. One angle of a triangle is $2\pi/5$. Another angle is 8°. Express the third angle in radians.

59. Through how many radians does the minute hand of a clock rotate in 50 min.? In 8 hr.?

60. Through how many radians does the hour hand of a clock rotate in 2 hr.? In 1 week?

29. Length of a circular arc. In a circle of radius r, let an arc of length a be subtended by a central angle θ. Then

$$a = r\theta, \quad \text{where } \theta \text{ is in radians.}$$

To prove this, recall that in any circle the arc subtended by a central angle is proportional to this angle. Hence if 1 radian subtends an arc equal to the radius, then θ radians subtend an arc equal to θ times the radius. It is to be remembered that *the central angle must be measured in radians.*

In the equation $a = r\theta$, if two of the quantities a, r, θ are known, the third can be found.

Example. A circle has a radius of 100 in. (*a*) How long is the arc subtended by a central angle of 72°? (*b*) How large is the central angle that subtends an arc of 30 in.?

*Solution.** (*a*) Since

$$180° = \pi \text{ radians,}$$

$$1° = \frac{\pi}{180} \text{ radians,}$$

$$72° = 72 \cdot \frac{\pi}{180} \text{ radians} = \frac{2\pi}{5} \text{ radians.}$$

---

* In all discussions and problems in this chapter, all figures are to be considered as exact. They are not approximations. For the sake of uniformity write all approximate results with three-figure accuracy. It may be convenient to use $\dfrac{1}{\pi} = 0.3183$.

Using
$$a = r\theta, \text{ where } \theta \text{ is in radians,}$$

$$a = 100 \cdot \frac{2\pi}{5} = \textbf{40}\boldsymbol{\pi} \textbf{ in.} \text{ (or } \textit{126 in.}\text{).}$$

(b) Using

$$a = r\theta,$$

$$30 = 100\theta,$$

$$\theta = \frac{30}{100} = \frac{\textbf{3}}{\textbf{10}} \textbf{ radian} \left(\text{or } \frac{3}{10} \cdot \frac{180°}{\pi} = \frac{\textbf{54}°}{\boldsymbol{\pi}} = \textit{17° 10}'\right).$$

The bold-faced results are exact; the italicized answers are merely three-figure approximations.

EXERCISE 19

1. On a circle of radius 180 ft., find the length of the arc subtended by a central angle of 80°.

2. Find the number of radians in the central angle that subtends an arc of 6 in. on a circle of diameter 5 ft. Express the angle in degrees and minutes.

3. Find the radius of a circle on which a central angle of $\frac{3}{10}$ radian subtends an arc of 60 ft.

4. Find the radius of a circle on which a central angle of 51° 0′ subtends an arc of 100 in.

5. If a locomotive wheel with a diameter of 5 ft. rolls 3.75 ft., through how many degrees and minutes does it turn?

6. A highway curve is to be laid out on a circle. What radius should be used if the road is to change its direction by 9° 10′ in a distance of 96 ft.?

In Probs. 7 to 12, assume that the earth is a sphere of radius 4000 miles. Write results with two-figure accuracy.

7. How far is it from the equator to Tampa, Fla., latitude 28° N? How far is Tampa from the north pole (Fig. 33)?

8. Butte, Mont., is 3200 miles from the equator. Find the latitude of Butte.

9. Port Huron, Mich. (latitude 43° N), is due north of Havana, Cuba (latitude 23° N). How far is Havana from Port Huron?

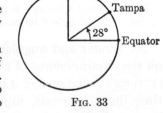

FIG. 33

10. Helsinki, Finland, is 6200 miles due north of Kimberley, South Africa. If the latitude of Kimberley is 29° S, find the latitude of Helsinki.

11. The north pole is 420 miles closer to Chicago than to Tokyo. If the latitude of Tokyo is 36° N, find the latitude of Chicago.

12. The latitude of Fairbanks, Alaska, is 65° N. The latitude of Adelaide, Australia, is 35° S. How many miles is Adelaide south of Fairbanks?

In Probs. 13 to 15, the angle being small, we can assume, with little error, that the chord is equal to its subtended arc. Write results with two-figure accuracy.

13. A railroad boxcar, known to be 13 ft. high, subtends an angle of 2° at the eye of an observer on level ground. How far is the boxcar from the observer (Fig. 34)?

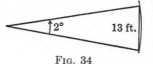

14. At a distance of 800 ft., a tree subtends an angle of 3° at the eye of an observer. Find the height of the tree.

15. The moon has a diameter of 2160 miles and is 240,000 miles from the earth. The sun has a diameter of 864,000 miles and is 93,000,000 miles from the earth. Compare the angle subtended by the moon at the earth with the angle subtended by the sun at the earth. Get results to the nearest minute.

FIG. 34

16. A sector of a circle is the part of the circle bounded by an arc and the radii drawn to its extremities (Fig. 35). By geometry, the area of a sector is equal to one-half its arc times the radius of the circle. Show that

$$\text{area of sector } OAB = \tfrac{1}{2}r^2\theta, \text{ where } \theta \text{ is in radians.}$$

17. On a circle of radius 20.0 in., the length of arc RS is 37.0 in. If the tangent lines at R and S intersect at T, find the length of RT.

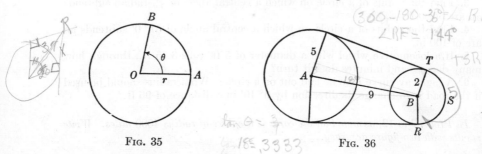

FIG. 35   FIG. 36

18. The radius of a circle is 100 in. If A and B are two points on the circumference and if the tangent lines at these two points intersect at an angle of 36° 0′, find the length of the arc AB.

19. In Fig. 36, if $AB = 9$, find the length of arc RST.

20. An isosceles triangle is inscribed in a circle of radius 100.0 in. Find the angles of the triangle if its base subtends an arc of 143.7 in.

30. Linear and angular velocity.

Consider a point P moving on the circumference of a circle with radius r and center O. If P traverses a distance of a linear units (inches, feet, miles, etc.) in t time units (seconds, minutes, etc.), then $a/t = v$ is called the linear velocity of P. If the radius OP swings through θ angular units (degrees, radians, etc.), in t time units, then $\theta/t = \alpha$ is called the angular velocity of P. If, further, θ is in radians and α

is in radians per unit of time, then we can divide $a = r\theta$, by t, and get

$$\frac{a}{t} = r \cdot \frac{\theta}{t},$$

$$v = \frac{a}{t}$$

or

$$v = r\alpha,$$

provided α is in radians per time unit. This means that the linear velocity of a point on the circumference of a circle is equal to the radius times the angular velocity of the point, in radians per unit of time.

The angular velocity of a rotating body is quite often expressed in revolutions per minute (rpm). This can be readily converted into radians per minute, by remembering that one revolution represents 2π radians.

Example. A flywheel 6 ft. in diameter makes 40 rpm. (a) Find its angular velocity in radians per second. (b) Find the speed of the belt that drives the flywheel.

Solution. (a) Since 40 rpm represents $40(2\pi) = 80\pi$ radians per minute,

$$\alpha = \frac{80\pi}{60} = \frac{4\pi}{3} \text{ radians per second.}$$

(b) The speed of the belt, if it does not slip, is equal to the linear velocity, of a point on the rim of the flywheel. Using

$$v = r\alpha,$$

we have

$$v = 3\left(\frac{4\pi}{3}\right) = 4\pi \text{ ft. per sec., or 12.6 ft. per sec.}$$

5280 ft mi
1760 yd mi
one one to an

EXERCISE 20

1. A wheel of an automobile is making 792 rpm. Find the speed of the auto in miles per hour if the diameter of the wheel is 28 in.

2. A locomotive is traveling 31.4 mph. Find in feet the radius of the drive wheels if they are making 220 rpm.

3. It takes 12 min. to run 200 ft. of movie film at uniform speed through a certain projector. The film is unwound from one reel, which becomes progressively smaller in diameter, and is rewound on another, which becomes larger. Find the number of revolutions per minute of each of the two reels when one roll of film is 4 in. in diameter and the other is 3 in. in diameter.

4. Find the linear speed of a point on the equator due to the rotation of the earth. Use 3960 miles as the radius of the equator. Express result in miles per hour with three-figure accuracy.

5. A pulley 12 in. in diameter is driven by a belt that moves 2000 ft. per min. How many revolutions per minute are made by the pulley?

6. A bicycle is driven by the pedals, which are attached to the sprocket wheel, which has a diameter of 11 in. A chain connects the sprocket to a smaller cog wheel of diameter 3 in. This wheel is fastened to the bicycle's rear wheel, whose diameter is 24 in. Find the speed of the bicycle in miles per hour when the sprocket is making 1 revolution per second.

7. A cogwheel is driven by a chain that travels 2 ft. per sec. Find in inches the diameter of the wheel if it makes 72 rpm.

8. A truck is traveling 20 mph. How many revolutions per second are made by the wheels, which have a diameter of 32 in.?

CHAPTER 6

GRAPHS OF THE TRIGONOMETRIC FUNCTIONS

31. Periodic functions. Since coterminal angles have the same trigonometric functions, we know that any trigonometric function of θ is exactly equal to the same function of $\theta + n\cdot 360°$, where n is any integer. For example, $\sin 10° = \sin 370° = \sin 730° = \sin(-350°) = $ etc. Hence $\sin \theta$ takes on all of its possible values as θ ranges from $0°$ to $360°$; then it repeats these values as θ moves from $360°$ to $720°$, from $720°$ to $1080°$, etc. In view of the fact that

$$\sin \theta = \sin(\theta + 360°),$$

we say that *the sine is a periodic function of period* $360°$. It repeats itself periodically every $360°$.

In general, a function $f(\theta)$ is said to be periodic and of period p, provided

$$f(\theta + p) = f(\theta),$$

where p is the smallest positive constant for which this is true. Since

$$\cos(\theta + 360°) = \cos \theta,$$

we can say that *the cosine is a periodic function with a period of* $360°$.

32. Variations of the sine and cosine. Knowing that the sine and cosine functions have a period of $360°$, we shall confine ourselves to

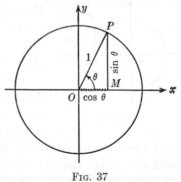

FIG. 37

investigating their behavior as the angle increases from $0°$ to $360°$. Consider any angle θ in standard position (Fig. 37). On the terminal side of θ, choose the point $P(x, y)$ whose radius vector is 1. As θ varies, make P move so that r is always 1. This will keep P on a circle with center O and radius 1. Recalling that $\sin \theta = y/r = MP/1 = MP$, we see that the length of the *directed*

55

segment MP is equal to sin θ. Now try to visualize θ as increasing from 0° to 90°. Accordingly sin θ (or MP) increases from 0 to 1. As θ increases from 90° to 180°, sin θ decreases from 1 to 0. As θ swings through the third and fourth quadrants, P is below the x-axis. Hence sin θ (or MP) is negative.

Similarly, cos $\theta = x/r = OM$. As θ increases from 0° to 90°, cos θ decreases from 1 to 0. A study of the variations of sin θ and cos θ as θ goes from 0° to 360° reveals the following results:

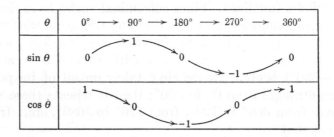

The arrow pointing upward means the function is increasing; downward, decreasing.

33. Variation of the tangent. In discussing tan $\theta = y/x$, we shall keep x numerically equal to 1. For θ in Q I, we have

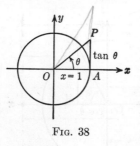

Fig. 38

tan $\theta = AP$, the length of the tangent line to the unit circle at A (Fig. 38). For $\theta = 0°$, P coincides with A, and tan 0° = 0. As θ increases toward 90°, P moves upward from A, and tan θ increases. When $\theta = 90°$, P is on the y-axis and $x = 0$ (it cannot be 1). Hence tan 90° = $y/0$ = *does not exist.* But as θ approaches 90°, tan θ (or AP) increases rapidly. In fact we can make tan θ just as large as we please by taking θ sufficiently close to 90°. A situation like this is expressed briefly by tan 90° = ∞ (read "tan 90° is infinite"). Remember, however, that *tan 90° = ∞ is just an abbreviation for: tan 90° does not exist; but by taking θ sufficiently close to 90° (never letting it equal 90°), we can make tan θ as large numerically as we please.* Memorize this statement and think of it when you see the symbol ∞.

In Q II (Fig. 39), keep $x = -1$; then P moves on the tangent line to the unit circle at B; and tan $\theta = y/x = y/-1 = -y$

$= -BP$ (a negative number since BP is positive). As soon as θ leaves 90°, P starts down on the tangent line. As θ increases from 90° to 180°, BP decreases from very large positive numbers to 0, and $\tan \theta$ increases from very large negative values to 0. Using our symbolic notation, we say that as θ increases from 90° to 180°, $\tan \theta$ increases from $-\infty$ to 0.* By a similar process, the variation of $\tan \theta$ in Q III and Q IV can be investigated.

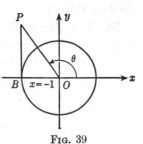

FIG. 39

The variation in $\cot \theta$ can be studied by recalling that $\cot \theta = 1/\tan \theta$. Since $\tan \theta$ is always increasing, $\cot \theta$ is always decreasing. When $\tan \theta$ becomes infinite, $\cot \theta$ approaches 0; when $\tan \theta$ approaches 0, $\cot \theta$ becomes infinite.

The variations in $\sec \theta$ and $\csc \theta$ can be investigated through their reciprocals.

In summary we have

θ	Q I 0° → 90°	Q II 90° → 180°	Q III 180° → 270°	Q IV 270° → 360°
$\sin \theta$	0 ↗ 1	1 ↘ 0	0 ↘ -1	-1 ↗ 0
$\cos \theta$	1 ↘ 0	0 ↘ -1	-1 ↗ 0	0 ↗ 1
$\tan \theta$	0 ↗ ∞	-∞ ↗ 0	0 ↗ ∞	-∞ ↗ 0
$\cot \theta$	∞ ↘ 0	0 ↘ -∞	∞ ↘ 0	0 ↘ -∞
$\sec \theta$	1 ↗ ∞	-∞ ↗ -1	-1 ↘ -∞	∞ ↘ 1
$\csc \theta$	∞ ↘ 1	1 ↗ ∞	-∞ ↗ -1	-1 ↘ -∞

Notice that in Q I the sine, tangent, and secant increase while their cofunctions decrease. Also observe that the sine and cosine

---

* The notation $\tan 90°^- = +\infty$ is frequently used to mean that as θ approaches 90° through values *less* than 90° (such as 89°, 89.9°, 89.99°, etc.), $\tan \theta$ *increases* without limit. The statement $\tan 90°^+ = -\infty$ is used to indicate that as θ approaches 90° through values *greater* than 90°, $\tan \theta$ *decreases* without limit. Both statements may be incorporated in the single form $\tan 90° = \infty$, which implies that as θ approaches 90° (from either side), $\tan \theta$ *increases numerically* without limit.

range from −1 to 1, the tangent and cotangent take on all values, and the secant and cosecant are always numerically equal to or greater than 1.

34. The graph of sin θ. A complete "picture story" of the variation of the sine is presented by its graph. Let us draw a system of coordinate axes and label the horizontal axis as θ and the vertical axis as sin θ. Since the radian is the natural measure of angles, let the θ-axis be laid off in radians. This means that the number 1 on the vertical scale and 1 radian on the horizontal scale are represented by the same distance. *Hence 180° on the θ-axis should be π times as long as 1 unit on the (sin θ)-axis.* Using trigonometric tables and the related-angle theory we form the following table:

θ in degrees ...	0°	30°	60°	90°	120°	150°	180°	210°	240°	270°	300°	330°	360°
θ in radians ...	0	$\dfrac{\pi}{6}$	$\dfrac{\pi}{3}$	$\dfrac{\pi}{2}$	$\dfrac{2\pi}{3}$	$\dfrac{5\pi}{6}$	π	$\dfrac{7\pi}{6}$	$\dfrac{4\pi}{3}$	$\dfrac{3\pi}{2}$	$\dfrac{5\pi}{3}$	$\dfrac{11\pi}{6}$	2π
sin θ..........	0	.5	.87	1	.87	.5	0	−.5	−.87	−1	−.87	−.5	0

After plotting these values on the coordinate axes,* we obtain the following curve:

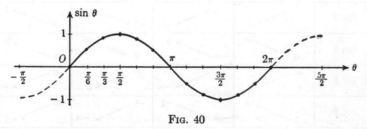

Fig. 40

The student should practice drawing the 0° to 360° portion of this curve until he can make a hasty sketch of it from memory. The sine curve† can be used to remember the sine of 0°, 90°,

---

* A very good approximation to the sine curve can be drawn on quadrille paper. Let 4 quadrille *spaces* represent 1 *unit* vertically and let 1 quadrille space represent 15° horizontally. For θ = 15°, sin θ = .26; the corresponding point would be plotted 1 *space* to the right and 4(.26) = 1.04 *spaces* up from the origin. For θ = 45°, sin θ = .71; the corresponding point would be plotted 3 *spaces* to the right and 4(.71) = 2.88 *spaces* up from the origin.

† Sometimes called the *sinusoid.*

180°, 270° and also to remember the sign of the sine in the various quadrants. For example, if you encounter sin 270°, make a rapid sketch or form a mental picture of the sine curve and notice that sin 270° = −1. Also, the sine curve enables us to remember that

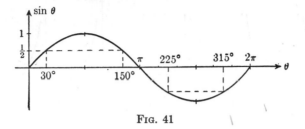

FIG. 41

sin θ is positive in Q I and Q II (because in these quadrants the curve is above the horizontal axis) and sin θ is negative in Q III and Q IV (because here the curve is below the horizontal axis).

Furthermore, the sine curve recalls the related-angle theory. For example, it is obvious from the curve (see Fig. 41) that

$$\sin 150° = \sin 30° = \tfrac{1}{2},$$

and
$$\sin 225° = \sin 315° = -\frac{\sqrt{2}}{2}.$$

Because of its wave form, the sine curve is very important in the study of wave motion in electrical engineering and physics. The maximum distance of the curve from the θ-axis is called the *amplitude* of the curve or wave. The period of the function representing the wave is called the *wave length* of the curve. The sine curve has an amplitude of 1 and a wave length of 2π.

35. Graphs of the other trigonometric functions. By using methods exactly like those employed in the preceding article, we can draw the graphs of the other trigonometric functions. For

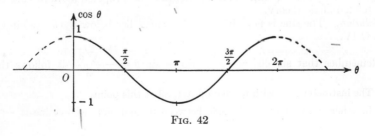

FIG. 42

reference purpose we exhibit these graphs. The student should draw each of them by preparing a table of values, plotting the points, and then drawing a smooth curve through these points.

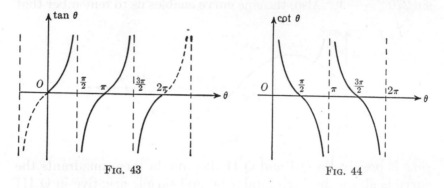

FIG. 43   FIG. 44

The student should be able to draw from memory a hasty sketch of sin θ, cos θ, tan θ.*

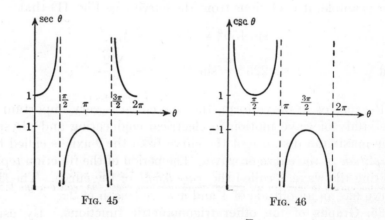

FIG. 45   FIG. 46

Example. Solve the equation† sin $\theta = -\dfrac{\sqrt{3}}{2}$ for all values of θ between $0°$ and $360°$. Use the sine curve to identify the proper quadrants and check the related-angle theory.

Solution. The sine is negative (the sine curve lies below the θ-axis) in Q III and Q IV.

Remember that sin $60° = \dfrac{\sqrt{3}}{2}$. Since sin $\theta = -\dfrac{\sqrt{3}}{2}$, it follows that θ

* The instructor may wish to take up Art. 83 at this point.

† In other words, find every angle between $0°$ and $360°$ whose sine is $-\dfrac{\sqrt{3}}{2}$.

must be equal to those angles in Q III and Q IV that have 60° for their related angle.

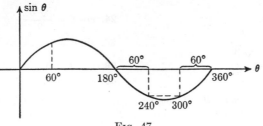

$$\text{Fig. } 47$$

In Q III: $\theta = 180° + 60° = 240°.$
In Q IV: $\theta = 360° - 60° = 300°.$

Hence if $$\sin \theta = -\frac{\sqrt{3}}{2},$$

then $$\theta = 240°, 300°.$$

EXERCISE 21

1. Sketch the sine curve by drawing a smooth curve through the points obtained by assigning to θ the values $-90°, -75°, -60°, -45°, -30°, -15°, 0°, 15°, 30°, \ldots, 360°.$
2. Sketch the cosine curve. Locate points every 15° from 0° to 360°.
3. Sketch the tangent curve. Locate points every 15° from $-90°$ to 360°.
4. Sketch the cotangent curve.
5. Sketch the secant curve.
6. Sketch the cosecant curve.
7. Explain briefly what is meant by the statement "sec 90° = ∞."
8. Explain briefly what is meant by the statement, "cot 180° = ∞."
9. What is the period of tan θ?
10. Discuss in detail the variation of the secant.

Solve the following equations for values of θ in the range $0° \leq \theta < 360°$ (i.e., solve for values of θ that are equal to or greater than 0° and less than 360°). Use the curves to identify the proper quadrants and check the related-angle theory. Do not use tables.

11. $\cos \theta = \dfrac{\sqrt{2}}{2}.$

12. $\sec \theta = 2.$

13. $\cos \theta = -\dfrac{\sqrt{3}}{2}.$

14. $\cos \theta = -\frac{1}{2}.$

15. $\sin \theta = -\frac{1}{2}.$

16. $\sin \theta = 0.$

17. $\sin \theta = \frac{1}{2}.$

18. $\sin \theta = \dfrac{\sqrt{2}}{2}.$

19. $\sin \theta = \dfrac{\sqrt{3}}{2}.$

20. $\sin \theta = -\dfrac{\sqrt{2}}{2}.$

21. $\tan \theta = -1.$

22. $\tan \theta = -\dfrac{1}{\sqrt{3}}$

Solve the following equations for values of θ in the range $0 \leq \theta < 2\pi$ (radians). Do not use tables.

23. $\tan \theta = 0$.

24. $\cos \theta = \dfrac{\sqrt{3}}{2}$.

25. $\csc \theta = -\dfrac{2}{\sqrt{3}}$.

26. $\sin \theta = -1$.

27. $\cos \theta = -1$.

28. $\cot \theta = 0$.

29. $\cos \theta = 0$.

30. $\sec \theta = 0$.

Use tables to solve the following equations for values of θ in the range $0° \leq \theta < 360°$. Obtain results correct to the nearest degree.

31. $\cos \theta = -0.7986$.

32. $\sin \theta = 0.9063$.

33. $\sin \theta = -\frac{1}{6}$.

34. $\cos \theta = \frac{1}{4}$.

35. $\tan \theta = 10$.

36. $\tan \theta = -0.3$.

37. $\cot \theta = 0.7$.

38. $\cot \theta = -29$.

39. Graph $\sin 2\theta$ as a function of θ (label the vertical axis $\sin 2\theta$ and the horizontal axis θ). State the amplitude and wave length of the curve.

40. Graph $2 \sin \theta$ as a function of θ. State the amplitude and wave length of the curve.

41. Graph $\sin (\theta + 30°)$ as a function of θ. State the amplitude and wave length of the curve.

42. Correct the following statement: $\sec 270° = \infty$ means (*a*) $\sec 270°$ does not exist, and (*b*) by taking θ sufficiently close to 270°, we can make $\sec 270°$ as large numerically as we please.

CHAPTER 7

FUNCTIONS OF TWO ANGLES

36. Functions of the sum of two angles. The trigonometric identities in Chap. 3 are relations among the trigonometric functions of one angle. We shall now consider functions of an angle which is the sum of two angles. It seems reasonable to say that if the functions of 30° and 45° are known, the functions of 75° can be obtained. For instance, is $\sin 30° + \sin 45° = \sin 75°$? Obviously this is false because $\frac{1}{2} + \frac{\sqrt{2}}{2} = .5 + .7 = 1.2$ which would make $\sin 75°$ greater than 1. This proves that, in general, $\sin (A + B) \neq \sin A + \sin B$.* Likewise $\sin 2A$ is not identically equal to $2 \sin A$ because $\sin 60° \neq 2 \sin 30°$. It is, however, possible to express $\sin (A + B)$ in terms of the functions of the separate angles A and B. And it is possible to express $\sin 2A$ in terms of the functions of A. These, and other, formulas will be developed in the following articles.

37. Sin $(A + B)$ and cos $(A + B)$. If A and B are any two angles, then

[1] $\qquad \sin (A + B) = \sin A \cos B + \cos A \sin B,$

[2] $\qquad \cos (A + B) = \cos A \cos B - \sin A \sin B.$

Proof. Let A and B be any two positive acute angles whose sum, $A + B$, is also acute. Place A in standard position and place B so its initial side coincides with the terminal side of A and its vertex falls at the origin O (Fig. 48). Choose P as any point on the terminal side of angle $(A + B)$, which is in standard position. From P drop a perpendicular to the initial side of B at Q. Draw PM and QS perpendicular to the x-axis and draw QR perpendicular to PM. Then angle RPQ equals angle A because they are acute angles with their sides respectively perpen-

---

* The symbol $\neq$ is read "is not equal to."

63

dicular. Using the definition of the sine of an angle, we have

$$\sin (A + B) = \frac{MP}{OP} = \frac{MR + RP}{OP} = \frac{SQ + RP}{OP}$$

$$= \frac{SQ}{OP} + \frac{RP}{OP}$$

$$= \frac{SQ}{*} \cdot \frac{*}{OP} + \frac{RP}{\dagger} \cdot \frac{\dagger}{OP}$$

$$= \frac{SQ}{OQ} \cdot \frac{OQ}{OP} + \frac{RP}{QP} \cdot \frac{QP}{OP}$$

$$= \sin A \cos B + \cos A \sin B.$$

(handwritten margin note: chose line involved in both triangles)

Using the definition of the cosine of an angle, we have

$$\cos (A + B) = \frac{OM}{OP} = \frac{OS - MS}{OP} = \frac{OS - RQ}{OP}$$

$$= \frac{OS}{OP} - \frac{RQ}{OP}$$

$$= \frac{OS}{OQ} \cdot \frac{OQ}{OP} - \frac{RQ}{QP} \cdot \frac{QP}{OP}$$

$$= \cos A \cos B - \sin A \sin B.$$

These proofs are not general because we considered only the case in which A and B are positive acute angles with a sum of less than 90°. Formulas [1] and [2] are, however, true for all values of A and B. A general proof is given in the Appendix.

It is impossible to overemphasize the importance of these results. In addition to learning formulas [1] and [2], the student should be able to state them in words. These statements are:

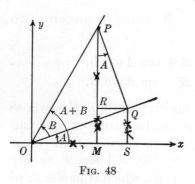

Fig. 48

[1] *The sine of the sum of two angles is equal to the sine of the first times the cosine of the second plus the cosine of the first times the sine of the second.*

---

* Since SQ and OP lie in different triangles SOQ and POQ, we multiply top and bottom of the fraction by OQ, the common side of the two triangles.

† The common side of triangles RQP and OQP is QP.

[2] *The cosine of the sum of two angles is equal to the cosine of the first times the cosine of the second minus the sine of the first times the sine of the second.*

It is equally important for the student to be able to use these formulas backward. For example, when

$$\cos 7\theta \cos 2\theta - \sin 7\theta \sin 2\theta$$

is encountered, it should be recognized as the expansion of $\cos (7\theta + 2\theta)$ or $\cos 9\theta$.

Example 1. Compute $\sin 75°$ and $\cos 75°$ from the functions of $30°$ and $45°$.
Solution.

$$\sin 75° = \sin (30° + 45°)$$
$$= \sin 30° \cos 45° + \cos 30° \sin 45°$$
$$= \frac{1}{2} \cdot \frac{\sqrt{2}}{2} + \frac{\sqrt{3}}{2} \cdot \frac{\sqrt{2}}{2}$$
$$= \frac{\sqrt{2}}{4} + \frac{\sqrt{6}}{4} = \frac{\sqrt{2} + \sqrt{6}}{4}$$

or

$$\frac{1.414 + 2.449}{4} = \frac{3.863}{4} = .966.$$

$$\cos 75° = \cos (30° + 45°) = \cos 30° \cos 45° - \sin 30° \sin 45°$$
$$= \frac{\sqrt{3}}{2} \cdot \frac{\sqrt{2}}{2} - \frac{1}{2} \cdot \frac{\sqrt{2}}{2}$$
$$= \frac{\sqrt{6} - \sqrt{2}}{4} \text{ or } .259.$$

Notice that these decimal approximations agree with the "story" as presented by the sine and cosine curves. Angles near $90°$ have sines close to 1 and cosines close to 0.

Example 2. Given $\sin A = \frac{5}{13}$, with A in Q I, and $\cos B = -\frac{4}{5}$, with B in Q II. Find (a) $\sin (A + B)$, (b) $\cos (A + B)$, (c) the quadrant in which $(A + B)$ lies.

Solution. First find $\cos A$ and $\sin B$ by drawing triangles of reference (Fig. 49). Hence

$$\cos A = \tfrac{12}{13}, \qquad \text{and} \qquad \sin B = \tfrac{3}{5}.$$

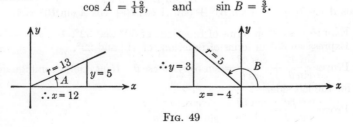

FIG. 49

(a) $$\sin (A + B) = \sin A \cos B + \cos A \sin B$$

$$= \left(\frac{5}{13}\right)\left(\frac{-4}{5}\right) + \left(\frac{12}{13}\right)\left(\frac{3}{5}\right)$$

$$= -\tfrac{20}{65} + \tfrac{36}{65} = \tfrac{16}{65}.$$

(b) $$\cos (A + B) = \cos A \cos B - \sin A \sin B$$

$$= \left(\frac{12}{13}\right)\left(\frac{-4}{5}\right) - \left(\frac{5}{13}\right)\left(\frac{3}{5}\right)$$

$$= -\tfrac{48}{65} - \tfrac{15}{65} = -\tfrac{63}{65}.$$

(c) The angle $(A + B)$ lies in Q II because $\sin (A + B)$ is positive and $\cos (A + B)$ is negative.

EXERCISE 22

1. Compute $\sin 195°$ from the functions of $60°$ and $135°$.
2. Compute $\cos 255°$ from the functions of $45°$ and $210°$.
3. Compute $\cos 285°$ from the functions of $60°$ and $225°$.
4. Compute $\sin 345°$ from the functions of $30°$ and $315°$.
5. Use tables to show that

$$\sin 10° + \sin 40° \neq \sin 50°,$$
$$\cos \ 5° + \cos 10° \neq \cos 15°.$$

Simplify by reducing to a single term.

6. $\sin 200° \cos 70° + \cos 200° \sin 70°$.
7. $\sin \dfrac{3\theta}{4} \cos \dfrac{\theta}{4} + \cos \dfrac{3\theta}{4} \sin \dfrac{\theta}{4}$.
8. $\cos 5\theta \cos 3\theta - \sin 5\theta \sin 3\theta$.
9. $\sin 160° \sin 20° - \cos 160° \cos 20°$.

Prove the following identities.

10. $\cos (\pi + \theta) = - \cos \theta$.
11. $\cos \left(\dfrac{3\pi}{2} + \theta\right) = \sin \theta$.
12. $\sin \left(\dfrac{\pi}{2} + \theta\right) = \cos \theta$.
13. $\sin (45° + \theta) - \cos (225° + \theta) = \sqrt{2} \cos \theta$.
14. $\sin (330° + \theta) + \cos (60° + \theta) = 0$.
15. $\sin (C - D) \cos D + \cos (C - D) \sin D = \sin C$.
16. $(\cos A \cos B - \sin A \sin B)^2 + (\sin A \cos B + \cos A \sin B)^2 = 1$.

17. Express $\cos 82°$ in terms of functions of $50°$ and $32°$.
18. Express $\sin 33°$ in terms of functions of $11°$ and $22°$.
19. Prove $\dfrac{\sin 4\theta}{\sin \theta} + \dfrac{\cos 4\theta}{\cos \theta} = \sin 5\theta \sec \theta \csc \theta$. *Hint:* Get a common denominator for the left side.
20. Prove $\dfrac{\cos 5\theta}{\sin 3\theta} - \dfrac{\sin 5\theta}{\cos 3\theta} = \dfrac{\cos 8\theta}{\sin 3\theta \cos 3\theta}$.

21. Given $\sin A = \frac{1}{3}$ with A in Q I, and $\sin B = \frac{2}{3}$ with B in Q I. Find $\sin (A + B)$.

22. Given $\sin (C - D) = \frac{7}{25}$ with $(C - D)$ in Q I, and $\sin D = \frac{4}{5}$ with D in Q I. Find $\sin C$.

23. Given $\cos A = \frac{9}{41}$ with A in Q I, and $\sin B = -\frac{4}{5}$ with B in Q III. Find (a) $\sin (A + B)$, (b) $\cos (A + B)$, (c) the quadrant in which $(A + B)$ lies.

24. Given $\sin A = \frac{15}{17}$ with A in Q II, and $\tan B = \frac{5}{12}$ with B in Q III. Find (a) $\sin (A + B)$, (b) $\cos (A + B)$, (c) the quadrant in which $(A + B)$ lies.

25. Prove the identity

$$\sin (A + B + C) = \sin A \cos B \cos C + \cos A \sin B \cos C$$
$$+ \cos A \cos B \sin C - \sin A \sin B \sin C.$$

Hint: $\sin (A + B + C) = \sin ([A + B] + C)$.

26. Prove the identity

$$\cos (A + B) + C) = \cos A \cos B \cos C - \sin A \sin B \cos C$$
$$- \sin A \cos B \sin C - \cos A \sin B \sin C.$$

27. If A and B are complementary angles, prove that

$$\cos (5A + 2B) = - \cos 3A.$$

28. If A and B are complementary angles, prove that

$$\sin (9A + B) = \cos 8A.$$

38. Tan $(A + B)$. Since $\tan \theta = \dfrac{\sin \theta}{\cos \theta}$,

$$\tan (A + B) = \frac{\sin (A + B)}{\cos (A + B)} = \frac{\sin A \cos B + \cos A \sin B}{\cos A \cos B - \sin A \sin B}.$$

Dividing top and bottom of this fraction by $\cos A \cos B$, we get

$$\tan (A + B) = \frac{\dfrac{\sin A \cos B}{\cos A \cos B} + \dfrac{\cos A \sin B}{\cos A \cos B}}{\dfrac{\cos A \cos B}{\cos A \cos B} - \dfrac{\sin A \sin B}{\cos A \cos B}}$$

$$= \frac{\dfrac{\sin A}{\cos A} + \dfrac{\sin B}{\cos B}}{1 - \dfrac{\sin A}{\cos A} \cdot \dfrac{\sin B}{\cos B}},$$

or

[3]
$$\tan (A + B) = \frac{\tan A + \tan B}{1 - \tan A \tan B}.$$

Stated in words, we have

[3] *The tangent of the sum of two angles is equal to the sum of their tangents divided by* 1 *minus the product of their tangents.*

39. Sin $(A - B)$, cos $(A - B)$, and tan $(A - B)$. If A and B are any two angles, then

[4] $$\sin (A - B) = \sin A \cos B - \cos A \sin B,$$

[5] $$\cos (A - B) = \cos A \cos B + \sin A \sin B,$$

[6] $$\tan (A - B) = \frac{\tan A - \tan B}{1 + \tan A \tan B}.$$

Proof. Recall that $\sin (-B) = - \sin B$, $\cos (-B) = \cos B$, and $\tan (-B) = - \tan B$. Then

$$\sin (A - B) = \sin (A + [-B]) *$$
$$= \sin A \cos [-B] + \cos A \sin [-B]$$
$$= \sin A \cos B + (\cos A)(- \sin B)$$
$$= \sin A \cos B - \cos A \sin B.$$

Formulas [5] and [6] are proved by a similar method. The student should then state formulas [4], [5], and [6] in words.

In comparing [1], [4], [2], and [5],

$$\sin (A + B) = \sin A \cos B + \cos A \sin B,$$
$$\sin (A - B) = \sin A \cos B - \cos A \sin B,$$
$$\cos (A + B) = \cos A \cos B - \sin A \sin B,$$
$$\cos (A - B) = \cos A \cos B + \sin A \sin B,$$

we notice that "the sines have the same sign but the cosines have different signs."

There is no need for formulas involving the cotangent, secant, and cosecant of $(A + B)$ and $(A - B)$ because they can be readily expressed in terms of their reciprocals.

EXERCISE 23

1. Compute tan 75° from tan 45° and tan 30°.
2. Compute tan 165° from tan 225° and tan 60°.
3. Compute cos 105° from the functions of 135° and 30°.
4. Compute sin 285° from the functions of 315° and 30°.

* This method may be used to convert any "sum formula" to a "difference formula."

Simplify by reducing to a single term.

5. $\cos 9\theta \cos 2\theta + \sin 9\theta \sin 2\theta$.

6. $\sin 80° \cos 50° - \cos 80° \sin 50°$.

7. $\dfrac{\tan 72° - \tan 12°}{1 + \tan 72° \tan 12°}$.

8. $\dfrac{\tan 3\theta + \tan 2\theta}{1 - \tan 3\theta \tan 2\theta}$.

Prove the following identities.

9. $\tan (60° - \theta) = \dfrac{\sqrt{3} - \tan \theta}{1 + \sqrt{3} \tan \theta}$.

10. $\tan (45° + \theta) = \dfrac{1 + \tan \theta}{1 - \tan \theta}$.

11. $\sin (\theta - 270°) = \cos \theta$.

12. $\cos (180° - \theta) = - \cos \theta$.

13. Given $\sin A = -\frac{8}{17}$ with A in Q IV, and $\tan B = \frac{3}{4}$ with B in Q I. Find (a) $\sin (A - B)$, (b) $\cos (A - B)$, (c) $\tan (A + B)$, (d) $\tan (A - B)$.

14. Given $\cos A = -\frac{5}{13}$ with A in Q III, and $\tan B = -\frac{24}{7}$ with B in Q II. Find (a) $\sin (A - B)$, (b) $\cos (A - B)$, (c) $\tan (A + B)$, (d) $\tan (A - B)$.

15. Given $\tan A = \frac{1}{4}$ with A in Q I, and $\tan B = \frac{3}{5}$ with B in Q I. Show that $A + B = 45°$.

16. Given $\sin (C + D) = \frac{7}{8}$ with $(C + D)$ in Q I, and $\sin C = \frac{2}{8}$ with C in Q I. Find $\sin D$.

Identify as true or false and give reasons.

17. $6 \sin 4\theta \cos 3\theta - 6 \cos 4\theta \sin 3\theta = \sin \theta$.

18. $9 \cos 7\theta \cos 2\theta + 9 \sin 7\theta \sin 2\theta = 9 \cos 5\theta$.

19. $\tan \theta + \tan 2\theta = \tan 3\theta$.

20. $\tan 20° = \dfrac{1 - \tan 25°}{1 + \tan 25°}$.

21. Express $\tan 40°$ in terms of $\tan 50°$ and $\tan 10°$.

22. Express $\tan 85°$ in terms of $\tan 20°$ and $\tan 65°$.

23. Express $\sin 11°$ in terms of functions of $77°$ and $66°$.

24. Express $\cos 6°$ in terms of functions of $10°$ and $4°$.

Prove the following identities.

25. $\cos (60° - \theta) + \sin (30° - \theta) = \cos \theta$.

26. $\cos (30° - \theta) - \sin (60° - \theta) = \sin \theta$.

27. $(\cos B \sin A - \cos A \sin B)^2 + (\sin A \sin B + \cos A \cos B)^2 = 1$.

28. $\dfrac{\tan (A + B) - \tan C}{1 + \tan (A + B) \tan C} = \dfrac{\tan A + \tan (B - C)}{1 - \tan A \tan (B - C)}$.

29. $\tan (A + B + C) = \dfrac{\tan A + \tan B + \tan C - \tan A \tan B \tan C}{1 - \tan A \tan B - \tan B \tan C - \tan C \tan A}$.

30. $\cot (A + B) = \dfrac{\cot A \cot B - 1}{\cot A + \cot B}$.

31. $\cot (A - B) = \dfrac{\cot A \cot B + 1}{\cot B - \cot A}$.

32. In Fig. 50, if $a > b$, show that $x = b\sqrt{\dfrac{a+b}{a-b}}$.

33. If A and B are supplementary angles, prove that $\tan(2A - B) = \tan 3A$.

34. If A and B are complementary angles, prove that $\cos(A - 5B) = \sin 6B$.

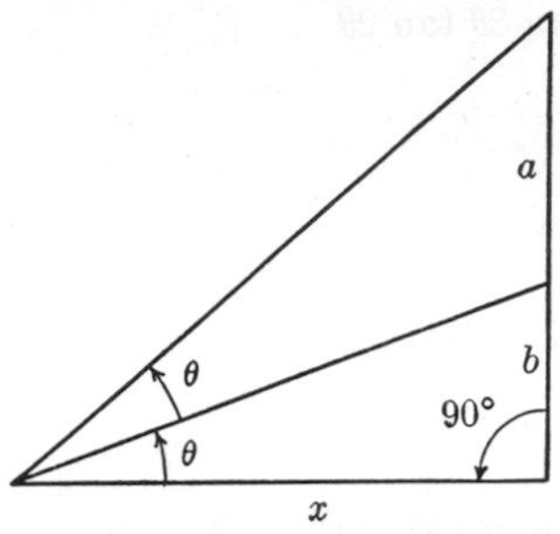

35. Express $4\sin\theta + 3\cos\theta$ in the form $k\sin(\theta + A)$, where k and A are constants.

Solution. Multiply and divide the expression by $\sqrt{4^2 + 3^2} = 5$:

$$5[\tfrac{4}{5}\sin\theta + \tfrac{3}{5}\cos\theta]$$

or $\qquad 5[(\sin\theta)\tfrac{4}{5} + (\cos\theta)\tfrac{3}{5}]$.

Put $\quad \tfrac{4}{5} = \cos A;\qquad$ then $\qquad \tfrac{3}{5} = \sin A.$

Our expression becomes

$$5[\sin\theta\cos A + \cos\theta\sin A] = 5\sin(\theta + A).$$

FIG. 50

From tables we find that if $\cos A = \tfrac{4}{5}$, then $A = 36° 52'$. Hence

$$4\sin\theta + 3\cos\theta = 5\sin(\theta + 36° 52').$$

36. Express $15\sin\theta + 8\cos\theta$ in the form $k\sin(\theta + A)$.

37. Express $\sin\theta + \cos\theta$ in the form $k\sin(\theta + A)$.

38. Express $5\sin\theta - 12\cos\theta$ in the form $k\sin(\theta - A)$.

40. Double-angle formulas. If A is any angle, then

[7] $\qquad\qquad$ **$\sin 2A = 2\sin A\cos A,$**

[8a] $\qquad\qquad$ **$\cos 2A = \cos^2 A - \sin^2 A$**

[8b] $\qquad\qquad\qquad\quad$ **$= 1 - 2\sin^2 A$**

[8c] $\qquad\qquad\qquad\quad$ **$= 2\cos^2 A - 1.$**

Proof. $\quad \sin 2A = \sin(A + A)$

$\qquad\qquad\qquad = \sin A\cos A + \cos A\sin A$

$\qquad\qquad\qquad = 2\sin A\cos A.$

$\qquad\quad \cos 2A = \cos(A + A)$

$\qquad\qquad\qquad = \cos A\cos A - \sin A\sin A$

$\qquad\qquad\qquad = \cos^2 A - \sin^2 A$

$\qquad\qquad\qquad = 1 - \sin^2 A - \sin^2 A$

$\qquad\qquad\qquad = 1 - 2\sin^2 A,$ etc.

Stated in words, formula [7] says

The sine of twice an angle is equal to twice the sine of the angle times the cosine of the angle.

The student should state the three forms of [8] in words.

Formulas [7] and [8] are called double-angle formulas because the angle on the left side is double the angle on the right side. Formula [7] could have been written

$$\sin B = 2 \sin \frac{B}{2} \cos \frac{B}{2}$$

because B is the double of $B/2$. In other words, [7] and [8] are used to express the sine and cosine of an angle in terms of the functions of an angle that is half as large. To illustrate,

$$\sin 60° = 2 \sin 30° \cos 30° = 2 \left(\frac{1}{2}\right)\left(\frac{\sqrt{3}}{2}\right) = \frac{\sqrt{3}}{2},$$

$$\cos 14\theta = 2 \cos^2 7\theta - 1,$$

$$\cos \frac{8\theta}{9} = 1 - 2 \sin^2 \frac{4\theta}{9}.$$

41. Half-angle formulas.   If θ is any angle, then

[9]
$$\sin \frac{\theta}{2} = \pm \sqrt{\frac{1 - \cos \theta}{2}},$$

[10]
$$\cos \frac{\theta}{2} = \pm \sqrt{\frac{1 + \cos \theta}{2}}.$$

The choice of the sign in front of the radical is determined by the quadrant in which $\theta/2$ lies.

Proof. Formula [8*b*] says

$$\cos 2A = 1 - 2 \sin^2 A.$$

Let $A = \theta/2$; then $2A = \theta$, and

$$\cos \theta = 1 - 2 \sin^2 \frac{\theta}{2}.$$

Transposing,

$$2 \sin^2 \frac{\theta}{2} = 1 - \cos \theta,$$

$$\sin^2 \frac{\theta}{2} = \frac{1 - \cos \theta}{2},$$

$$\sin \frac{\theta}{2} = \pm \sqrt{\frac{1 - \cos \theta}{2}}.$$

By a similar method [10] can be derived from [8*c*].

Formulas [9] and [10] are called half-angle formulas because the angle on the left side is half the angle on the right side. To illustrate,

$$\sin 30° = \sqrt{\frac{1 - \cos 60°}{2}} = \sqrt{\frac{1 - \frac{1}{2}}{2}} = \sqrt{\frac{\frac{1}{2}}{2}} = \sqrt{\frac{1}{4}} = \frac{1}{2}.$$

$$\cos 170° = -\sqrt{\frac{1 + \cos 340°}{2}}.$$

(Here the minus sign is chosen because 170° is in Q II and has a negative cosine.)

$$\sin C = \pm \sqrt{\frac{1 - \cos 2C}{2}}.$$

Notice that in the double-angle formulas the large angle is on the left side while in the half-angle formulas the small angle is on the left side. In fact, the half-angle formulas are merely the double-angle formulas used backward (reading from right to left).

It is desirable to read the left side of [9]: "the sine of half of θ" rather than to say "the sine of θ over 2" which might be construed as $\dfrac{\sin \theta}{2}$.

Example 1. Prove the identity $\cos 3\theta = 4 \cos^3 \theta - 3 \cos \theta$.
Proof.

$\cos 3\theta$	$4 \cos^3 \theta - 3 \cos \theta$

$\cos 3\theta$
$= \cos (2\theta + \theta)$
$= \cos 2\theta \cos \theta - \sin 2\theta \sin \theta$
$= (2 \cos^2 \theta - 1) * \cos \theta - (2 \sin \theta \cos \theta) \sin \theta$
$= 2 \cos^3 \theta - \cos \theta - 2 \sin^2 \theta \cos \theta$
$= 2 \cos^3 \theta - \cos \theta - 2(1 - \cos^2 \theta) \cos \theta$
$= 2 \cos^3 \theta - \cos \theta - 2 \cos \theta + 2 \cos^3 \theta$
$= 4 \cos^3 \theta - 3 \cos \theta.$

This identity is frequently used in proving that it is impossible to trisect a general angle with ruler and compasses.

Example 2. Express $\cos 20\theta$ in terms of $\sin 5\theta$.
Solution. Since 20θ is the double of 10θ, and 10θ is the double of 5θ, we shall employ double-angle formulas:

$$\cos 20\theta$$
$$= 1 - 2 \sin^2 10\theta$$

* Formula [8c] is used because the right side involves only $\cos \theta$.

$$= 1 - 2(2 \sin 5\theta \cos 5\theta)^2$$
$$= 1 - 8 \sin^2 5\theta \cos^2 5\theta$$
$$= 1 - 8 \sin^2 5\theta (1 - \sin^2 5\theta)$$
$$= 1 - 8 \sin^2 5\theta + 8 \sin^4 5\theta.$$

Example 3. By using half-angle formulas, reduce $\sin^4 A$ to an expression involving no even exponents.

Solution. Upon squaring both sides of [9], we obtain

$$\sin^2 \frac{\theta}{2} = \frac{1 - \cos \theta}{2} = \frac{1}{2}(1 - \cos \theta).$$

Replacing $\frac{\theta}{2}$ with A gives $\sin^2 A = \frac{1}{2}(1 - \cos 2A)$. This equation enables us to change the exponent from 2 to 1, with a doubling of the angle. Hence

$$\sin^4 A = (\sin^2 A)^2 = [\tfrac{1}{2}(1 - \cos 2A)]^2$$
$$= \tfrac{1}{4}(1 - 2\cos 2A + \cos^2 2A).$$

If $\cos^2 2A$ is replaced by $\frac{1}{2}(1 + \cos 4A)$, we get

$$\sin^4 A = \tfrac{3}{8} - \tfrac{1}{2}\cos 2A + \tfrac{1}{8}\cos 4A.$$

Such transformations are needed in the integration of even powers of sines and cosines in calculus.

EXERCISE 24

1. Use tables to show that

$$2 \sin 5° \neq \sin 10°,$$

$$2 \cos 20° \neq \cos 40°.$$

2. Use double-angle formulas to compute $\sin 90°$ and $\cos 90°$ from the functions of $45°$.

3. Compute $\sin 22\frac{1}{2}°$ and $\cos 22\frac{1}{2}°$ from the functions of $45°$. Leave results in radical form.

4. Compute $\sin 105°$ and $\cos 105°$ from the functions of $210°$. Leave results in radical form.

Simplify by reducing to a single term.

5. $2 \cos^2 6\theta - 1$.

6. $5 - 10 \sin^2 16°$.

7. $2 \sin \dfrac{\theta}{3} \cos \dfrac{\theta}{3}$.

8. $3 \cos^2 5° - 3 \sin^2 5°$.

9. $\sqrt{\dfrac{1 - \cos 10\theta}{2}}$.

10. $-\sqrt{\dfrac{1 + \cos 230°}{2}}$.

11. $1 - \sin^2 7B$.

12. $\cos^2 \dfrac{40}{5} + \sin^2 \dfrac{40}{5}$.

13. Given $\sin A = \frac{12}{13}$ with A in Q I.* Find $\sin 2A$ and $\sin \dfrac{A}{2}$.

* Assume the given angle is between $0°$ and $360°$.

14. Given $\cos B = -\frac{1}{6}$ with B in Q II.* Find $\cos 2B$ and $\cos \frac{B}{2}$.

15. Given $\cos 10A = \frac{5}{8}$ with $10A$ in Q IV.* Find $\cos 20A$ and $\cos 5A$.

16. Given $\sin \frac{A}{2} = -\frac{3}{5}$ with $\frac{A}{2}$ in Q III.* Find $\sin A$ and $\sin \frac{A}{4}$.

17. Express $\cos 140°$ in terms of a function of $280°$.

18. Express $\sin 10°$ in terms of a function of $20°$.

19. Express $\sin 200°$ in terms of functions of $100°$.

20. Express $\cos 160°$ in terms of $\cos 80°$.

21. Express $\cos 8\theta$ in terms of $\sin 4\theta$.

22. Express $\sin 7\theta$ in terms of functions of $\frac{7\theta}{2}$.

23 Express $\sin^2 2\theta$ in terms of a function of 4θ.

24. Express $\cos 10\theta$ in terms of a function of 20θ.

Identify as true or false and give reasons. Do not use tables.

25. $\sin \frac{B}{2} = 2 \sin \frac{B}{4} \cos \frac{B}{4}$.

26. $\cos^2 \frac{\theta}{6} - \sin^2 \frac{\theta}{6} = \cos \frac{\theta}{3}$.

27. $8 - 16 \sin^2 3B = 8 \cos 6B$.

28. $12 \sin 6° \cos 6° = 6 \sin 12°$.

29. $\left(\frac{1 + \cos 70°}{2} \right)^{\frac{5}{2}} = \cos^5 35°$.

30. $\sqrt{8(1 - \cos A)} = \pm 4 \sin \frac{A}{2}$.

31. $16 \sin^4 B \cos^4 B = \sin^4 2B$.

32. $\frac{1}{2} \cos 18\theta + \sin^2 9\theta = \frac{1}{2}$.

33. $\sin^2 A - \cos^2 A = \cos(-2A)$.

34. $\sin 2\theta \cos 2\theta = \frac{1}{2} \sin 4\theta$.

35. $\sqrt{\frac{1 - \cos 400°}{2}} = \sin 200°$.

36. $\pm \sqrt{\frac{1 + \cos 2A}{72}} = \frac{1}{6} \cos A$.

Prove each of the following identities by transforming one side to the other.

37. $\cos^2 2A + 4 \sin^2 A \cos^2 A = 1$.

38. $2 \sin^2 \frac{A}{2} + \cos A = 1$.

39. $\frac{1 - \tan^2 A}{1 + \tan^2 A} = \cos 2A$.

40. $\frac{\sin^3 \theta + \cos^3 \theta}{\sin \theta + \cos \theta} = 1 - \frac{1}{2} \sin 2\theta$.

41. $\frac{\cos \theta}{\cos \theta - \sin \theta} - \frac{\sin \theta}{\cos \theta + \sin \theta} = \sec 2\theta$.

42. $\frac{\sin 2A + \cos 2A}{\sin A \cos A} = 2 + \cot A - \tan A$.

43. $\frac{\cos 4A}{\sin A} + \frac{\sin 4A}{\cos A} = \frac{2 \cos 3A}{\sin 2A}$.

44. $\frac{\sin 4A}{2 \sin 2A} = \cos^4 A - \sin^4 A$.

45. $\frac{1}{2} \sin^2 2\theta + \cos 2\theta + 2 \sin^4 \theta = 1$.

46. $\tan 2A = \frac{2 \tan A}{1 - \tan^2 A}$.

47. $\tan \frac{\theta}{2} = \frac{1 - \cos \theta}{\sin \theta} = \frac{\sin \theta}{1 + \cos \theta}$.

48. $\sin 3\theta = 3 \sin \theta - 4 \sin^3 \theta$.

49. $\frac{\cos A - \cos 2A}{\sin^2 A} = \frac{1 + 2 \cos A}{1 + \cos A}$.

50. $2 \sin^2 3\theta(1 + \cos 6\theta) = \sin^2 6\theta$.

51. $(2 \sin^2 2\theta - 1)^2 = 1 - \sin^2 4\theta$.

* Assume the given angle is between $0°$ and $360°$.

52. $\dfrac{1 + \sin^2 \dfrac{\theta}{2}}{1 + \cos^2 \dfrac{\theta}{2}} = \dfrac{3 - \cos \theta}{3 + \cos \theta}.$

53. $\dfrac{\cos 2A}{1 - \sin 2A} = \dfrac{\cot A + 1}{\cot A - 1}.$

54. $\dfrac{2 \sin 2A}{(\cos 2A - 1)^2} = \csc^2 A \cot A.$

55. $\cos 10A + \cos 5A = (\cos 5A + 1)(2 \cos 5A - 1).$

56. $\dfrac{a + b \sin 2\theta + a \cos 2\theta}{b + a \sin 2\theta - b \cos 2\theta} = \cot \theta.$

57. $\dfrac{2(1 + \sin 2A)}{2 \cos 2A + \sin 4A} = \sec 2A.$

58. $1 - \cos 3A = \dfrac{1 - \cos 6A}{2(1 + \cos 3A)}.$

59. $\dfrac{\cos \dfrac{\theta}{2} + \sin \dfrac{\theta}{2}}{\cos \dfrac{\theta}{2} - \sin \dfrac{\theta}{2}} = \sec \theta + \tan \theta.$

60. $\dfrac{\sin 2A + 2 \cos 2A + 1}{\cos 2A} = \dfrac{3 \cos A - \sin A}{\cos A - \sin A}.$

61. Reduce $\sin^4 2\theta$ to $\frac{3}{8} - \frac{1}{2} \cos 4\theta + \frac{1}{8} \cos 8\theta.$

62. Reduce $\cos^4 \theta$ to $\frac{3}{8} + \frac{1}{2} \cos 2\theta + \frac{1}{8} \cos 4\theta.$

63. Reduce $\sin^2 \theta \cos^2 \theta$ to $\frac{1}{8}(1 - \cos 4\theta).$

42. Product to sum formulas; sum to product formulas. It is sometimes necessary to convert a product of two trigonometric functions into a sum of two functions, and vice versa. For this reason we develop the following formulas. They are not nearly so important as the preceding ten formulas.

When [1] and [4] are added, we get

$$\sin (A + B) + \sin (A - B) = 2 \sin A \cos B,$$

or

(11) $\sin A \cos B = \frac{1}{2}[\sin (A + B) + \sin (A - B)].$

Upon subtracting [1] and [4], we obtain

(12) $\cos A \sin B = \frac{1}{2}[\sin (A + B) - \sin (A - B)].$

Similarly, by adding and subtracting [2] and [5], we get

(13) $\cos A \cos B = \frac{1}{2}[\cos (A + B) + \cos (A - B)].$
(14) $\sin A \sin B = \frac{1}{2}[\cos (A - B) - \cos (A + B)].$

Formulas (11), (12), (13), and (14) are used to convert a product of sines and cosines into a sum or difference * of sines and cosines. They are used in certain problems in integral calculus.

When [11] is used backward (from right to left), it converts a sum into a product. Thus

(1) $\sin (A + B) + \sin (A - B) = 2 \sin A \cos B.$

For convenience we shall change notation by making the substitutions

$$A + B = C \quad \text{and} \quad A - B = D.$$

Adding these two equations and dividing by 2, we then obtain $A = \frac{1}{2}(C + D)$. Subtracting and dividing by 2, we get $B = \frac{1}{2}(C - D)$. Substituting in (1), we obtain

(15) $\sin C + \sin D = 2 \sin \frac{1}{2}(C + D) \cos \frac{1}{2}(C - D).$

Similarly,

(16) $\sin C - \sin D = 2 \cos \frac{1}{2}(C + D) \sin \frac{1}{2}(C - D).$
(17) $\cos C + \cos D = 2 \cos \frac{1}{2}(C + D) \cos \frac{1}{2}(C - D).$
(18) $\cos C - \cos D = -2 \sin \frac{1}{2}(C + D) \sin \frac{1}{2}(C - D).$

Formulas (15), (16), (17), and (18) are used to convert sums and differences into products. Formula (16) is usually employed in the derivation of the formula for the derivative of the sine in differential calculus.

Formula [1] should not be confused with formula (15). The former deals with the sine of the sum of two angles; the latter deals with the sum of the sines of two angles.

Example 1. Reduce $\cos 5\theta \cos 3\theta$ to a sum.
Solution. Using (13), we get

$$\cos 5\theta \cos 3\theta = \frac{1}{2}[\cos (5\theta + 3\theta) + \cos (5\theta - 3\theta)]$$
$$= \frac{1}{2} \cos 8\theta + \frac{1}{2} \cos 2\theta.$$

Example 2. Prove the identity $\dfrac{\sin 7\theta - \sin 3\theta}{\cos 7\theta + \cos 3\theta} = \tan 2\theta.$
Proof.

$$\frac{\sin 7\theta - \sin 3\theta}{\cos 7\theta + \cos 3\theta} \qquad\qquad \tan 2\theta$$

$$= \frac{2 \cos \frac{1}{2}(7\theta + 3\theta) \sin \frac{1}{2}(7\theta - 3\theta)}{2 \cos \frac{1}{2}(7\theta + 3\theta) \cos \frac{1}{2}(7\theta - 3\theta)}$$

$$= \frac{\sin 2\theta}{\cos 2\theta}$$

$$= \tan 2\theta.$$

* The expression "sum or difference" is called the "algebraic sum."

EXERCISE 25

Express each of the following as an algebraic sum of sines and cosines.

1. $2 \sin 5\theta \sin 3\theta$.
2. $10 \sin 6\theta \cos \theta$.
3. $\cos 75° \cos 15°$.
4. $\sin 4\theta \sin 8\theta$.
5. $4 \sin 37\frac{1}{2}° \cos 7\frac{1}{2}°$.
6. $6 \cos 2\theta \cos 5\theta$.

Express each of the following as a product.

7. $\cos 2\theta - \cos \theta$.
8. $\sin 19A - \sin 11A$.
9. $\cos A + \cos (A + 60°)$.
10. $\sin 36° + \cos 66°$.

Prove the following identities.

11. $\dfrac{\sin 6\theta - \sin 2\theta}{\cos 7\theta + \cos \theta} = \dfrac{\sin 2\theta}{\cos 3\theta}$.

12. $\dfrac{\cos 70° + \cos 50°}{\sin 280° + \sin 260°} = -\dfrac{1}{2}$.

13. $\dfrac{\sin 100° + \sin 200°}{\cos 80° - \cos 20°} = -\cot 50°$.

14. $\dfrac{\cos 9\theta - \cos 5\theta}{\sin 17\theta - \sin 3\theta} = -\sin 2\theta \sec 10\theta$.

15. $\sin 20° + \sin 40° = \sin 80°$.

16. $\dfrac{\cos (A + B + C) - \cos (A - B - C)}{\sin (A + B + C) - \sin (A - B - C)} = -\tan A$.

17. $\dfrac{\cos 10A - \cos 6A}{\sin 5A - \sin A} + \dfrac{\sin 15A + \sin A}{\cos 10A + \cos 4A} = 0$.

18. $\dfrac{\sin A + \sin 4A + \sin 7A}{\cos A + \cos 4A + \cos 7A} = \tan 4A$.

19. $\sin 9\theta \cos \theta - \cos 7\theta \sin 3\theta = \sin 6\theta \cos 2\theta$.

20. If $A + B + C = 90°$, prove

$$\sin 2A + \sin 2B + \sin 2C = 4 \cos A \cos B \cos C.$$

Hint: $\sin 2C = 2 \sin C \cos C,$ $\sin (A + B) - \cos C$.

20.

$(A+B)+C$ are complimentary angles

$2 \sin \tfrac{1}{2}(2A+2B) \cos \tfrac{1}{2}(2A+2B) + \sin 2C$

$2 \sin(A+B) \cos(A-B) + 2 \sin C \cos C$

$2 \cos C \cos(A+B) + 2 \sin C \cos C$

$2 \cos C [\cos(A+B) + \sin C]$

$2 \cos C [\cos(A+B) + \cos(A+B)]$

$2 \cos C [2 \cos(A-B)+(A+B)] \cos \tfrac{1}{2}[(A-B)-(A+B)]\}$

$2 \cos C \cdot 2 \cos A \cos B$

$4 \cos A \cos B \cos C$

CHAPTER 8

TRIGONOMETRIC EQUATIONS

43. Trigonometric equations. A conditional equation is an equation that does *not* hold true for all permissible values of the letters involved. (The student should review Art. 22 before proceeding.) If a conditional equation involves trigonometric functions, it is called a trigonometric equation, in contrast to a trigonometric identity. *A solution of a trigonometric equation is a value of the angle that satisfies the equation.* For example, $\theta = 90°$ is a solution of the equation $\sin \theta = 1 + \cos \theta$. Any angle coterminal with $90°$ is also a solution. Thus $\theta = 450°, 810°$, etc., are also solutions. In this book, *to solve a trigonometric equation shall mean to find all positive (or zero) solutions less than $360°$.*

44. Solving a trigonometric equation. The process of finding the solutions of a trigonometric equation involves algebraic as well as trigonometric methods. There is no general rule, but the following suggestions will take care of most cases.

(*A*). *If only one function of a single angle is involved, solve algebraically for the values of the function.* Then determine the corresponding angles.

Example 1. Solve for θ: $4 \cos^2 \theta = 3$.
Solution. Here $\cos^2 \theta = \frac{3}{4}$.
Hence

$$\cos \theta = \frac{\sqrt{3}}{2}. \qquad\qquad \cos \theta = -\frac{\sqrt{3}}{2}.$$
$$\theta = 30°, 330°. \qquad\qquad \theta = 150°, 210°.$$

Therefore $\qquad\qquad \theta = 30°, 150°, 210°, 330°.$

Example 2. Solve for θ: $4 \sin^2 \theta = 3 \sin \theta$.
Solution. Transpose $3 \sin \theta$ to make the right side 0; then factor:

$$\sin \theta (4 \sin \theta - 3) = 0$$

$\sin \theta = 0.$ $\qquad\qquad$ $4 \sin \theta - 3 = 0.$
$\theta = 0°, 180°.$ $\qquad\qquad$ $\sin \theta = \frac{3}{4} = .75.$
$\qquad\qquad\qquad\qquad\qquad \theta = 48° 35', 131° 25'.$

Hence $\qquad\qquad\qquad \theta = 0°, 48° 35', 131° 25', 180°.$

The student is warned to guard against dividing both sides of this equation by the variable factor $\sin \theta$. Had this been done, the solutions $0°$ and $180°$ would have been lost.

Example 3. Solve for θ: $\qquad \sin^2 \theta - 5 \sin \theta - 3 = 0.$

Solution. The left side is not factorable. The roots of the quadratic equation $ax^2 + bx + c = 0$ are

$$x = \frac{-b \pm \sqrt{b^2 - 4ac}}{2a}.$$

In this case $a = 1$, $b = -5$, $c = -3$, and $x = \sin \theta$. The formula gives us

$$\sin \theta = \frac{5 \pm \sqrt{25 + 12}}{2} = \frac{5 \pm 6.0828}{2}.$$

$\sin \theta = 5.5414.$	$\sin \theta = -0.5414.$
θ is impossible.	(Related angle is $32° 47'$)
	θ is in Q III, IV.
	$\theta = 212° 47', 327° 13'.$

Hence $\qquad\qquad\qquad \theta = 212° 47', 327° 13'.$

(B). *If one side of the equation is zero and the other side is factorable,* set each such factor equal to zero *and solve the resulting equations.*

Example 4. Solve for θ: $\qquad \cos 2\theta \csc \theta - 2 \cos 2\theta = 0.$

Solution. Factor the left side:

$$\cos 2\theta (\csc \theta - 2) = 0.$$

$\cos 2\theta = 0.$	$\csc \theta - 2 = 0.$
$2\theta = 90°, 270°, 450°, 630°.$	$\csc \theta = 2.$
$\theta = 45°, 135°, 225°, 315°.$	$\sin \theta = \frac{1}{2}.$
	$\theta = 30°, 150°.$

Hence $\qquad\qquad \theta = 30°, 45°, 135°, 150°, 225°, 315°.$

In order to solve $\cos 2\theta = 0$ for all values of θ in the range $0° \leqq \theta < 360°$, it is necessary to find all values of 2θ in the range $0° \leqq 2\theta < 720°$.

(C). *If several functions of a single angle are involved,* use the fundamental relations to *express everything in terms of a single function.* Then proceed as in (A).

Example 5. Solve for θ: $\sin^2 \theta - \cos^2 \theta - \cos \theta = 1$.

Solution.   Replace $\sin^2 \theta$ with $1 - \cos^2 \theta$; collect terms:

$$2 \cos^2 \theta + \cos \theta = 0.$$
$$\cos \theta (2 \cos \theta + 1) = 0.$$

$$\cos \theta = 0.$$
$$\theta = 90°, 270°.$$

$$2 \cos \theta + 1 = 0.$$
$$\cos \theta = -\tfrac{1}{2}.$$
(Related angle is 60°)
$$\theta \text{ is in Q II, III.}$$
$$\theta = 120°, 240°.$$

Hence $\theta = 90°, 120°, 240°, 270°.$

Example 6. Solve for θ: $\sec \theta = \tan \theta - 1$.

Solution.   Replace $\sec \theta$ with $\pm \sqrt{1 + \tan^2 \theta}$; square both sides:

$$1 + \tan^2 \theta = \tan^2 \theta - 2 \tan \theta + 1,$$
$$2 \tan \theta = 0, \quad \text{or} \quad \tan \theta = 0.$$

Hence $\theta = 0°, 180°.$

Inasmuch as we squared the equation, we may have introduced some extraneous roots. Consequently, we must check these values in the original equation.

Check for $\theta = 0°$: $\sec 0° = \tan 0° - 1.$

$$1 = -1. \quad \text{False.}$$

Check for $\theta = 180°$: $\sec 180° = \tan 180° - 1.$

$$-1 = -1. \quad \text{True.}$$

Therefore $\theta = 0°$ is an *extraneous* root and $\theta = 180°$ is a true root. The only solution of the equation is $\theta = 180°$.

(D) *If several angles are involved,* use the fundamental identities to *express everything in terms of a single angle.* Then proceed as in (C).

Example 7. Solve for θ: $\cos 2\theta = 3 \sin \theta + 2$.

Solution.   This equation involves two angles. It is not convenient to replace $\sin \theta$ with a function of 2θ because this would introduce the radical

$$\pm \sqrt{\frac{1 - \cos 2\theta}{2}}.$$

It is better to replace $\cos 2\theta$ with one of its three forms. Since the right side involves only $\sin \theta$, we choose the form $\cos 2\theta = 1 - 2 \sin^2 \theta$ in order to reduce everything immediately to the same function of a single angle. This gives us

$$1 - 2 \sin^2 \theta = 3 \sin \theta + 2,$$

or $2 \sin^2 \theta + 3 \sin \theta + 1 = 0.$

Factor:

$$(2 \sin \theta + 1)(\sin \theta + 1) = 0.$$

$$\sin \theta = -\tfrac{1}{2}. \qquad\qquad \sin \theta = -1.$$
$$\theta = 210°, 330°. \qquad\qquad \theta = 270°.$$

Hence $\qquad\qquad \theta = 210°, 270°, 330°.$

EXERCISE 26

Solve the following equations.

1. $\sin (\theta + 10°) = \dfrac{\sqrt{3}}{2}.$

2. $\cos (\theta - 5°) = -\dfrac{\sqrt{3}}{2}.$

3. $4 \sin^2 \theta = 3.$

4. $2 \cos^2 \theta - 1 = 0.$

5. $\tan^2 \theta - 3 = 0.$

6. $\csc^2 \theta = 1.$

7. $(2 \cos \theta - \sqrt{3})(\sqrt{2} \sin \theta + 1) = 0.$

8. $(\sin \theta - 1)(2 \cos \theta + \sqrt{3}) = 0.$

9. $\sin 2\theta \cos \theta = 0.$

10. $\cot \theta (\sec 2\theta - 2) = 0.$

11. $\sin 3\theta \cos \theta + \sin 3\theta + \cos \theta + 1 = 0.$

12. $\sqrt{3} \cos 2\theta \tan \theta + \cos 2\theta = 0.$

13. $\sqrt{2} \sin \theta \sec 5\theta - \sec 5\theta = 0.$

14. $2 \sin \theta \tan \theta + \sqrt{3} \tan \theta = 0.$

15. $2 \cos^3 \theta = \cos \theta.$

16. $3 \csc^3 \theta - 4 \csc \theta = 0.$

17. $\tan^2 \theta - \tan \theta = 0.$

18. $2 \sin^2 \theta = 21 \sin \theta + 11.$

19. $2 \cos^2 \theta + 7 \sin \theta = 5.$

20. $\sin^2 \theta = 7 \cos \theta + 7.$

21. $5 \tan^2 \theta - 11 \sec \theta + 7 = 0.$

22. $\sin \theta + \sqrt{3} \cos \theta = 0.$

23. $\cos 2\theta = \cos \theta.$

24. $\sin 2\theta + \sqrt{2} \cos \theta = 0.$

25. $\sin 2\theta + \sin \theta = 0.$

26. $\cos 2\theta = 1 - \sin \theta.$

27. $\sin 6\theta = \sin 3\theta.$

28. $\cos 2\theta = 2 \sin^2 \theta + 2 \sin \theta + 1.$

29. $\cos 2\theta + 2 \cos^2 \theta = 2.$

30. $\sin \theta = \sqrt{3} \cos \dfrac{\theta}{2}.$

31. $\csc \theta = 1 + \cot \theta.$

32. $\sqrt{2} \sec \theta = 1 - \tan \theta.$

33. $2 + \sin \theta = \sqrt{3} \cos \theta.$

34. $\cos \theta - 1 = \sqrt{3} \sin \theta.$

35. $\sec^2 \theta - 5 \tan \theta + 3 = 0.$

36. $8 \cos^2 \theta + 6 \sin \theta = 9.$

37. $5 \cos^2 \theta + 9 \cos \theta + 2 = 0.$

38. $\sin^2 \theta - 6 \sin \theta - 1 = 0.$

39. $4 \sin \theta + 3 \cos \theta = 1.$ *Hint:* See Prob. 35, page 70.

40. $8 \sin \theta = 5 \cos \theta.$

41. $\csc \theta \cot \theta - 1000 \sec \theta \tan \theta = 0.$

42. $7 \sin \theta = 7 + \cos \theta.$

43. $4 \csc \theta \sec \theta = \sec \theta.$

44. $\sin^2 \theta + 6 = 5 \sin \theta.$

45. $\cos \theta - \sin \theta = \sqrt{2}.$

46. $2 \csc \theta + \sqrt{4 + \csc^2 \theta} = 0.$

47. $2 \sin \theta + \cot \theta = \csc \theta.$

48. $12 \cos^4 \theta = \sin^2 \theta.$

49. $\sin \theta + \csc \theta = 1.9.$

50. $\cos 2\theta = 2 \cos^2 \theta.$

51. $\dfrac{\tan 3\theta - \tan \theta}{1 + \tan 3\theta \tan \theta} = \dfrac{1}{\sqrt{3}}.$

52. $\cos 7\theta \cos 5\theta + \sin 7\theta \sin 5\theta = 1$.

53. $\cos \theta + \cos 7\theta = 4 \cos 3\theta$. *Hint:* Express the left side as a product.

54. $\sin 5\theta - \sin \theta = 2 \sin 2\theta$.   **55.** $\cos^2 2\theta - \sin^2 2\theta = -1$.

56. $\sin 2\theta + 2 \cos \theta = 1 + \sin \theta$.

57. $\sqrt{2} \sin \dfrac{\theta}{2} + \sqrt{1 - \cos \theta} = \sqrt{2}$.

58. $3 \sec^2 \theta - \cot^2 \theta = 1$.   **59.** $\sin 3\theta = \cos (\theta + 50°)$.

60. $\tan (2\theta + 5°) = \cot (\theta - 20°)$.

$90° - 3\theta = \theta + 50°$

$4\theta = -40°$

$\theta = 10°$, and $190°$

original panel

$I + III \ Q$

60 $\tan(2\theta + 5°) = \cot(\theta - 20°)$

$\theta - 20° = 90° - 2\theta - 5°$

$3\theta = 105°$

$\theta = 35°$

CHAPTER 9

LOGARITHMS

45. The uses of logarithms. Logarithms are used to shorten the labor involved in computing products and quotients, raising to a power, and extracting roots. For example, the operation of multiplying 234.56 by 9876.5 can be reduced to the operation of adding the logarithms of these numbers, namely, 2.37025 and 3.99460. Since the solution of triangles (Chaps. 10 and 11) involves such computations, we shall first consider the theory of logarithms.

46. Some laws of exponents. A logarithm, as we shall see later, is an exponent. Accordingly we shall first review the following laws of exponents.

(1) $a^m \cdot a^n = a^{m+n}$.   *Example.* $2^3 \cdot 2^4 = 2^7$.

(2) $(a^m)^n = a^{mn}$.   *Example.* $(2^3)^4 = 2^{12}$.

(3) $\dfrac{a^m}{a^n} = a^{m-n}$.   *Example.* $\dfrac{2^8}{2^2} = 2^6$.

(4) $a^{\frac{m}{n}} = (\sqrt[n]{a})^m = \sqrt[n]{a^m}$.   *Example.* $8^{\frac{4}{3}} = (\sqrt[3]{8})^4 = 2^4 = 16$.

(5) $a^0 = 1$.   *Example.* $(\frac{2}{3})^0 = 1$.

(6) $a^{-n} = \dfrac{1}{a^n}$.   *Example.* $3^{-2} = \dfrac{1}{3^2} = \dfrac{1}{9}$.

Although these laws are true for all values of m and n and for positive and negative values of a, we shall use them for just positive values of a.

47. Definition of logarithm. *The* **logarithm** *of a number to a given base is the exponent which must be placed on the base to produce the number.** Thus the logarithm of 9 to the base 3 (written $\log_3 9$) is 2 because $3^2 = 9$.

---

* This exponent need not be rational. For example, $\log_{10} 2$ is an irrational number which, rounded off to five decimal places, becomes 0.30103. If the exponent $\dfrac{30,103}{100,000}$ is placed on 10, the result is 2 *approximately*.

Illustrations.

$$\log_2 8 = 3 \quad \text{because} \quad 2^3 = 8.$$
$$\log_7 1 = 0 \quad \text{because} \quad 7^0 = 1.$$
$$\log_3 \tfrac{1}{3} = -1 \quad \text{because} \quad 3^{-1} = \tfrac{1}{3}.$$
$$\log_2 \frac{1}{16} = -4 \quad \text{because} \quad 2^{-4} = \frac{1}{2^4} = \frac{1}{16}.$$
$$\log_{25} 5 = \tfrac{1}{2} \quad \text{because} \quad (25)^{\frac{1}{2}} = \sqrt{25} = 5.$$
$$\log_8 4 = \tfrac{2}{3} \quad \text{because} \quad 8^{\frac{2}{3}} = (\sqrt[3]{8})^2 = 2^2 = 4.$$
$$\log_6 6 = 1 \quad \text{because} \quad 6^1 = 6.$$

The definition of logarithm implies that

if
$$\log_b N = x,$$
then
$$b^x = N.$$

These two equations, the former logarithmic and the latter exponential, say the same thing in two different ways. We shall assume in further discussions that N is a positive number and that b is a positive number different from 1. Explain the necessity for such restrictions.

Since, by the definition of logarithm, $\log_b N$ is the exponent which must be placed on b to produce N, it follows that if $\log_b N$ is applied as an exponent to the base b, then the result must be N:

$$b^{\log_b N} = N.$$

EXERCISE 27

Find the value of each of the following logarithms.

1. $\log_{10} 100.$
2. $\log_9 \tfrac{1}{9}.$
3. $\log_3 3.$
4. $\log_2 32.$
5. $\log_2 1.$
6. $\log_{36} 6.$
7. $\log_{4/7} \tfrac{7}{4}.$
8. $\log_9 \tfrac{1}{81}.$
9. $\log_{125} 25.$
10. $\log_{1000} \tfrac{1}{10}.$
11. $\log_{49} \tfrac{1}{7}.$
12. $\log_3 1.$
13. $\log_2 \tfrac{1}{64}$
14. $\log_{\sqrt{2}} 8.$
15. $\log_{16} 32.$
16. $\log_{27} 3.$

Find the unknown N, b, or x in the following.

17. $\log_{81} N = -\tfrac{3}{4}.$
18. $\log_{32} N = \tfrac{6}{5}.$
19. $\log_b \tfrac{1}{81} = -4.$
20. $\log_b \tfrac{1}{10} = -1.$
21. $\log_b 125 = -3.$
22. $\log_{1/4} 16 = x.$
23. $\log_{12} N = 0.$
24. $10^{\log_{10} 3} = x.$
25. $e^{\log_e 8} = x.$
26. $\log_b 2^7 = 7.$
27. $\log_3 3^{10} = x.$
28. $\log_{32} N = -\tfrac{3}{5}.$

Express as a logarithmic equation.

29. $12^{-1} = \frac{1}{12}$.

30. $10^{-5} = \frac{1}{100,000}$.

31. $125^{4/3} = 625$.

32. $r^s = t$.

Express as an exponential equation.

33. $\log_b a = c$.

34. $\log_6 1 = 0$.

35. $\log_2 \frac{1}{1024} = -10$.

36. $\log_{128} \frac{1}{16} = -\frac{4}{7}$.

Identify as true or false and give reasons.

37. $\log_8 \sqrt[3]{2} = \frac{1}{9}$. *True*

38. $\log_9 \frac{\sqrt[4]{27}}{3} = -\frac{1}{8}$.

39. $\log_2 32^r = 5r$. *True*

40. $\log_{16} 2^m = \frac{m}{4}$.

48. Properties of logarithms.

As a consequence of the definition of logarithm, we have three properties or laws of logarithms. They are used in computations involving logarithms.

Property 1.   The logarithm of a product is equal to the sum of the logarithms of the factors; i.e.,

$$\log MN = \log M + \log N.*$$

Proof. Let $x = \log_a M$ and $y = \log_a N$.

Express in exponential form: $M = a^x$ and $N = a^y$.

Multiply the equations: $MN = a^x a^y = a^{x+y}$.

Change to logarithmic form: $\log_a MN = x + y$.

$$\log_a MN = \log_a M + \log_a N.$$

The proof is similar for a product of more than two factors.

Illustrations.

$$\log 35 = \log 5 \cdot 7 = \log 5 + \log 7;$$
$$\log 30 = \log 2 \cdot 3 \cdot 5 = \log 2 + \log 3 + \log 5.$$

Property 2.   The logarithm of a fraction is equal to the logarithm of the numerator minus the logarithm of the denominator; i.e.,

$$\log \frac{M}{N} = \log M - \log N.$$

Proof. Let $x = \log_a M$ and $y = \log_a N$.

Express in exponential form: $M = a^x$ and $N = a^y$.

Divide the equations: $\frac{M}{N} = \frac{a^x}{a^y} = a^{x-y}$.

* The base is the same for all the logarithms.

Change to logarithmic form: $\log_a \dfrac{M}{N} = x - y.$

$$\log_a \frac{M}{N} = \log_a M - \log_a N.$$

Illustrations.

$$\log \tfrac{2}{3} = \log 2 - \log 3;$$

$$\log \frac{6}{35} = \log \frac{2 \cdot 3}{5 \cdot 7} = \log 2 + \log 3 - (\log 5 + \log 7).$$

Property 3.   The logarithm of the kth power of a number is equal to k times the logarithm of the number; i.e.

$$\log N^k = k \log N.$$

Proof.   Let $x = \log_a N.$

Express in exponential form: $N = a^x.$

Raise to the kth power: $N^k = (a^x)^k = a^{kx},$

Change to logarithmic form: $\log_a N^k = kx.$

$$\log_a N^k = k \log_a N.$$

Illustrations.

$$\log 8 = \log 2^3 = 3 \log 2;$$

$$\log \sqrt{3} = \log 3^{1/2} = \tfrac{1}{2} \log 3;$$

$$\log \frac{125}{49} = \log \frac{5^3}{7^2} = \log 5^3 - \log 7^2 = 3 \log 5 - 2 \log 7.$$

NOTE.   Since $\sqrt[r]{M} = M^{\frac{1}{r}}, \log \sqrt[r]{M} = \dfrac{1}{r} \log M.$

EXERCISE 28

Given $\log_{10} 2 = 0.30$, $\log_{10} 3 = 0.48$, $\log_{10} 7 = 0.85$, *find the following logarithms.*   (Remember $\log_{10} 10 = 1.$)

1. $\log_{10} 14.$
2. $\log_{10} \tfrac{3}{2}.$
3. $\log_{10} \tfrac{2}{7}.$
4. $\log_{10} 16.$
5. $\log_{10} \sqrt[4]{3}.$
6. $\log_{10} \sqrt{7}.$
7. $\log_{10} 243.$
8. $\log_{10} \sqrt[3]{5}.$
9. $\log_{10} \tfrac{8}{3}$
10. $\log_{10} 256.$
11. $\log_{10} \sqrt[6]{2}.$
12. $\log_{10} \tfrac{6}{7}.$
13. $\log_{10} 70,000.$
14. $\log_{10} \tfrac{14}{45}.$
15. $\log_{10} 210.$
16. $\log_{10} \tfrac{21}{2}.$

Express as a single logarithm.   (Assume all logarithms have the same base.)

17. $\log (5 - x) + \log x.$
18. $\log x - \log y - \log z.$

19. $\log P + n \log (1 + i)$.

20. $\log a - \frac{1}{2} \log b$.

21. $\log a - \frac{1}{5} \log b + 7 \log c$.

22. $\frac{1}{6} \log r + 8 \log s$.

23. $\frac{1}{3} \log \pi - \log 2$.

24. $\log x - 3 \log y - \log z + 2 \log w$.

Identify as true or false and give reasons. (In each equation the base is assumed to be the same for all the logarithms.)

25. $\log a = - \log \dfrac{1}{a}$.

26. $6^{5 \log_6 y} = y^5$. *true*

27. $b^{(\frac{1}{3}) \log_b x} = \sqrt[3]{x}$. *power of (log)*

28. $\sqrt[5]{a} = \frac{1}{5} \log a$.

29. $(\log t)^7 = 7 \log t$.

30. $\log \sqrt{ab} = \sqrt{\log a + \log b}$.

31. $(\log x + \log y)^{10} = 10 \log x + 10 \log y$.

32. $\log \dfrac{a}{bc} = \dfrac{\log a}{\log b + \log c}$.

33. $\log a = n \log \sqrt[n]{a}$.

34. $\dfrac{r}{s} = \log r - \log s$. *true*

35. $\dfrac{1}{2} \log r - \dfrac{1}{3} \log s - \dfrac{1}{6} \log t = \dfrac{1}{6} \log \dfrac{r^3}{s^2 t}$.

36. $2 \log \log r = \log (\log r)^2$.

49. Systems of logarithms. There are only two important systems of logarithms in use today. The *natural*, or *Napierian*, system employs the base e, where e is approximately 2.71828. This system is encountered in calculus and higher mathematics. The *common*, or *Briggs*, system employs the base 10. This system is most convenient for computation because our number system uses the base 10. Henceforth, in this text, when the base of a logarithm is not specified, we are to understand that the base is 10. Thus $\log N$ means $\log_{10} N$. And, unless stated to the contrary, the word *logarithm* shall mean common logarithm.

50. Characteristic and mantissa. We know that

$\log 1000$	$= 3$	because	$10^3 = 1000$,
$\log 100$	$= 2$	because	$10^2 = 100$,
$\log 10$	$= 1$	because	$10^1 = 10$,
$\log 1$	$= 0$	because	$10^0 = 1$,
$\log .1$	$= -1$	because	$10^{-1} = .1$,
$\log .01$	$= -2$	because	$10^{-2} = .01$,
$\log .001$	$= -3$	because	$10^{-3} = .001$.

It seems reasonable to assume that, as a number increases, its logarithm increases.* Consequently, any number lying between 10 and 100 must have a logarithm between 1 and 2. This logarithm can be written in the form 1 plus a positive decimal.† For example, log 45.7 = 1 + .65992 = 1.65992. Likewise, any number between .001 and .01 must have a logarithm between −3 and −2. This logarithm can be written in the form −3 plus a positive decimal. For example, log .006 = −3 + .77815, which can be written log .006 = 7.77815 − 10 because −3 = 7 − 10.

As a matter of convenience, *every logarithm is usually written as the sum of an integer* (positive, negative, or zero) *plus a positive decimal.*† The integer is called the **characteristic** of the logarithm; the positive decimal is called the **mantissa** of the logarithm.

Illustrations.

Logarithm	Characteristic	Mantissa
4.56789	4	.56789
0.23456	0	.23456
3.00000	3	.00000
8.77665 − 10 or −2 + .77665	8 − 10 or −2	.77665
7.11111 − 10 or −2.88889	7 − 10 or −3	.11111

51. Method of determining characteristics. *If a number has a decimal point immediately to the right of its first nonzero digit, then the decimal point is said to be in* **standard position.** For example, the decimal point is in standard position in each of the following: 6.507, 4.17, 3.2, and 8. Consequently, *if a number N has its decimal point in standard position,* then N is between 1 and 10, and log N is between 0 and 1; therefore, *the characteristic of log N is 0.*

Theorem 1. Whenever a number is multiplied by 10, its logarithm is increased by 1.

Proof. Let log N be the logarithm of any number N. Then

$$\log 10N = \log 10 + \log N, \qquad \text{(Property 1)}$$
$$\log 10N = 1 + \log N.$$

* This is proved in more advanced texts.
† Positive decimal here means a number n such that $0 \leqq n < 1$.

574 = 5.74 × 10² = characteristic

It is therefore apparent that when a number is multiplied by 10 (*i.e.*, if the decimal point is moved one place to the right), the characteristic of its logarithm is increased by 1, but the mantissa is unaltered.

Illustration.   If log 2.345 = 0.37014, then log 23.45 = 1.37014.

By repeating this process, we see that if a number is *multiplied* by 10^k (*i.e.*, if the decimal point is moved k places to the right), the characteristic of its logarithm is *increased* by k.   It also follows that if a number is *divided* by 10^k (*i.e.*, if the decimal point is moved k places to the left), the characteristic of its logarithm is *decreased* by k.

Illustration.   If log 2.345 = 0.37014, then

$$\log 234.5 = 2.37014 \qquad \text{and} \qquad \log 23450 = 4.37014,$$

and

$$\log 0.2345 = 9.37014 - 10 \qquad \text{and} \qquad \log 0.002345 = 7.37014 - 10.$$

We may sum up our discussion in the following

Theorem 2.   If the decimal point in a number is k places to the $\left\{ \begin{matrix} \text{right} \\ \text{left} \end{matrix} \right\}$ of standard position, then the characteristic of the logarithm of the number is $\left\{ \begin{matrix} k \\ -k \end{matrix} \right\}.$

Illustration.   The characteristic of log 8765 is 3 because the decimal point is understood to be after the 5, which is 3 places to the right of standard position (*i.e.*, after the 8).

The characteristic of log 0.08765 is -2 or $8 - 10$ because the decimal point is 2 places to the left of standard position.

An alternate method used in finding characteristics is:

1. For a number N that is greater than 1, the characteristic is one less than the number of digits to the left of the decimal point in N.

2. For a number N that is less than 1, the characteristic is negative and is numerically equal to one more than the number of zeros between the decimal point and the first nonzero digit in N.

Illustrations:

Number	Characteristic of Logarithm
456780	5
456.78	2
4.5678	0
0.45678	$9 - 10$ or -1
0.045678	$8 - 10$ or -2
0.00045678	$6 - 10$ or -4

Theorem 3. *The mantissa of the logarithm of a number N is independent of the position of the decimal point in N.* This means that two numbers differing only in the position of the decimal point have logarithms with the same mantissa. The proof of this theorem is embodied in that of Theorem 1 and the discussion that follows it.

Illustration. The following numbers have logarithms with the same mantissa:

$$0.04689, \quad 4.689, \quad 46.89, \quad 46890.$$

Theorem 2 serves two purposes:

1. If we look at the position of the decimal point in a *number*, we can determine the characteristic of its *logarithm*.

2. If we look at the characteristic of the *logarithm* of a number, we can determine the position of the decimal point in the *number*.

Example 1. Given log 1.616 = 0.20844.
(a) Find log 0.01616.   (b) Find N if log N = 5.20844.
(c) Find N if log N = 6.20844 − 10.
Solution.
   (a)   log 0.01616 = 8.20844 − 10.

Since the decimal point in 0.01616 is **2** places to the *left* of standard position, the characteristic is −**2** or 8 − 10. The mantissa is the same as that for log 1.616.

   (b) If   log N = **5**.20844,
                             N = 161600.

Since log N and log 1.616 have the same mantissa, N is obtainable from 1.616 by moving the decimal point **5** places to the right (from standard position).

   (c) If   log N = 6.20844 − 10,
                             N = 0.0001616.

Since the characteristic of log N is −4, we obtain N from 1.616 by moving the decimal point 4 places to the left.

Note. Theorems 1, 2, 3 of this article are valid only if the base of the logarithms is 10. For any other base, the process of finding the characteristic would not be so simple.

EXERCISE 29

Given log 3.612 = 0.55775 *and* log 7.777 = 0.89081, *find the value of the following.*

1. log 36,120.   2. log 0.03612.
3. log 0.007777.   4. log 777.7.
5. log 0.7777.   6. log 7777.

7. log 36.12.
9. log 0.000 07777.
11. log 77,770,000.

8. log 0.000 3612.
10. log 3,612,000.
12. log 0.3612.

Given log 3.333 = 0.52284 *and* log 64.28 = 1.80808, *find N for each of the following.*

13. log N = 9.80808 − 10.
15. log N = 4.52284.
17. log N = 5.52284.
19. log N = 7.80808 − 10.
21. log N = 4.52284 − 10.
23. log N = 8.52284 − 20.
25. log N = −3.19192.
27. log N = −1.19192.

14. log N = 0.80808.
16. log N = 5.52284 − 10.
18. log N = 8.52284 − 10.
20. log N = 9.80808
22. log N = 2.80808.
24. log N = 3.80808.
26. log N = −2.47716.
28. log N = −0.47716.

Hint: For Probs. 25 to 28, first write log N in a form where the decimal part is positive. For example: −3.19192 = 6.80808 − 10.

52. A five-place table of mantissas. In Table II (pages 8–25 in the tables) there are listed, to five decimal places, the mantissas (with the decimal points omitted) of the logarithms of all whole numbers from 1 to 9999. Since the mantissa is independent of the decimal point in the number, Table II can be used to find the mantissa of the logarithm of any four-figure number. The problems we shall need to consider are:

1. Given a number N, to find log N.
2. Given log N, to find N.

53. Given *N*, to find log *N*. The procedure of finding the logarithm of a given number is illustrated by the following examples.

Example 1. Find log 0.003467.
Solution. The characteristic of log 0.003467 is 7 − 10. To find the mantissa, look for 346 in the left-hand column headed "N" on page 12. In the line beginning with 346, move over to the column headed by 7. Here we find 995, which represents the last three figures of the five-place mantissa. The first two figures, 53, are found in the column headed by 0. Hence the mantissa of log 3467 (and log 0.003467) is .53995. Therefore,

$$\log 0.003467 = 7.53995 - 10.$$

Example 2. Find log 346.8.
Solution. The required characteristic is 2. To find the mantissa, go down the N column to 346 and then over to the 8 column and find 008. The asterisk (*) indicates that we are to prefix the 54 of the following line instead of using the 53 as in the preceding example. Hence the mantissa of log 3468 is .54008. Therefore,

$$\log 346.8 = 2.54008.$$

54. Given log N, to find N. The procedure of finding a number whose logarithm is given is illustrated by the following examples.

Example 1. Given log $N = 4.38686$, find N.

Solution. Look for the mantissa .38686 in the body part of Table II. It appears on page 10 in the 243 line and the 7 column. Hence N is 2437 with the decimal point placed in accordance with a characteristic of 4. Therefore,

if
$$\log N = 4.38686,$$
$$N = 24370.$$

Example 2. Given log $N = 8.09202 - 10$, find N.

Solution. The mantissa .09202 appears in the 123 line and in the 6 column. Hence N is 1236 with the decimal point moved 2 places to the left of standard position (because the characteristic is $8 - 10$ or -2). Therefore,

if
$$\log N = 8.09202 - 10,$$
$$N = 0.01236.$$

EXERCISE 30

Use a five-place table to find the value of each of the following.

1. log 5.744.
2. log 42.88.
3. log 8449.
4. log 3.269.
5. log 0.003895.
6. log 0.000 6167.
7. log 0.2634.
8. log 0.07946.
9. log 736,000.
10. log 928.1.
11. log 0.000 06821.
12. log 51,120.

Use a five-place table to determine the value of N in each of the following.

13. log $N = 3.47378$.
14. log $N = 9.06558 - 10$.
15. log $N = 0.09968$.
16. log $N = 2.95727$.
17. log $N = 8.78003 - 10$.
18. log $N = 4.89020$.
19. log $N = 1.64018$.
20. log $N = 7.45010 - 10$.
21. log $N = 6.92122$.
22. log $N = 5.93902 - 10$.
23. log $N = 6.97955 - 10$.
24. log $N = 5.67679$.

55. Interpolation. We have already seen (Art. 52) that the logarithm of a four-figure number can be found in Table II. The logarithm of a five-figure number can also be found from the table by interpolation (Art. 16). It is to be remembered that, since the mantissas of the logarithms of most integers are unending decimals, a five-place table merely rounds off these mantissas to five-figure accuracy. For this reason a five-place table will not give satisfactory results when we are dealing with six-figure numbers. Consequently, whenever we encounter a six-figure number, we shall round it off to five-figure accuracy before using Table II.

Example 1.   Find log 24357.

Solution.   The characteristic is 4. The mantissa lies between the mantissas for 24350 and 24360.

mantissa of log 24350   = .38650

mantissa of log 24357   7)   =

mantissa of log 24360   = .38668

$\Big)$ 10 $\Big)$ 18

Using the same procedure as in Art. 16, we take $\frac{7}{10}$ of the tabular difference 18 to get our difference 12.6 → 13 and add this to the top mantissa. Hence, mantissa of log 24357 is .38663. Therefore,

$$\log 24357 = 4.38663.$$

Instead of writing this three-line arrangement, we can interpolate mentally by using the tables of proportional parts which are at the right of each page. To find $\frac{7}{10}$ of 18, locate the short column with 18 at the top. Follow down to the line that has 7 at the left and read 12.6 in the 18 column. Thus $\frac{7}{10}(18)$ = 12.6.

Example 2.   Find log 0.17083.

Solution.   The characteristic is $9 - 10$. From page 9, the mantissa of log 17080 is .23249. The tabular difference is 25. Using the proportional parts table, we find $\frac{3}{10}(25) = 7.5$, which must be rounded off to 7 to make the final result even.*   Hence

$$\log 0.17083 = 9.23256 - 10.$$

Example 3.   Given $\log N = 8.38591 - 10$, find N.

Solution.   From page 10,

mantissa of log 24310   = .38578

mantissa of log N = .38591

mantissa of log 24320   = .38596

$\Big)$ 10 $\Big)$ 13 $\Big)$ 18

Proceeding as in Art. 16, we take $\frac{13}{18}$ of 10 and get $7\frac{2}{9}$ → 7, which when added to 24310 gives 24317. Hence

if $\log N = 8.38591 - 10,$
                              $N = 0.024317.$

Here again we can dispense with the three-line arrangement and save time by using the tables of proportional parts. Obviously the result of taking $\frac{13}{18}$ of 10 is the answer to the question, "How many tenths of 18 will be equal to 13."†   In the proportional parts table for 18, look for the number nearest to 13. This number is 12.6 and to its left we find 7. Hence, 7 must be added to 24310.

* See footnote on p. 19.

† If $x = \frac{13}{18}(10)$, then $\frac{x}{10}(18) = 13$.

Example 4. Given log $N = 1.52255$, find N.

Solution. From page 12, mantissa of log 33300 is .52244. The tabular difference is 13 and our difference is $(255 - 244) = 11$. In the proportional parts table for 13, we seek the number nearest to 11. This number is 10.4 and it corresponds to 8. Hence

if
$$\log N = 1.52255,$$
$$N = 33.308.$$

It is to be noted that, in going from a number to its logarithm, we work from left to right in the small proportional parts table as well as in the large table (Table II). In going from a logarithm to the corresponding number, the movement is from right to left in both the small and large tables.

EXERCISE 31

Find the value of each of the following. (Use tables of proportional parts—not the three-line arrangement.)

1. log 0.041517.
2. log 5.8604.
3. log 0.000 33302.
4. log 0.0093812.
5. log 8267.5.
6. log 0.30841.
7. log 1.7423.
8. log 29.147.
9. log 0.000 000 67676.
10. log 72,459.
11. log 501,340.
12. log 0.000 045786.
13. log 127.93.
14. log 0.000 000 0025298.
15. log 0.000 0097379.
16. log 8,824,100.

Find the value of N in each of the following. (Use tables of proportional parts.)

17. log $N = 0.00451$.
18. log $N = 3.69298$.
19. log $N = 9.84769 - 10$.
20. log $N = 8.80757 - 10$.
21. log $N = 8.26417$.
22. log $N = 6.43533 - 10$.
23. log $N = 2.77260$.
24. log $N = 4.55428$.
25. log $N = 7.96025 - 10$.
26. log $N = 7.37026$.
27. log $N = 6.49117$.
28. log $N = 2.01102 - 10$.
29. log $N = 1.30405$.
30. log $N = 4.15413 - 10$.
31. log $N = 5.54522 - 10$.
32. log $N = 0.72091$.

56. Logarithmic computation. When logarithms are used to compute products, quotients, and powers of numbers, it is advisable to:

1. Make a complete outline indicating the operations to be performed.

2. Fill in all characteristics.

3. Fill in mantissas.

4. Perform the operations outlined in step 1.

These suggestions are offered in the hope that accuracy, speed, and neatness will result.   Every logarithm appearing in the solution should be labeled.

Example 1.   Use logarithms to compute $\dfrac{(2345)(0.6699)}{9.876}$.

Solution.   Let $N = \dfrac{(2345)(0.6699)}{9.876}$.

Then $\log N = \log 2345 + \log 0.6699 - \log 9.876$.

After preparing the outline and filling in the characteristics, we have

$$\log 2345 = 3.$$
$$\log 0.6699 = 9. \qquad -10$$
$$\overline{} \text{ Add}$$
$$\log \text{numerator} =$$
$$\log 9.876 = 0.$$
$$\overline{} \text{ Subtract}$$
$$\log N =$$
$$N =$$

After supplying the mantissas and performing the indicated operations, we get

$$\log 2345 = \quad 3.37014$$
$$\log 0.6699 = \quad 9.82601 - 10$$
$$\overline{} \text{ A}$$
$$\log \text{numerator} = 13.19615 - 10$$
$$\log 9.876 = \quad 0.99458$$
$$\overline{} \text{ S}$$
$$\log N = 12.20157 - 10$$
$$N = 159.1$$

Notice that no interpolation was performed in finding N from $\log N$. The original numbers are all four-figure numbers; hence the computed result should have no more than four-figure accuracy. Since the mantissa .20157 is best approximated by the tabular mantissa .20167, the best four-figure approximation of N is 159.1.

In all logarithmic computations we are really expressing the original numbers as powers of 10.   For example, since $\log 2345 = 3.37014$, it follows that $2345 = 10^{3.37014}$.

Consequently $N = \dfrac{(10^{3.37014})(10^{9.82601-10})}{10^{0.99458}}$.

Applying the laws of exponents,

$$N = 10^{3.37014+(9.82601-10)-0.99458}$$
$$= 10^{2.20157} = 159.1$$

Example 2.   Use logarithms to compute

$$N = \frac{(1.2346)^3}{(60370)(0.045023)}.$$

Solution.   Take the logarithm of each side:

$$\log N = 3 \log 1.2346 - (\log 60370 + \log 0.045023).$$

After taking the four suggested steps, we get

$$\begin{array}{ll}
\log 1.2346 = \underline{\quad 0.09153 \quad} \\
3 \log 1.2346 = \overline{\quad 0.27459 \quad} \; 3
\end{array}
\qquad
\begin{array}{l}
\log 60370 = 4.78082 \\
\log 0.045023 = 8.65344 - 10
\end{array}$$

$$\begin{array}{ll}
\log \text{num.} = 10.27459 - 10 \\
\log \text{den.} = 3.43426
\end{array}
\qquad
\begin{array}{l}
\text{—————— A} \\
\end{array}$$

$$\log \text{den.} = 13.43426 - 10$$
$$= 3.43426$$

$$\begin{array}{c}
\text{—————— S} \\
\log N = 6.84033 - 10 \\
N = 0.00069236
\end{array}$$

It is to be noticed that log num. was changed from 0.27459 to 10.27459 − 10 to avoid subtracting 3.43426 from a smaller number.

Example 3. Compute $\sqrt[7]{\dfrac{345.80}{4589}}$.

Solution. Let $N = \sqrt[7]{\dfrac{345.80}{4589}}$.

Then $\log N = \frac{1}{7} [\log 345.80 - \log 4589]$.
After taking the four suggested steps, we have

$$\begin{array}{rl}
\log 345.80 = & 12.53882 - 10 \\
\log 4589 = & 3.66172 \\
& \text{—————— S} \\
\log \text{radicand} = & 8.87710 - 10 \\
\log \text{radicand} = & 68.87710 - 70 \\
& 7 \text{ ——————} \\
\log N = & 9.83959 - 10 \\
N = & 0.6912.
\end{array}$$

Notice that log radicand was changed from 8.87710 − 10 to 68.87710 − 70 to facilitate the division by 7. Had we divided 8.87710 − 10 by 7, the result, 1.26816 − 1.42857 = −0.16041, would involve a *negative* decimal that does not appear in our table of *positive* mantissas.

The final result is written with only four-figure accuracy because the least accurate number, 4589, in the original data has only four significant figures.

Example 4. Use logarithms to compute

$$x = \frac{(-1.2346)^3}{(-60370)(-0.045023)}.$$

Solution. The value of x is negative since $\dfrac{(-)^3}{(-)(-)} = \dfrac{-}{+} = -$. Discard all minus signs in x and then use logarithms to compute the value of the corresponding expression in which all numbers are positive. This was done in Example 2 with the result 0.00069236. Hence

$$x = -0.00069236.$$

EXERCISE 32

Use logarithms to compute the following correct to four-figure accuracy. (In finding N from log N, do not interpolate.)

1. $(62.84)(0.007193)$.

2. $(888.5)(0.4606)(0.05177)$.

3. $(3.142)^5(0.06698)$.

4. $(0.0002581)(676.3)$.

5. $\dfrac{(0.8743)^2}{561.1}$.

6. $\dfrac{0.004832}{19.56}$.

7. $\dfrac{3{,}728{,}000}{7296}$.

8. $\dfrac{\sqrt{22507}}{0.6713}$.

9. $[(0.01941)(456.7)]^7$.

10. $(9.999)^{10}$.

11. $(0.9876)^{100}$.

12. $\left(\dfrac{78.56}{3721}\right)^5$.

13. $\dfrac{89{,}140}{\sqrt[4]{567800}}$.

14. $\sqrt[5]{(0.9283)(0.002777)}$.

15. $\dfrac{(1776)(0.006446)}{(3.095)(516.2)}$.

16. $\dfrac{(8.540)(222.6)}{0.09481}$.

17. $\sqrt[3]{0.0007418}$.

18. $\sqrt[6]{\dfrac{0.04321}{78910}}$.

19. $\sqrt[7]{(0.001492)(54.40)}$.

20. $\sqrt[9]{0.0002056}$.

21. $\dfrac{-3.854}{(-86.11)(-0.001812)}$.

22. $\left[\dfrac{(-4753)(-0.6318)}{-99.44}\right]^4$.

23. $(-207.4)(-0.7563)(-0.03334)$.

24. $(-4189)(-0.8839)^6$.

25. $(\log 9247)(\log 1{,}074{,}000)$.

26. $\dfrac{\log 3767}{0.0005755}$.

27. $\sqrt{\dfrac{\log 58210}{\log 8.445}}$.

28. $(\log 22.08)^3$.

29. $(0.7071)^{-6}$.

30. $\dfrac{(1.576)^5 + 4.167}{67230}$.

31. $\dfrac{0.09292}{\sqrt[3]{582400} + 14.23}$.

32. $[(33770)(0.008945)]^{-4}$.

Use logarithms to compute the following correct to five-figure accuracy.

33. $(4.4309)(585.41)(0.00062530)$.

34. $(0.0076543)^2(246.88)$.

35. $(1781.3)(9.0464)$.

36. $\dfrac{0.022748}{8.1326}$.

37. $\sqrt[7]{\dfrac{0.032196}{9.5263}}$.

38. $\sqrt[7]{0.00085234}$.

39. $\sqrt[3]{0.000075767}$.

40. $\sqrt[3]{(0.0044022)(0.00069253)}$.

41. $(34578)^{3/6}$.

42. $(0.50376)^{-8}$.

43. $\left(\dfrac{47932}{159.26}\right)^{-3}$.

44. $\dfrac{(72.421)^4(0.65870)}{23567}$.

Use logarithms to compute the following to as much accuracy as is warranted by the numbers involved.

45. $\dfrac{0.0647}{7428}$.

46. $(34.879)(0.096520)$.

47. $(0.0005440)^2(10.01)^9(21,645)$.

48. $\dfrac{(87.439)^4}{(432.60)^3}$.

49. $\sqrt[100]{30,405}$.

50. $(0.00289)\sqrt[8]{7409.0}$.

51. $\dfrac{0.049152}{\sqrt[6]{8352.0}}$.

52. $\sqrt[4]{177500}\sqrt[5]{0.0000972}$.

53. $\dfrac{(0.9116)^4\sqrt{0.00005168}}{48.960}$.

54. $\dfrac{\sqrt[3]{3,847,000}}{\sqrt[4]{0.06290}}$.

55. $\dfrac{2563\sqrt[5]{0.00712}}{0.83490}$.

56. $\sqrt{\dfrac{(1.020)^3(0.05182)}{9586.4}}$.

57. At the end of each year a man deposits \$1000 in a savings bank that pays 3 per cent interest, compounded annually. A mathematical formula for the amount S of this annuity at the end of 20 years gives

$$S = 1000\left[\frac{(1.03)^{20} - 1}{.03}\right].$$

Use logarithms to compute S to five-figure accuracy.

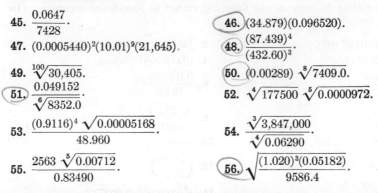

CHAPTER 10

RIGHT TRIANGLES

57. Logarithms of trigonometric functions. In Table III (pages 28–72 in the tables) there are listed, to five decimal places, the logarithms of the sine, cosine, tangent, and cotangent for acute angles at intervals of one minute. This table is a combination of Tables I and II. We could find the value of log sin 41° 40′ by using Table I to find sin 41° 40′ = .6648, and then using Table II to find log .6648 = 9.82269 − 10. It is much easier, however, to use Table III and read immediately

$$\log \sin 41° \, 40′ = 9.82269 - 10.$$

The sine or cosine of any acute angle is less than 1. The same is true of the tangent of an angle between 0° and 45°, or the cotangent of an angle between 45° and 90°. Consequently, the characteristics of the logarithms of such functions are negative. To conserve space in the tables, the "−10" of negative characteristics has been omitted. For the sake of uniformity, the table is so constructed that a "−10" is to be understood with each entry. For example, the table entry for log tan 85° 25′ is 11.09601. But we are to understand that

$$\log \tan 85° \, 25′ = 11.09601 - 10 = 1.09601.$$

Table III can be used to read directly the logarithms of the trigonometric functions of angles measured to the nearest minute. By using interpolation, we can extend this to angles measured to the nearest tenth of a minute. The tabular differences for log sin and log cos appear in the columns marked "d"; those for log tan and log cot appear in the column marked "cd" (common difference). These columns save us the labor of performing the subtraction to obtain the tabular difference.

99

Example 1. Find log tan 73° 14.7′.
Solution. On page 44, we find

$$\log \tan 73° \, 14' = 10.52103 - 10.$$

In the "cd" column, we find the tabular difference is 45. Using the table of proportional parts for 45, we find $\frac{7}{10}(45) = 31.5 \rightarrow 31.$* Hence

$$\log \tan 73° \, 14.7' = 0.52134.$$

Example 2. Find θ if log cos $\theta = 9.86082 - 10$.
Solution. On page 71, we find

$$\log \cos 43° \, 27' = 9.86092 - 10.$$

The tabular difference is 12, and our difference is 10. In the proportional parts column headed by 12 we seek the number closest to 10. This number is 9.6, and it corresponds to 8. Hence,

if $\log \cos \theta = 9.86082 - 10,$
          $\theta = 43° \, 27.8'.$

EXERCISE 33

Evaluate the following.

1. log sin 19° 47′.	**2.** log tan 78° 32′.
3. log cot 83° 29′.	**4.** log cos 37° 11′.
5. log cos 52° 6.8′.	**6.** log cot 21° 58.4′.
7. log tan 44° 44.6′.	**8.** log sin 45° 35.2′.
9. log cot 41° 37.1′.	**10.** log cos 70° 13.5′.
11. log sin 66° 20.7′.	**12.** log tan 9° 52.3′.
13. log tan 86° 41.9′.	**14.** log sin 36° 36.8′.
15. log cos 15° 18.3′.	**16.** log cot 59° 24.6′.

Find the value of θ.

17. log cot $\theta = 9.70058 - 10$.	**18.** log cos $\theta = 9.91712 - 10$.
19. log sin $\theta = 9.30336 - 10$.	**20.** log tan $\theta = 1.41879$.
21. log tan $\theta = 9.99763 - 10$.	**22.** log sin $\theta = 9.85058 - 10$.
23. log cos $\theta = 9.98340 - 10$.	**24.** log cot $\theta = 0.10144$.
25. log sin $\theta = 9.87325 - 10$.	**26.** log tan $\theta = 9.18791 - 10$.
27. log cot $\theta = 0.17627$.	**28.** log cos $\theta = 9.67814 - 10$.
29. log cos $\theta = 9.98677 - 10$.	**30.** log cot $\theta = 9.12580 - 10$.
31. log tan $\theta = 0.10690$.	**32.** log sin $\theta = 9.69339 - 10$.
33. log cot $\theta = 0.39104$.	**34.** log cos $\theta = 0.01123$.
35. log sin $\theta = 8.89300 - 10$.	**36.** log tan $\theta = 9.48355 - 10$.

58. Logarithmic solution of right triangles. The solution of right triangles is discussed in Art. 18.† Since all computations involved are either multiplication or division, we can usually perform them with less labor by using logarithms.

---

* To make final result *even.*
† The student should review this article before proceeding.

In solving a triangle with logarithms the following steps are suggested:

1. Draw the triangle to scale and label numerically the parts that are known.

2. Make a complete outline indicating the operations to be performed.

3. Fill in all logarithms.

4. Perform the operations outlined in step 2.

5. Check the solution.

It is desirable to find as many as possible of the required parts directly from the given parts.

Example 1. Solve the right triangle ABC, for which $A = 23° 45'$ and $b = 67.89$.

Solution.

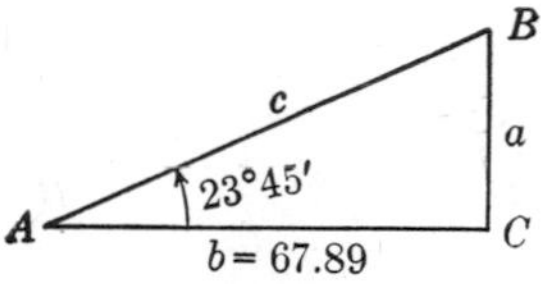

(1) $$B = 90° - 23° 45'$$
$$= 66° 15'.$$

FIG. 51

(2) To find a, use $\tan 23° 45' = \dfrac{a}{67.89}$.

Hence
$$a = 67.89 \tan 23° 45'.$$
$$\log 67.89 = 1.83181$$
$$\log \tan 23° 45' = 9.64346 - 10$$
$$\overline{} \text{A}$$
$$\log a = 11.47527 - 10$$
$$a = 29.87.$$

(3) To find c, use $\cos 23° 45' = \dfrac{67.89}{c}$. Hence $c = \dfrac{67.89}{\cos 23° 45'}$.

$$\log 67.89 = 11.83181 - 10$$
$$\log \cos 23° 45' = 9.96157 - 10$$
$$\overline{} \text{S}$$
$$\log c = 1.87024$$
$$c = 74.17.$$

(4) A fairly good check * may be obtained by finding c in another way. Use $\sin 23° 45' = \dfrac{a}{c}$. Hence $c = \dfrac{a}{\sin 23° 45'}$.

$$\log a = 11.47527 - 10$$
$$\log \sin 23° 45' = 9.60503 - 10$$
$$\overline{} \text{S}$$
$$\log c = 1.87024$$
$$c = 74.17.$$

* The instructor may prefer to use the following check. Since $c^2 = a^2 + b^2$, $a^2 = c^2 - b^2 = (c + b)(c - b)$. Hence $2 \log a = \log (c + b) + \log (c - b)$. Likewise, $2 \log b = \log (c + a) + \log (c - a)$.

In this case the two values for log c are exactly the same. Sometimes there is a small discrepancy in the last digit. This is due to the fact that the mantissas in the tables are five-decimal *approximations*.

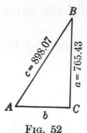

FIG. 52

This problem illustrates four-figure accuracy in the known parts and the computed parts. No interpolations should be made in finding a and c. Why?

Example 2. Solve the right triangle ABC, for which $a = 765.43$ and $c = 898.07$.

Solution.

(1) To find A, use $\sin A = \dfrac{765.43}{898.07}$.

$$\log 765.43 = 12.88391 - 10$$
$$\log 898.07 = 2.95331$$
$$\overline{}\ \text{S}$$
$$\log \sin A = 9.93060 - 10$$
$$A = 58° 27.9'.$$

(2) $$B = 90° - 58° 27.9' = 31° 32.1'.$$

(3) To find b, use $\cos A = \dfrac{b}{898.07}$. Hence $b = 898.07 \cos A$.

$$\log 898.07 = 2.95331$$
$$\log \cos A = 9.71852 - 10$$
$$\overline{}\ \text{A}$$
$$\log b = 12.67183 - 10$$
$$b = 469.71.$$

(4) Check by finding the last part, b, in another way: $b = \dfrac{765.43}{\tan A}$.

EXERCISE 34

Make a complete outline of the logarithmic solution of the right triangle in which the following parts are known.

1. A, c.   **2.** B, a.   **3.** a, b.   **4.** b, c.

Use logarithms to solve the following right triangles. Check as directed by the instructor.

5. $A = 78° 59', a = 68.57.$ **6.** $B = 28° 43', c = 3883.$
7. $A = 40° 2', c = 2.320.$ **8.** $B = 68° 14', a = 0.1775.$
9. $a = 5.886, b = 7.435.$ **10.** $b = 906.6, c = 943.6.$
11. $a = 0.04837, c = 0.06295.$ **12.** $a = 30.15, b = 19.58.$
13. $b = 8008.3, c = 29384.$ **14.** $a = 2.9536, b = 5.3971.$
15. $B = 45° 58.3', b = 369.12.$ **16.** $A = 17° 25.6', c = 40.669.$
17. $B = 39° 40.7', c = 555.16.$ **18.** $A = 80° 13.2', b = 13.924.$
19. $a = 71727, b = 26405.$ **20.** $a = 437.89, c = 917.48.$

59. Vectors. A *vector quantity* is a quantity having magnitude and direction. Examples of vector quantities are forces, velocities, accelerations, and displacements. A *vector* is a directed line segment. A vector quantity can be represented by means of a vector if (1) the direction of the vector is the same as that of the vector quantity and (2) the length of the vector represents, to some convenient scale, the magnitude of the

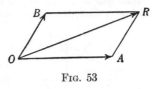

Fig. 53

vector quantity. For example, a velocity of 30 mph in a northerly direction can be represented by a 3-in. line segment pointed north.

In physics it is shown that the *resultant* (or vector sum) of two vectors is the diagonal of a parallelogram having the two given vectors as adjacent sides. In Fig. 53, vector OR is the resultant of vectors OA and OB. If the lengths and directions of OA and

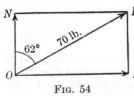

Fig. 54

OB are known, then the length and direction of OR can be found by solving triangle OAR.

Two vectors having a certain resultant are said to be *components* of that resultant. If the two vectors are at right angles to each other, they are called *rectangular components*. It is possible to resolve a given vector into components along any two specified directions. For example (Fig. 54), a force of 70 lb. acting in the direction N 62° E can be resolved into an easterly force and a northerly force by solving the right triangle ORN.

Example 1. An airplane with an *air speed* (speed in still air) of 178 mph is headed due north. If a west wind of 27.5 mph is blowing, find the direction traveled by the plane and its *ground speed* (actual speed with respect to the ground).

Solution. To find θ (see Fig. 55) use

$$\tan \theta = \frac{27.5}{178}.$$

Logarithmic computation gives

$$\theta = 8° 47'.$$

To find OR, use $\cos \theta = \dfrac{178}{OR}$. Hence $OR = \dfrac{178}{\cos \theta}$. Using logarithms, we find

$$OR = 180.1.$$

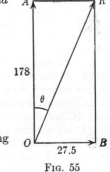

Fig. 55

Inasmuch as the original data indicate only three-figure accuracy, the results should be rounded off to three-figure accuracy. Hence the ground speed of the plane is 180 mph in the direction N 8° 50′ E.

Example 2. What is the minimum force required to prevent a 367-lb. barrel from rolling down a plane that makes an angle of 17° 30′ with the horizontal? Find the force of the barrel against the plane.

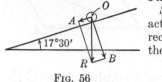

Fɪɢ. 56

Solution. The weight or force of 367 lb., *OR*, acting vertically downward can be resolved into two rectangular components, one parallel to the plane and the other perpendicular to it (see Fig. 56). Hence

$$OA = OR \sin \angle ORA = 367 \sin 17° 30′.$$

Computing this product with logarithms, we find *OA* = 110.4 lb. The force required to prevent the barrel from rolling is 111 lb. (to the nearest pound).

The force of the barrel against the plane is

$$OB = OR \cos \angle ROB = 367 \cos 17° 30′.$$

Using logarithms, we find *OB* = 350 lb.

EXERCISE 35

1. Ribbon Fall in Yosemite National Park is the highest waterfall in North America. From a point 4704 ft. from, and in the same horizontal plane with, the top of Ribbon Fall, the angle of depression of the foot of the fall is 18° 55′. Find the height of Ribbon Fall.

2. The angle of elevation of the top of the Chicago Civic Opera Building from a point on the ground 677 ft. from its base is 39° 20′. Find the height of the building.

3. The angle of elevation of the top of the Cathedral of Cologne from a point on the ground 254 ft. from its base is 63° 36′. How high is the Cathedral?

4. A dirigible is 2106 ft. directly above one end of Brooklyn Bridge. The angle of depression of the other end of the bridge from the balloon is 52° 52′. How long is the bridge?

5. Pullman, Wash., is 220 miles N 12° W from Boise, Idaho. An airplane leaves Boise at noon and flies due north at 150 mph. When will the plane be closest to Pullman?

6. Find the perimeter of a regular polygon of 100 sides that is circumscribed about a circle of diameter 1.0000. Compare this number with the circumference of the circle.

7. A balloon is rising at 120 ft. per min. and is carried eastward by a west wind. If the sun is directly overhead and the balloon's shadow is moving 365 ft. per min. on level ground, what is the angle of ascent of the balloon?

8. Through a point *A* on the outside of a circle with center *O*, tangents *AB* and *AC* are drawn to the circle. If *AO* = 36.72 and the radius of the circle is 15.84, find the angle *BAC* made by the two tangents.

9. The pilot of an airplane wants to fly due south. His plane has a cruising speed of 275 mph in still air. In what direction should he head his plane if a west wind of 32.5 mph is blowing? Find the actual speed of the plane.

10. A pilot wishes to fly 300 miles due north in 2 hr. If the wind is blowing at 17.5 mph from the east, in what direction should he head his plane and what air speed must he maintain in order to arrive at his destination on time?

11. The wind is blowing from the south at 28.5 mph. The pilot of an airplane finds that if he heads his plane in the direction S 80° 0′ W, he will move due west. Find the plane's air speed and its ground speed.

12. A motorboat, capable of a speed of 408 ft. per min. in still water, is at the south bank of a river that flows due west. By heading the boat in the direction N 20° 0′ E, the pilot is able to make it move due north across the river. Find the speed of the current and the time required to cross the river if it is 1917 ft. wide at this point.

13. A force of 1815 lb. is required to keep a truck from rolling down a hill that makes an angle of 21° 30′ with the horizontal. Find the weight of the truck.

14. A force of 195 lb. is needed to keep a 342-lb. barrel from rolling down an inclined plane. What angle does the plane make with the horizontal?

15. Find the tension in a cable that is pulling a 3395-lb. automobile up a ramp that makes an angle of 14° 50′ with the horizontal.

16. From a train traveling due east at 2250 ft. per min., a stone is thrown due south at 1470 ft. per min. Find the direction and speed of the stone.

17. A brick wall 12.75 ft. high runs east and west. The angle of elevation of the sun is 20° 15′, and its bearing is S 30° 30′ W. How wide is the shadow cast by the fence on level ground?

18. Two men are walking along a straight sidewalk carrying a large stone between them. One man exerts a force of 92.5 lb. at an angle of 10° 0′ with the vertical. Find the force exerted by the other man if he pushes at an angle of 20° 0′ with the vertical. Find the weight of the stone. *Hint:* The horizontal components of the two forces must counterbalance each other.

19. The Great Pyramid of Gizeh, Egypt, has a square base. Its faces are isosceles triangles that intersect in the four edges. Before vandals removed the outer limestone casing and the top 31 ft. of the pyramid, each edge was 719 ft. 2.6 in. long and made an angle of 42° 0.6′ with the horizontal. Find the original height and the length of a side of the base.

20. Three forces of 22.22 lb., 41.41 lb., and 65.30 lb. act in the directions N 22° 22′ E, N 41° 41′ E, and N 65° 30′ E, respectively. Find the magnitudes of two forces, one acting due west and the other acting due south, that will counterbalance the three given forces. *Hint:* The force that acts due west must neutralize the easterly components of the three given forces.

Solve * each of the following oblique triangles by dividing it into right triangles. Draw figures.

21. $A = 81° 38′$, $B = 59° 9′$, $b = 4073$.

Solution. Let h represent the length of the perpendicular CD from C to AB. Then use the equations

$$C = 180° - (A + B), \qquad AD = 4073 \cos 81° 38′, \qquad h = 4073 \sin 81° 38′,$$

$$DB = \frac{h}{\tan 59° 9′}, \qquad c = AD + DB, \qquad a = \frac{h}{\sin 59° 9′}.$$

* May be omitted at the discretion of the instructor.

Computation gives $C = 39° 13'$, $AD = 592.7$, $\log h = 3.60526$ (the value of h need not be found), $DB = 2407$, $c = 3000$, $a = 4694$. The student is expected to perform the computations.

22. $A = 57° 49'$, $B = 80° 22'$, $b = 93.65$.

23. $A = 48° 33'$, $b = 666.3$, $c = 567.4$. *Hint:* Let h be the length of the perpendicular CD from C to AB. Use the equations

$$AD = 666.3 \cos 48° 33', \qquad h = 666.3 \sin 48° 33', \qquad DB = 567.4 - AD,$$

$$\tan B = \frac{h}{DB}, \qquad C = 180° - (48° 33' + B), \qquad a = \frac{h}{\sin B}.$$

24. $A = 71° 52'$, $b = 7576$, $c = 8293$.

25. $A = 108° 24'$, $B = 41° 37'$, $a = 6916$.

26. $A = 125° 13'$, $b = 4506$, $c = 5172$.

CHAPTER 11

OBLIQUE TRIANGLES

60. Introduction. A triangle that does not contain a right angle is called an oblique triangle. Since the ratio of two sides of an *oblique* triangle does not represent a function of an angle of the triangle, additional formulas are needed for solving oblique triangles. These formulas are the law of cosines, the law of sines, the law of tangents, and the half-angle formulas.

The six parts of a triangle are its three sides a, b, c, and the opposite angles A, B, C, respectively. <u>If three parts, one of which is a side, are given, the remaining parts can be determined</u>. For convenience, we shall divide the possibilities into the following four cases:

SAA: Given one side and two angles.

SSA: Given two sides and the angle opposite one of them.

SAS: Given two sides and the included angle.

SSS: Given three sides.

61. The law of cosines. *The square of any side of a triangle is equal to the sum of the squares of the other two sides minus twice their product times the cosine of the included angle;*

$$a^2 = b^2 + c^2 - 2bc \cos A,$$
$$b^2 = c^2 + a^2 - 2ca \cos B,$$
$$c^2 = a^2 + b^2 - 2ab \cos C.$$

Proof. I. If all the angles are acute: Draw CD perpendicular to AB. Then

$$a^2 = h^2 + \overline{DB}^2$$
$$= h^2 + (c - AD)^2$$
$$= \underbrace{h^2 + \overline{AD}^2}_{b^2} + c^2 - 2cAD$$
$$= \quad b^2 \quad + c^2 - 2c(b \cos A).$$
$$a^2 = b^2 + c^2 - 2bc \cos A.$$

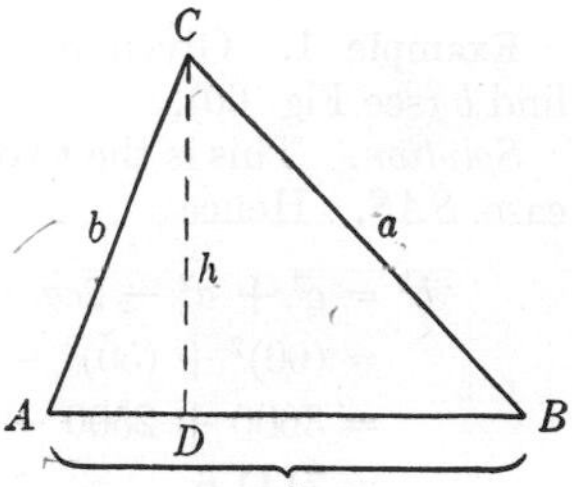

Fig. 57

II. If one angle is obtuse: Draw CD perpendicular to AB extended. Notice that if AB is considered a positive directed segment, then AD is negative in Fig. 58 while DB is negative in Fig. 59. With this understanding, the proofs for Figs. 58 and 59 are exactly the same as that for Fig. 57. The student should verify this.

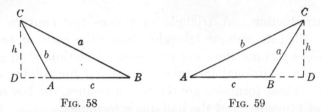

FIG. 58   FIG. 59

This is a general proof because a may be used to represent any side of the given triangle. The other two forms of the law of cosines can be obtained from the first form by the method of *cyclic permutation* in which

$$a \text{ is changed to } b, \quad A \text{ is changed to } B,$$
$$b \text{ is changed to } c, \quad B \text{ is changed to } C,$$
$$c \text{ is changed to } a, \quad C \text{ is changed to } A.$$

If $A = 90°$, $\cos A = 0$, and $a^2 = b^2 + c^2 - 2bc \cos A$ reduces to the form $a^2 = b^2 + c^2$. We conclude that the Pythagorean theorem is a special case of the law of cosines; *i.e.*, the law of cosines is a generalization of the Pythagorean theorem.

62. Applications of the law of cosines: *SAS* and *SSS*. The law of cosines is used in many geometric problems, one of which is the solution of triangles. Since three sides and one angle are involved in every form of the law of cosines, it can be used to solve the *SAS* and *SSS* cases described in Art. 60.

Example 1. Given $a = 50$, $c = 60$, $B = 100°$, find b (see Fig. 60).

Solution. This is the two sides and included angle case, *SAS*. Hence

$$b^2 = c^2 + a^2 - 2ca \cos B$$
$$= (60)^2 + (50)^2 - 2(60)(50) \cos 100°$$
$$= 3600 + 2500 - 6000(-.1736)$$
$$= 7141.6.$$
$$b = 85.$$

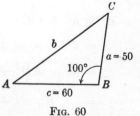

FIG. 60

This example illustrates two-figure accuracy in the given data and the computed result. Notice that cos $100° = - $ cos $80° = -.1736$.

The square root of 7141.6 may be obtained by use of logarithms or by using Table IV, with interpolation.

Example 2. Given $a = 8.00$, $b = 5.00$, $c = 4.00$, find the largest and smallest angles.

Solution. The largest and smallest angles lie opposite the largest and smallest sides, respectively.

To find A, use

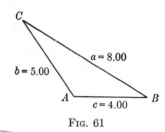

$$a^2 = b^2 + c^2 - 2bc \cos A,$$
$$64 = 25 + 16 - 40 \cos A,$$
$$40 \cos A = 41 - 64 = -23,$$
$$\cos A = -\tfrac{23}{40} = -.5750,$$
[Related angle is 54° 50′]
$$A = 180° - 54° 50' = 125° 10'.$$

Fig. 61

To find C, use

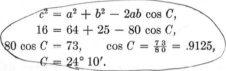

$$c^2 = a^2 + b^2 - 2ab \cos C,$$
$$16 = 64 + 25 - 80 \cos C,$$
$$80 \cos C = 73, \qquad \cos C = \tfrac{73}{80} = .9125,$$
$$C = 24° 10'.$$

This example illustrates three-figure accuracy.

EXERCISE 36

1. Given $a = 7.0$, $b = 8.0$, $c = 2.0$, find B.
2. Given $a = 90$, $b = 50$, $c = 70$, find A.
3. Given $a = 400$, $b = 500$, $c = 600$, find C.
4. Given $a = 10$, $b = 11$, $c = 12$, find B.
5. Given $b = 30$, $c = 10$, $A = 49°$, find a.
6. Given $a = 100$, $b = 400$, $C = 76° 10'$, find c.
7. Given $a = 15$, $c = 20$, $B = 124°$, find b.
8. Given $b = 6.0$, $c = 1.0$, $A = 153°$, find a.
9. Given $a = 1.2$, $b = 2.5$, $C = 99°$, find c.
10. Given $a = 2.0$, $c = 6.0$, $B = 144°$, find b.
11. Given $a = 3.0$, $b = 7.0$, $c = 8.0$, find A, B, and C.
12. Given $a = 50$, $b = 30$, $c = 70$, find A, B, and C.

13. In walking around a triangular lot, a pedestrian starts at one corner and walks 400 ft. due east to the second corner. He then turns sharply to his left and walks 900 ft. to the third corner. In what direction should he now travel to reach his starting point, which is 600 ft. away?

14. An airplane is moving with an air speed of 100 mph. The wind, blowing from the north at 20 mph, causes the plane to travel with a ground speed of only 90 mph. Find the direction the plane is heading and the direction it travels.

15. Jerusalem is 14 miles S 65° W from Jericho. Bethlehem is 18 miles S 51° W from Jericho. How far is Bethlehem from Jerusalem?

16. Two points, A and B, are separated by a large building. To find the distance AB, a third point C is chosen. Measurements yield $CA = 800$ ft., $CB = 1000$ ft., angle $ACB = 22°\,0'$. Find AB.

17. Discuss the equation $c^2 = a^2 + b^2 - 2ab \cos C$, (a) when C approaches $180°$, (b) when C approaches $0°$.

63. The law of sines. *In any triangle the sides are proportional to the sines of the opposite angles;*

$$\frac{a}{\sin A} = \frac{b}{\sin B} = \frac{c}{\sin C}.$$

Proof. Consider the two cases: all angles acute (Fig. 62) and one angle obtuse (Fig. 63). Let h be the perpendicular from C to AB (or AB extended).

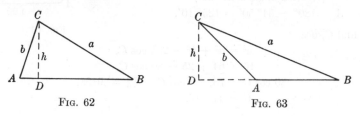

FIG. 62   FIG. 63

In either case

$$\sin B = \frac{h}{a}\,; \quad \text{hence} \quad h = a \sin B.$$

Also *

$$\sin A = \frac{h}{b}\,; \quad \text{hence} \quad h = b \sin A.$$

Equate the two values of h: $a \sin B = b \sin A.$

Divide by $\sin A \sin B$: $\dfrac{a}{\sin A} = \dfrac{b}{\sin B}.$

Similarly, $\dfrac{a}{\sin A} = \dfrac{c}{\sin C}.$

Therefore $\dfrac{a}{\sin A} = \dfrac{b}{\sin B} = \dfrac{c}{\sin C}.$

The law of sines is equivalent to the following three equations:

$$\frac{a}{\sin A} = \frac{b}{\sin B}, \quad \frac{a}{\sin A} = \frac{c}{\sin C}, \quad \frac{b}{\sin B} = \frac{c}{\sin C}. \quad \text{If the three}$$

* In Fig. 63, $\sin A = \sin \angle CAD = \dfrac{h}{b}.$

given parts of the triangle include one side and the opposite angle, then one of these equations will involve three known quantities and one unknown. We can solve for this unknown by using ordinary algebraic methods. Thus, if a, c, C are the known parts, we can find A by solving the equation $\dfrac{\sin A}{a} = \dfrac{\sin C}{c}$;

$\sin A = \dfrac{a \sin C}{c}$. The law of sines is well adapted to the use of logarithms because it involves only ratios and products. Whenever four parts of a triangle are known (the fourth part may have been obtained from the other three), we can use the law of sines to find the remaining two parts. Why?

64. Applications of the law of sines: SAA. When one side and two angles of a triangle are known, we can immediately find the third angle from the relation $A + B + C = 180°$. The remaining two sides can then be found by using the law of sines.

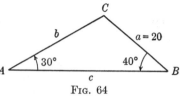

FIG. 64

Before continuing, the student should review the suggested procedure in Art. 58.

Example 1. Solve the triangle ABC, given $a = 20$, $A = 30°$, $B = 40°$.
Solution. (See Fig. 64.)

(1) $$C = 180° - (30° + 40°)$$
$$= 110°.$$

(2) To find b, use
$$b = \frac{a \sin B}{\sin A} = \frac{20 \sin 40°}{\sin 30°} = \frac{20(.6428)}{.5000} = 26.$$

(3) To find c, use
$$c = \frac{a \sin C}{\sin A} = \frac{20 \sin 110°}{\sin 30°} = \frac{20(.9397)}{.5000} = 38.$$

The values of b and c are rounded off to two-figure accuracy. The results can be checked by the law of cosines or by finding c with the formula $c = \dfrac{b \sin C}{\sin B}$.

Example 2. Solve the triangle ABC, given $b = 1906$, $A = 55° 44'$, $C = 81° 29'$.
Solution.

(1) $$B = 180° - (55° 44' + 81° 29')$$
$$= 42° 47'.$$

(2) $$a = \frac{b \sin A}{\sin B} = \frac{1906 \sin 55° 44'}{\sin 42° 47'}.$$

An outline of the logarithmic solution is:

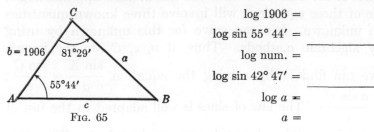

$$\log 1906 =$$
$$\log \sin 55° 44' = \underline{\hspace{3cm}} \; A$$
$$\log num. =$$
$$\log \sin 42° 47' = \underline{\hspace{3cm}} \; S$$
$$\log a =$$
$$a =$$

Fig. 65

The student should fill in the outline and find $a = 2319$.

$$(3) \qquad\qquad c = \frac{b \sin C}{\sin B} = \frac{1906 \sin 81° 29'}{\sin 42° 47'}.$$

After preparing the outline and then filling in the numbers, we have:

$$
\begin{aligned}
\log 1906 &= 3.28012 \\
\log \sin 81° 29' &= 9.99518 - 10 \\
&\overline{\hspace{4cm}} A \\
\log num. &= 13.27530 - 10 \\
\log \sin 42° 47' &= 9.83202 - 10 \\
&\overline{\hspace{4cm}} S \\
\log c &= 3.44328 \\
c &= 2775.
\end{aligned}
$$

The results may be checked by finding c again using $c = \dfrac{a \sin C}{\sin A}$ or by using the law of tangents (Art. 67).*

EXERCISE 37

Solve the following triangles without using logarithms.

1. $b = 300$, $A = 82° 10'$, $C = 73° 0'$.
2. $c = 50$, $A = 106°$, $C = 54°$.

Make an outline of the logarithmic solution of the oblique triangle in which the following parts are known.

3. a, A, C.   **4.** c, A, B.   **5.** c, B, C.   **6.** b, A, B.

Use logarithms to solve the following triangles.

7. $a = 3015$, $B = 62° 35'$, $C = 75° 15'$.
8. $a = 86.12$, $A = 84° 22'$, $B = 57° 8'$.
9. $a = 2.736$, $A = 28° 17'$, $C = 81° 42'$.
10. $b = 0.04973$, $A = 45° 56'$, $C = 69° 31'$.
11. $c = 502$, $A = 29° 40'$, $C = 90° 50'$.
12. $b = 7834$, $A = 37° 1'$, $B = 109° 43'$.
13. $c = 44309$, $A = 53° 53.0'$, $B = 22° 5.0'$.
14. $a = 58541$, $A = 86° 20.0'$, $B = 43° 10.0'$.

* The instructor may wish to use Mollweide's equations (Probs. 49 and 50 of Exercise 42).

15. $b = 0.80473$, $B = 79°\ 32.0'$, $C = 56°\ 49.0'$.
16. $a = 940.38$, $B = 25°\ 45.0'$, $C = 66°\ 0.0'$.

17. The largest angle of a triangle is twice the size of the smallest angle. Is the largest side twice as large as the smallest side? Find b if $A = 37°\ 30'$, $B = 75°\ 0'$, $a = 100$.

18. The world's tallest man-made structure is a television tower on the outskirts of Oklahoma City. From a point on level ground, the angle of elevation of the top of the tower is $28°\ 28'$. From another point, 2202 ft. closer to the base of the tower, the angle of elevation of the top is $66°\ 6'$. How high is the tower?

19. An airplane heads S 70° W. A 25-mph wind, blowing toward N 40° W, causes the plane to move in the direction S 75° W. Find the air speed and the ground speed of the plane.

20. Orono, Maine, is 250 miles N 33° E from Providence, R.I. Manchester, N.H., is due north of Providence. The bearing of Orono from Manchester is N 46° E. How far is Manchester from Orono? From Providence? *

21. Show that if $C = 90°$, the law of sines gives the definition of the sine of an acute angle.

22. Why does the law of sines fail to solve the *SAS* and *SSS* cases?

65. The ambiguous case: *SSA*.
If two sides and the angle opposite one of them are given, the triangle is not always uniquely determined. With the given parts, we may be able to construct two triangles, or only one triangle, or no triangle at all. Because of the possibility of two triangles, this is usually called the ambiguous case.

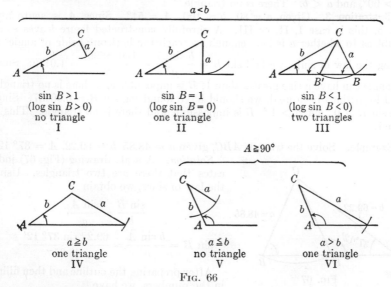

FIG. 66

* Ignore the curvature of the earth and assume only two-place accuracy. Get angles to the nearest degree. Get distances to the nearest multiple of 10 miles.

To avoid unnecessary confusion, we shall use A to designate the given angle, a to represent the opposite side, and b to indicate the other side. Construct angle A and lay off b as an adjacent side, thus fixing the vertex C. With C as center and a as radius, strike an arc cutting the other side adjacent to A. Figure 66 illustrates the various possibilities.

The last three cases (diagrams IV, V, and VI) can be quickly identified by merely noting the relative sizes of a and b. If A is acute and $a < b$, it is necessary to begin the solution before we can state how many triangles are possible. To do this, use the law of sines:

$$\frac{\sin B}{b} = \frac{\sin A}{a}, \qquad \sin B = \frac{b \sin A}{a}.$$

After determining the value of sin B (or log sin B with logarithms), we can definitely classify our problem as one of the various types. It is frequently possible to determine the number of solutions by merely constructing a figure to scale.

Illustration 1. Given $a = 100$, $b = 70$, $A = 80°$. This is case IV because $a > b$. There is one triangle.

Illustration 2. Given $a = 40$, $b = 42$, $A = 110°$. This is case V because $A > 90°$, and $a < b$. There is no triangle.

Illustration 3. Given $a = 80$, $b = 100$, $A = 54°$. Since A is acute and $a < b$, this is case I, II, or III. A carefully constructed figure leaves some doubt as to whether a is long enough to reach the horizontal side of angle A. Using the law of sines, we find $\sin B = \dfrac{b \sin A}{a} = \dfrac{100(.8090)}{80} = 1.0112$. Since no angle can have a sine greater than 1, B is impossible and there is no triangle. Had logarithms been used, we should have found log sin $B = 0.00487$. Since log sin $B > 0$, sin $B > 1$,* B is impossible, and there is no triangle. This is case I.

Example. Solve the triangle ABC, given $a = 48.85$, $b = 69.22$, $A = 37° \, 12'$.

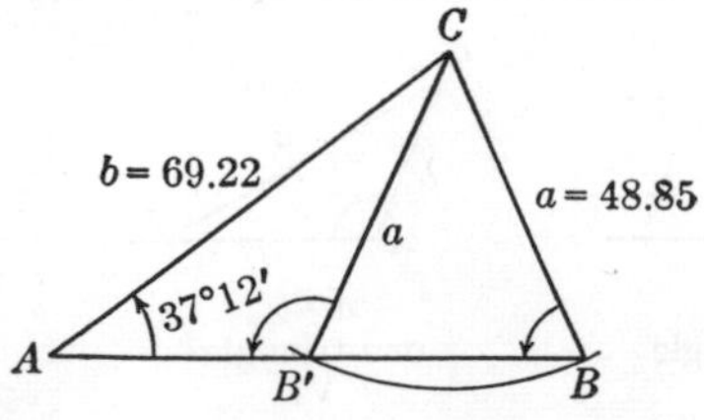

Solution. A scale drawing (Fig. 67) indicates that there are two triangles. Using the law of sines, we obtain

$$\frac{\sin B}{b} = \frac{\sin A}{a},$$

$$\sin B = \frac{b \sin A}{a} = \frac{69.22 \sin 37° \, 12'}{48.85}.$$

FIG. 67

After preparing the outline and then filling in the numbers, we have

* Recall that a number greater than 1 has a logarithm greater than 0.

$$\log 69.22 = 1.84023$$
$$\log \sin 37° 12' = 9.78147 - 10$$
$$\overline{\hspace{3cm}} \text{A}$$
$$\log \text{num.} = 11.62170 - 10$$
$$\log 48.85 = 1.68886$$
$$\overline{\hspace{3cm}} \text{S}$$
$$\log \sin B = 9.93284 - 10$$
$$B = 58° 57'.$$

Continuing with the solution of large triangle ABC (Fig. 68), we find

$$C = 180° - (37° 12' + 58° 57')$$
$$= 83° 51'.$$

To find c, use

$$\frac{c}{\sin C} = \frac{a}{\sin A}, \qquad c = \frac{a \sin C}{\sin A} = \frac{48.85 \sin 83° 51'}{\sin 37° 12'}.$$

Logarithmic computation gives

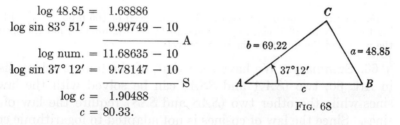

$$\log 48.85 = 1.68886$$
$$\log \sin 83° 51' = 9.99749 - 10$$
$$\overline{\hspace{3cm}} \text{A}$$
$$\log \text{num.} = 11.68635 - 10$$
$$\log \sin 37° 12' = 9.78147 - 10$$
$$\overline{\hspace{3cm}} \text{S}$$
$$\log c = 1.90488$$
$$c = 80.33.$$

Fig. 68

Hence the computed parts of triangle ABC are $B = 58° 57'$, $C = 83° 51'$, $c = 80.33$.

We shall now solve the small triangle $AB'C'$. Since triangle BCB' (Fig. 67) is isosceles, $\angle BB'C = B$. Hence

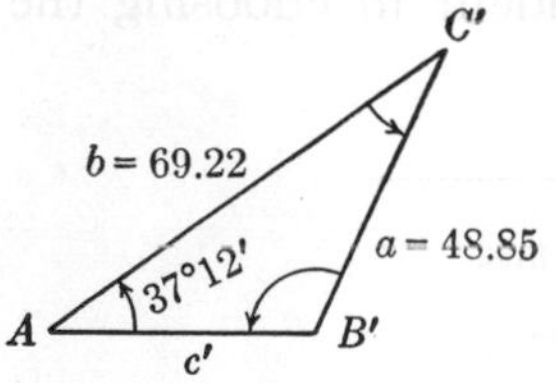

$$B' = 180° - B = 180° - 58° 57' = 121° 3'.$$

Also (see Fig. 69),

$$C' = 180° - (37° 12' + 121° 3') = 21° 45'.$$

Using the law of sines with logarithms, we find $c' = 29.94$.

Hence the computed parts of triangle $AB'C'$ are $B' = 121° 3'$, $C' = 21° 45'$, $c' = 29.94$.

FIG. 69

EXERCISE 38

Draw a figure and solve all possible triangles.

1. $a = 81.47$, $b = 92.65$, $A = 61° 42'$.
2. $a = 592.8$, $b = 713.6$, $A = 53° 11'$.
3. $a = 1861$, $b = 3488$, $A = 22° 57'$.
4. $a = 4.156$, $b = 6.390$, $A = 41° 41'$.
5. $a = 0.02903$, $b = 0.02414$, $A = 75° 38'$.
6. $a = 2956$, $b = 1812$, $A = 123° 45'$.

7. $a = 4.7631$, $b = 5.0884$, $A = 96° 4.7'$.

8. $a = 51.076$, $b = 82.190$, $A = 35° 26.0'$.

9. $a = 30405$, $c = 74859$, $A = 17° 33.8'$.

10. $b = 9.5847$, $c = 9.6003$, $B = 114° 11.4'$.

11. $b = 76.750$, $c = 57.630$, $C = 48° 40.0'$.

12. $a = 0.20406$, $c = 0.20406$, $C = 59° 26.9'$.

Some of the following problems can be solved more easily without using logarithms.

13. State College, Pa., is 210 miles due east of Wooster, Ohio. The bearing of Washington from Wooster is S 64° E. State College is 130 miles from Washington. How far is Washington from Wooster?

14. The distance ES from the earth to the sun is 93,000,000 miles. The distance MS from Mercury to the sun is 36,000,000 miles. How far is Mercury from the earth when the angle MES is 15°? (Get result to the nearest multiple of a million miles.)

15. On a hillside that makes an angle of 22° with the horizontal, a 40-ft. tree leans downhill. When the elevation of the sun is 47°, the tree's shadow is 80 ft. long and falls straight down the slope. Find the angle made by the tree with the vertical.

16. An airplane heads due east with an air speed of 165 mph. A wind blowing toward N 50° 0' E causes the plane to travel 182 mph. Find the speed of the wind and the direction the plane travels.

66. Summary. We have seen that, of the four problems listed in Art. 60, two (SAA and SSA) can be solved with the law of sines while the other two (SAS and SSS) require the law of cosines. Since the law of cosines is not adapted to logarithmic computation, we shall develop substitute formulas to be used in the SAS and SSS cases when the given sides are not easily squared. The following outline should assist the student in choosing the best plan of attack.

	Without logs	With logs
SAA	Law of sines	Law of sines
SSA	Law of sines	Law of sines
SAS	Law of cosines	Law of tangents
SSS	Law of cosines	Half-angle formulas

The law of sines can be used to complete the solution as soon as four parts are known.

67. The law of tangents. *In any triangle, the difference of two sides is to their sum as the tangent of half the difference of the opposite* *angles is to the tangent of half their sum;*

$$\frac{a-b}{a+b} = \frac{\tan \frac{1}{2}(A-B)}{\tan \frac{1}{2}(A+B)}, \qquad \frac{b-a}{b+a} = \frac{\tan \frac{1}{2}(B-A)}{\tan \frac{1}{2}(B+A)},$$

$$\frac{b-c}{b+c} = \frac{\tan \frac{1}{2}(B-C)}{\tan \frac{1}{2}(B+C)}, \qquad \frac{c-b}{c+b} = \frac{\tan \frac{1}{2}(C-B)}{\tan \frac{1}{2}(C+B)},$$

$$\frac{c-a}{c+a} = \frac{\tan \frac{1}{2}(C-A)}{\tan \frac{1}{2}(C+A)}, \qquad \frac{a-c}{a+c} = \frac{\tan \frac{1}{2}(A-C)}{\tan \frac{1}{2}(A+C)}.$$

Proof. Let the two given sides be a and b, with $a > b$. By the law of sines,

$$\frac{a}{b} = \frac{\sin A}{\sin B}.$$

Subtract 1 from each side; add 1 to each side:

$$\frac{a}{b} - 1 = \frac{\sin A}{\sin B} - 1, \qquad \frac{a}{b} + 1 = \frac{\sin A}{\sin B} + 1.$$

Hence

$$\frac{a-b}{b} = \frac{\sin A - \sin B}{\sin B}, \qquad \frac{a+b}{b} = \frac{\sin A + \sin B}{\sin B}.$$

Divide the first equation by the second:

$$\frac{a-b}{a+b} = \frac{\sin A - \sin B}{\sin A + \sin B}.$$

Apply formulas (16) and (15) of Art. 42:

$$\frac{a-b}{a+b} = \frac{2 \cos \frac{1}{2}(A+B) \sin \frac{1}{2}(A-B)}{2 \sin \frac{1}{2}(A+B) \cos \frac{1}{2}(A-B)}$$

$$= \cot \tfrac{1}{2}(A+B) \tan \tfrac{1}{2}(A-B) = \frac{\tan \frac{1}{2}(A-B)}{\tan \frac{1}{2}(A+B)}.$$

This proves the first of the six formulas.

If a and b are interchanged, then their opposite angles, A and B, must be interchanged and we get the second formula:

$$\frac{b - a}{b + a} = \frac{\tan \frac{1}{2}(B - A)}{\tan \frac{1}{2}(B + A)}.$$

The remaining formulas may be obtained by cyclic permutation (Art. 61).

68. Applications of the law of tangents: SAS. Suppose that the given parts are the sides a and b and the included angle C. If $a > b$, we use the following form of the law of tangents:

$$\tan \frac{1}{2}(A - B) = \frac{a - b}{a + b} \tan \frac{1}{2}(A + B).$$

Knowing a and b, we can find $(a - b)$ and $(a + b)$. Since C is given, we can find $\frac{1}{2}(A + B)$ by halving the relation $A + B = 180° - C$. Thus the three quantities on the right side of the

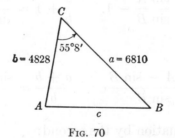

Fig. 70

equation are easily obtained from the given data. By applying the law of tangents, we find the value of $\frac{1}{2}(A - B)$. *Knowing $\frac{1}{2}(A + B)$ and $\frac{1}{2}(A - B)$, we add to get A, and subtract to get B.* The sixth part, c, can be found with the law of sines. The problem can be checked by finding c again with another form of the law of sines.

Example. Solve the triangle ABC, given $a = 6810$, $b = 4828$, $C = 55° 8'$ (Fig. 70).

Solution. Since $a > b$, use the first form of the law of tangents:

$$\tan \frac{1}{2}(A - B) = \frac{a - b}{a + b} \tan \frac{1}{2}(A + B).$$

$$a = 6810$$
$$b = 4828$$

$$a - b = 1982$$
$$a + b = 11638$$
$$A + B = 180° - 55° 8'$$
$$ = 124° 52'$$
$$\tfrac{1}{2}(A + B) = 62° 26'$$
$$\tfrac{1}{2}(A - B) = 18° 4'$$

$$A = 80° 30'$$
$$B = 44° 22'$$

$$\tan \tfrac{1}{2}(A - B) = \frac{1982}{11638} \tan 62° 26'$$

$$\log 1982 = 3.29710$$
$$\log \tan 62° 26' = 10.28229 - 10 A$$

$$\log \text{num.} = 13.57939 - 10$$
$$\log 11638 = 4.06588 S$$

$$\log \tan \tfrac{1}{2}(A - B) = 9.51351 - 10$$
$$\tfrac{1}{2}(A - B) = 18° 4'$$

To find c,

$$c = \frac{a \sin C}{\sin A} = \frac{6810 \sin 55° 8'}{\sin 80° 30'}$$

$$\log 6810 = 3.83315$$
$$\log \sin 55° 8' = 9.91407 - 10 A$$

$$\log \text{num.} = 13.74722 - 10$$
$$\log \sin 80° 30' = 9.99400 - 10 S$$

$$\log c = 3.75322$$
$$c = 5665$$

To check,

$$c = \frac{b \sin C}{\sin B} = \frac{4828 \sin 55° 8'}{\sin 44° 22'}$$

$$\log 4828 = 3.68377$$
$$\log \sin 55° 8' = 9.91407 - 10 A$$

$$\log \text{num.} = 13.59784 - 10$$
$$\log \sin 44° 22' = 9.84463 - 10 S$$

$$\log c = 3.75321$$
$$c = 5665$$

EXERCISE 39

Make a complete outline of the logarithmic solution and check of the oblique triangle in which the following parts are known.

1. b, c, A, with $b > c$.   **2.** a, c, B, with $a > c$.

3. a, c, B, with $c > a$.   **4.** b, c, A, with $c > b$.

Solve the following triangles. Check as directed by the instructor.

5. $a = 5221$, $b = 2778$, $C = 80° 0'$.

6. $a = 765.0$, $b = 164.2$, $C = 116° 0'$.

7. $a = 38.83$, $b = 23.76$, $C = 88° 0'$.

8. $a = 4.985$, $b = 3.147$, $C = 63° 16'$.

9. $a = 0.1906$, $c = 0.4378$, $B = 37° 54'$.

10. $b = 8.053$, $c = 9.127$, $A = 46° 38'$.

11. $b = 93049$, $c = 56751$, $A = 95° 41.8'$.

12. $a = 543.82$, $c = 418.07$, $B = 148° 6.2'$.

13. $a = 20.876$, $b = 37.108$, $C = 130° 27.6'$.
14. $a = 3512.6$, $b = 4590.2$, $C = 74° 11.0'$.

15. The sum of the two longest sides of a triangle is 940 ft. Two angles of the triangle are 54° 30' and 21° 30'. Find the sides of the triangle.

16. A television tower 572 ft. high stands on the top of a hill whose side makes an angle of 12° 0' with the horizontal. Find the angle of elevation of the sun if it casts an 838-ft. shadow on the side of the hill.

17. An airplane heads N 68° E with an air speed of 235 mph. A 37-mph wind is blowing toward S 10° E. Find the direction the plane travels and the plane's ground speed.

18. Laramie, Wyo., is 110 miles N 16° W from Denver, Colo. Kearney, Nebr., is 310 miles N 78° E from Denver. Find the bearing and the distance of Kearney from Laramie.*

69. The half-angle formulas. *In any triangle ABC,*

$$\tan \frac{A}{2} = \frac{r}{s-a}, \qquad \tan \frac{B}{2} = \frac{r}{s-b}, \qquad \tan \frac{C}{2} = \frac{r}{s-c},$$

where

$$r = \sqrt{\frac{(s-a)(s-b)(s-c)}{s}} \qquad and \qquad s = \frac{1}{2}(a+b+c).$$

Proof. It is shown in geometry † that the area of a triangle with sides a, b, c is $K = \sqrt{s(s-a)(s-b)(s-c)}$, where $s = \frac{1}{2}(a+b+c)$. In triangle ABC, let AO, BO, and CO be the

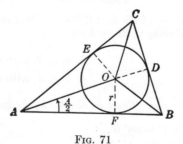

Fig. 71

bisectors of angles A, B, and C, respectively (Fig. 71). Then, by geometry, O is the center of the inscribed circle. *Let r be the*

---

* Ignore the curvature of the earth and assume only two-place accuracy. Get angles to the nearest degree. Get distances to the nearest multiple of 10 miles.

† This is proved in Art. 71.

radius of the inscribed circle. It is obvious that

$$\text{area } \triangle ABC = \text{area } \triangle AOB + \text{area } \triangle BOC + \text{area } \triangle COA$$

$$= \tfrac{1}{2}cr + \tfrac{1}{2}ar + \tfrac{1}{2}br$$

$$= r \cdot \tfrac{1}{2}(c + a + b) = rs.$$

Equate the two values of the area:

$$rs = \sqrt{s(s - a)(s - b)(s - c)},$$

$$r = \sqrt{\frac{(s - a)(s - b)(s - c)}{s}}.$$

In $\triangle ABC$, by geometry, $AF = AE$, $BF = BD$, and $CD = CE$. Why? Since the sum of these six segments equals the perimeter, $2s$,

$$2AF + 2BD + 2CD = 2s,$$

$$AF = s - (BD + CD) = s - a.$$

Similarly

$$BD = s - b \qquad \text{and} \qquad CE = s - c.$$

Since AO bisects angle A and $OF \perp AF$,

$$\tan \frac{A}{2} = \frac{FO}{AF} = \frac{r}{s - a}.$$

Similarly

$$\tan \frac{B}{2} = \frac{r}{s - b}, \qquad \text{and} \qquad \tan \frac{C}{2} = \frac{r}{s - c}.$$

70. Applications of the half-angle formulas: SSS. When the three sides are given, we first compute s, then $(s - a)$, $(s - b)$, $(s - c)$. Knowing these four quantities, we find r by use of logarithms. Then the half-angle formulas give us $A/2$, $B/2$, $C/2$. When these values are doubled, we get the three angles of the triangle. The half-angle formulas may be used to check other solutions.

Fig. 72

Example. Solve the triangle ABC, given $a = 76.54$, $b = 60.06$, $c = 54.32$.

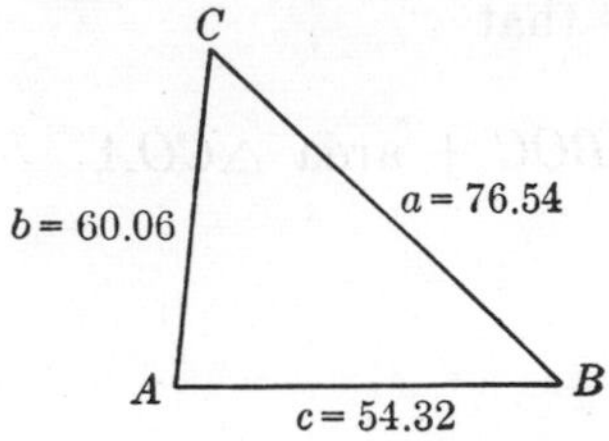

Solution.

$$
\begin{aligned}
a &= 76.54 \\
b &= 60.06 \\
c &= 54.32 \\
\hline
\;\;\;\; & \qquad\qquad \text{A} \\
2s &= 190.92 \\
s &= 95.46
\end{aligned}
$$

$$
\begin{aligned}
s - a &= 18.92 \\
s - b &= 35.40 \\
s - c &= 41.14 \\
\hline
& \qquad\qquad \text{A} \\
\text{Check *: } s &= 95.46
\end{aligned}
$$

$$
\begin{aligned}
\log (s - a) &= 1.27692 \\
\log (s - b) &= 1.54900 \\
\log (s - c) &= 1.61426 \\
\hline
& \qquad\qquad \text{A} \\
\log \text{num.} &= 4.44018 \\
\log s &= 1.97982 \\
\hline
& \qquad\qquad \text{S} \\
\log \text{radicand} &= 2.46036 \\
2 & \;\overline{} \\
\log r &= 1.23018
\end{aligned}
$$

$$ r = \sqrt{\frac{(s - a)(s - b)(s - c)}{s}} $$

$$ \tan \frac{A}{2} = \frac{r}{s - a} $$

$$
\begin{aligned}
\log r &= 1.23018 \\
\log (s - a) &= 1.27692 \\
\hline
& \qquad\qquad \text{S} \\
\log \tan \frac{A}{2} &= 9.95326 - 10 \\
\frac{A}{2} &= 41° 55.4' \\
A &= 83° 50.8'
\end{aligned}
$$

$$ \tan \frac{B}{2} = \frac{r}{s - b} $$

$$
\begin{aligned}
\log r &= 1.23018 \\
\log (s - b) &= 1.54900 \\
\hline
& \qquad\qquad \text{S} \\
\log \tan \frac{B}{2} &= 9.68118 - 10 \\
\frac{B}{2} &= 25° 38.3' \\
B &= 51° 16.6'
\end{aligned}
$$

$$ \tan \frac{C}{2} = \frac{r}{s - c} $$

$$
\begin{aligned}
\log r &= 1.23018 \\
\log (s - c) &= 1.61426 \\
\hline
& \qquad\qquad \text{S} \\
\log \tan \frac{C}{2} &= 9.61592 - 10 \\
\frac{C}{2} &= 22° 26.4' \\
C &= 44° 52.8'
\end{aligned}
$$

Rounding off these results to the nearest minute for four-figure accuracy, we get $A = 83° 51'$, $B = 51° 17'$, $C = 44° 53'$.

Check. $A + B + C = 180° 1'$.

The check is satisfactory.

* $(s - a) + (s - b) + (s - c) = 3s - (a + b + c) = s.$

EXERCISE 40

1. Make a complete outline of the logarithmic solution of an oblique triangle in which the three sides are given.

Use logarithms to solve the following triangles.

2. $a = 40.1$, $b = 69.3$, $c = 80.2$.
3. $a = 6287$, $b = 8591$, $c = 7374$.
4. $a = 1954$, $b = 1619$, $c = 1863$.
5. $a = 370.5$, $b = 549.9$, $c = 416.8$.
6. $a = 0.5940$, $b = 0.4888$, $c = 0.2056$.
7. $a = 310.8$, $b = 273.7$, $c = 565.5$.
8. $a = 5.4772$, $b = 7.0711$, $c = 4.1231$.
9. $a = 2.4495$, $b = 1.4142$, $c = 1.7321$.
10. $a = 60074$, $b = 72285$, $c = 61163$.
11. $a = 94.950$, $b = 81.828$, $c = 62.636$.

12. Make an attempt to solve the following triangle: $a = 5237$, $b = 2694$, $c = 7936$. Explain.

13. Two angles of a triangle are $44° 0'$ and $104° 0'$. The radius of the inscribed circle is 100 in. Find the sides of the triangle. (Solve without logs.)

14. An airplane travels with an air speed of 185 mph. A wind speed of 32 mph causes the plane to move 195 mph due east. In what direction is the plane heading? In what direction is the wind blowing?

15. Athens, Ga., is 130 miles S 89° W from Columbia, S.C. Gainesville, Fla., is 310 miles from Athens and 320 miles from Columbia. What is the bearing of Gainesville from Athens? From Columbia? * (Gainesville, of course, lies south of the Athens-Columbia line.)

16. Given $\quad \tan \dfrac{A}{2} = \dfrac{r}{s - a}$, $\quad$ where $\quad r = \sqrt{\dfrac{(s - a)(s - b)(s - c)}{s}}$

and $s = \frac{1}{2}(a + b + c)$. Prove that $\sin \dfrac{A}{2} = \sqrt{\dfrac{(s - b)(s - c)}{bc}}$.

71. The area of a triangle. I. *The area of a triangle is equal to one-half the product of any two sides times the sine of the included angle:*

$$K = \tfrac{1}{2}bc \sin A = \tfrac{1}{2}ca \sin B = \tfrac{1}{2}ab \sin C.$$

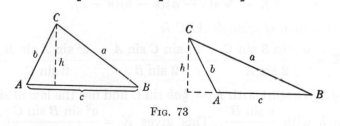

FIG. 73

---

* Ignore the curvature of the earth and assume only two-place accuracy. Get angles to the nearest degree. Get distances to the nearest multiple of 10 miles.

Proof. Let h be the altitude from C to AB (Fig. 73).

$$\text{Area } \triangle ABC = K = \tfrac{1}{2}ch = \tfrac{1}{2}bc \sin A,$$

since $h = b \sin A$. The other forms can be obtained by cyclic permutation.

II. *The area of triangle ABC is*

$$\boldsymbol{K = \sqrt{s(s - a)(s - b)(s - c)},}$$
$$\text{where } \boldsymbol{s = \tfrac{1}{2}(a + b + c).}$$

Proof. Since $K = \tfrac{1}{2}bc \sin A$,

$$K^2 = \frac{1}{4}\, b^2 c^2 \sin^2 A = \frac{b^2 c^2}{4}\,(1 - \cos^2 A)$$

$$= \frac{bc}{2}\,(1 + \cos A)\,\frac{bc}{2}\,(1 - \cos A).$$

Using the law of cosines, we get

$$K^2 = \frac{bc}{2}\left(1 + \frac{b^2 + c^2 - a^2}{2bc}\right)\frac{bc}{2}\left(1 - \frac{b^2 + c^2 - a^2}{2bc}\right)$$

$$= \frac{2bc + b^2 + c^2 - a^2}{4} \cdot \frac{2bc - b^2 - c^2 + a^2}{4}$$

$$= \frac{(b + c)^2 - a^2}{4} \cdot \frac{a^2 - (b - c)^2}{4}$$

$$= \frac{b + c + a}{2} \cdot \frac{b + c - a}{2} \cdot \frac{a - b + c}{2} \cdot \frac{a + b - c}{2}.$$

Let $s = \dfrac{1}{2}(a + b + c)$; then $\dfrac{b + c - a}{2} = s - a$, etc.

Hence

$$K^2 = s(s - a)(s - b)(s - c),$$
$$K = \sqrt{s(s - a)(s - b)(s - c)}.$$

III. *The area of triangle ABC is*

$$\boldsymbol{K = \frac{a^2 \sin B \sin C}{2 \sin A} = \frac{b^2 \sin C \sin A}{2 \sin B} = \frac{c^2 \sin A \sin B}{2 \sin C}.}$$

Proof. We start with $K = \tfrac{1}{2}ab \sin C$ and use the law of sines to replace b with $\dfrac{a \sin B}{\sin A}$. This gives $K = \dfrac{a^2 \sin B \sin C}{2 \sin A}$. This formula should be used when one side and two angles are given.

EXERCISE 41

Find the areas of the following triangles without using logarithms.

1. $a = 15$, $c = 40$, $B = 161°$.
2. $a = 20.0$, $b = 60.0$, $C = 80° 0'$.
3. $b = 10$, $A = 53°$, $C = 74°$.
4. $a = 30$, $A = 150°$, $C = 20°$.
5. $a = 45.0$, $b = 40.0$, $c = 13.0$.
6. $a = 25$, $b = 17$, $c = 10$.

Use logarithms to find the areas of the following triangles.

7. $b = 87.19$, $c = 64.63$, $A = 107° 22'$.
8. $a = 9.803$, $c = 7.216$, $B = 44° 2'$.
9. $a = 17.33$, $A = 52° 41'$, $B = 63° 9'$.
10. $c = 8.490$, $A = 132° 55'$, $B = 27° 46'$.
11. $a = 6.006$, $b = 8.008$, $c = 9.998$.
12. $a = 76.76$, $b = 48.48$, $c = 30.30$.

13. Use area formula I to derive an expression for the area of an equilateral triangle. Check your result by using formula II.

14. Use area formula II to show that the area of an isosceles triangle with sides a, a, b is $\dfrac{b}{4} \sqrt{4a^2 - b^2}$.

15. Find the number of acres in a triangular field whose sides are 106 yd., 127 yd., and 159 yd. (One acre contains 4840 sq. yd.)

16. The area of a triangle is 892.5 sq. ft. One angle is $57° 18'$. One of the sides adjacent to this angle is 19.65 ft. Find the other two sides of the triangle.

EXERCISE 42

(Miscellaneous Problems)

For each of the twelve following problems, (a) draw the triangle, (b) write the formulas that should be used to solve for the required parts, (c) make an outline of the solution, (d) find only the required parts.

1. $a = 9.0$, $b = 6.0$, $c = 8.0$. Find A.
2. $b = 40$, $c = 50$, $A = 146°$. Find a.
3. $a = 47.23$, $b = 39.66$, $A = 37° 25'$. Find B.
4. $b = 6.234$, $A = 77° 44'$, $C = 65° 56'$. Find c.
5. $b = 246.1$, $c = 713.9$, $A = 76° 14'$. Find B and C.
6. $a = 3177$, $b = 4566$, $c = 3925$. Find B.
7. $a = 2.00$, $c = 5.00$, $B = 65° 10'$. Find b.
8. $a = 40$, $b = 70$, $c = 90$. Find C.
9. $c = 5489$, $A = 29° 47'$, $B = 35° 10'$. Find a.
10. $a = 8.125$, $c = 9.625$, $A = 52° 40'$. Find C.
11. $a = 6271$, $b = 5723$, $c = 8046$. Find A.
12. $a = 926.7$, $c = 882.3$, $B = 95° 8'$. Find A.

13. Two ships leave a port at noon. One ship moves 12.5 mph in the direction N $49°$ E; the other travels 10 mph in the direction S $20°$ W. How far apart are they at 4 P.M.?

14. The Leaning Tower of Pisa makes an angle of 5° 20' with the vertical. When the angle of elevation of the sun is 22° 50', the shadow of the tower (falling on a horizontal plane) is 409 ft. long and appears on the side *from which* the tower leans. Find the distance from the bottom to the top of the tower.

15. A man in the horizontal plane of the base of the Woolworth Building finds the angle of elevation of the top of the building to be 40° 7'. After walking 423 ft. directly toward the base of the building, he observes that the angle of elevation of the top is now 56° 52'. How high is the Woolworth Building?

16. A tree stands vertically on a hillside whose inclination with the horizontal is 10°. From a point 100 ft. down the hill from the tree, the angle of elevation of the treetop is 32°. How tall is the tree?

17. A vertical tree stands on a hillside that makes an angle of 25° with the horizontal. From a point directly up the hill from the tree, the angle of elevation of the treetop is 50°. From a point 30 ft. farther up the hill, the angle of elevation of the treetop is 20°. How tall is the tree?

18. The distance between the centers of two intersecting circles is 10.0 in. The radii of the circles are 5.0 in. and 6.0 in., respectively. Find the acute angle made by the tangent lines at a point of intersection.

19. Each of three circles is tangent externally to the other two. If the radii are 20 in., 30 in., and 40 in., find the angles of the triangle formed by connecting the three centers.

20. Two straight roads intersect at an angle of 50° 0'. An auto on one road is 400 yards from the crossing. A truck on the other road is 500 yards from the intersection. Find the distance between the vehicles.

21. Santa Barbara, Calif., is 330 miles due south of Carson City, Nev. Stockton, Calif., is 120 miles from Carson City and 260 miles from Santa Barbara. Find the bearing of Stockton from Carson City. From Santa Barbara.* (Stockton, of course, lies west of the Carson City–Santa Barbara line.)

22. Warsaw, Poland, is 320 miles S 88° E from Berlin, Germany. The bearing of Prague, Czechoslovakia, from Berlin is S 14° E. The bearing of Prague from Warsaw is S 61° W. How far is Prague from Berlin? From Warsaw? *

23. Wichita, Kans., is 340 miles due north of Fort Worth, Tex. Fayetteville, Ark., is 290 miles N 37° E from Fort Worth. Find the bearing and the distance of Fayetteville from Wichita.*

24. Copenhagen, Denmark, is 300 miles S 13° E from Oslo, Norway. The bearing of Stockholm, Sweden, from Oslo is S 83° E. Stockholm is 320 miles from Copenhagen. What is the bearing of Stockholm from Copenhagen? How far is Stockholm from Oslo? *

25. A motorboat heads N 12° 30' W on a river that flows due east. The boat travels N 7° 30' E with a speed of 925 ft. per min. Find the speed of the current and the speed of the boat in still water.

26. An airplane heads N 25° W with an air speed of 100 mph. Find the speed and the direction of the wind that makes the plane travel north at 110 mph.

27. An airplane heads due north with an air speed of 120 mph. A wind of 30 mph causes the plane to travel N 10° E. Find the direction of the wind and the ground speed of the plane.

28. An airplane heads west with an air speed of 210 mph. A wind speed of

---

* Ignore the curvature of the earth and assume only two-place accuracy. Get angles to the nearest degree. Get distances to the nearest multiple of 10 miles.

20 mph causes the plane to travel with a ground speed of 200 mph. In what direction is the wind blowing? In what direction does the plane travel?

29. Three forces are in equilibrium. One force of 72.54 lb. acts in the direction N 23° 18′ E. The second force acts due south. Find the direction of the third force if its magnitude is 33.87 lb.

30. Forces of 614.7 lb. and 750.8 lb. act on a body. The smaller force acts due west; the larger force acts S 20° 21′ W. Find the direction and magnitude of the resultant.

31. One diagonal of a parallelogram makes angles of 31° 31′ and 42° 42′ with the sides. If the length of the diagonal is 29.29 in., how long are the sides?

32. Two sides of a parallelogram are 6.789 and 5.111. One diagonal is 2.468. Find the angles of the parallelogram.

33. A sailboat is moving 4.0 mph in the direction S 10° E. A motorboat with a speed of 12.0 mph is due west of the sailboat. In what direction should the motorboat travel if it is to overtake the sailboat in a minimum of time?

34. In a triangle $A = 78°\,45′$, $b = 5432$, and the median from C to the midpoint of c is 6040. Find c.

35. A train is moving at 50 mph on a straight track in the direction N 25° E. The sun rising in the direction N 70° E casts the train's shadow onto the front of a building that faces due east. How fast is the train's shadow moving?

36. A pole stands on level ground and leans eastward making an angle of 55° with the horizontal. The pole is supported by a 13-ft. prop whose base is 15 ft. from the base of the pole. Find the angle made by the prop with the horizontal.

37. A ladder leaning against a building has an angle of elevation of α. After the foot of the ladder is moved a ft. closer to the building, the angle of elevation is β. Show that the number of ft. in the length of the ladder is $\dfrac{a}{\cos \alpha - \cos \beta}$.

38. If R is the radius of the circle circumscribed about triangle ABC, prove that $2R = \dfrac{a}{\sin A} = \dfrac{b}{\sin B} = \dfrac{c}{\sin C}$. *Hint:* Let A be any acute angle of the triangle and let O be the center of the circle. Connect O with the mid-point M of BC. Then by geometry, angle MOB is equal to A.

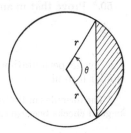

39. Show that the area of the shaded **segment** of the circle in Fig. 74 is equal to $\frac{1}{2}r^2\,(\theta - \sin \theta)$, where θ is in radians. (See Prob. 16, p. 52.)

40. Prove that the area of any quadrilateral equals one-half the product of its diagonals times the sine of the included angle.

FIG. 74

41. If a and b are two sides of a triangle and m is the length of the median from their common vertex to the mid-point of the third side c, show that $c = \sqrt{2a^2 + 2b^2 - 4m^2}$.

42. From a mountain village, the angle of elevation of a mountain peak is 19° 0′. After leaving the village and walking 2500 ft. down a slope of 13° 0′, directly toward the mountain, an observer finds the angle of elevation of the peak to be 28° 0°. How much higher is the peak than the village?

43. A 50-ft. flagpole stands on the top of a 45-ft. building. How far from the base of the building should a man stand if the flagpole and the building are to subtend equal angles at his eye, which is 5 ft. above the ground?

44. Two buildings standing on level ground are 40 ft. apart. From a point on the ground one-fourth of the way from the taller building T to the shorter building S, the angle of elevation of the top of T is twice the angle of elevation of the top of S. From a point on the ground three-fourths of the way from T to S, the angles of elevation of their tops are equal. Find the heights of the buildings.

45. In quadrilateral $ABCD$, $AB = 32.76$, $BC = 45.14$, $CD = 55.88$, angle $B = 111° 20'$, angle $C = 107° 18'$. Find AD.

46. The sides of a triangle are 3 ft., 7 ft., and 8 ft. From a point R on the shortest side 1 ft. from the vertex of the largest angle, a line RS is drawn intersecting the longest side at S. If RS divides the triangle into two equal areas, how far is S from the vertex of the smallest angle? (Solve without logs.)

47. The area of a triangle is $24\sqrt{3}$. The perimeter is 36. One angle is 60°. Find the sides of the triangle.

48. Given A, a, and b, use the law of cosines to show that

$$c = b \cos A \pm \sqrt{a^2 - b^2 \sin^2 A}.$$

Discuss this equation and interpret the geometric significance if (1) $a < b \sin A$, (2) $a = b \sin A$, (3) $a > b \sin A$, (4) $a = b$. Compare with the possibilities in the SSA case.

49.* Prove that in any triangle

$$\frac{a+b}{c} = \frac{\cos \frac{1}{2}(A - B)}{\sin \frac{1}{2}C}.$$

Hint: Add the equations $\dfrac{a}{c} = \dfrac{\sin A}{\sin C}$ and $\dfrac{b}{c} = \dfrac{\sin B}{\sin C}$. Apply formula [15] of Art. 42 to $\sin A + \sin B$. Replace $\sin C$ with $2 \sin \frac{1}{2}C \cos \frac{1}{2}C$. Notice that $\frac{1}{2}C$ is the complement of $\frac{1}{2}(A + B)$.

50.* Prove that in any triangle

$$\frac{a-b}{c} = \frac{\sin \frac{1}{2}(A - B)}{\cos \frac{1}{2}C}.$$

Use cyclic permutation and the interchange of pairs of letters to derive five similar formulas.

* The formulas in Probs. 49 and 50 are called **Mollweide's equations.** They serve as good checks because each of them involves all six parts of the triangle.

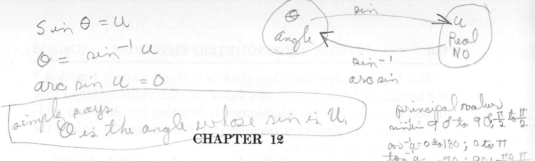

$\sin \theta = u$

$\theta = \sin^{-1} u$

$\text{arc sin } u = 0$

θ angle $\xrightarrow{\ \sin\ }$ u Real NO

$\sin^{-1}$ arc sin

simple says θ is the angle whose sin is u.

principal values: min of θ -to 90, $\frac{\pi}{2}$ to $\frac{\pi}{2}$

$\cos^{-1} u = 0$ to 180; 0 to π

$\tan^{-1} u$ -90; 90; $-\frac{\pi}{2}$ to $\frac{\pi}{2}$

CHAPTER 12

INVERSE TRIGONOMETRIC FUNCTIONS

72. Inverse trigonometric functions. The equation

$$u = \sin \theta$$

says that u is a *number* representing the sine of the angle θ. Another interpretation is

θ is an angle whose sine is u.

This statement is usually written in the form *

$\theta = \text{arc sin } u.$

With this understanding, we can say

$$\text{arc sin } \tfrac{1}{2} = 30°, \ 150°, \ 390°, \ -210°, \text{ etc.,}$$

because the sine of each of these angles is $\tfrac{1}{2}$. Values of arc sin $\tfrac{1}{2}$ can be obtained by finding all the points on the sine curve that are $\tfrac{1}{2}$ unit above the θ-axis (Fig. 75).

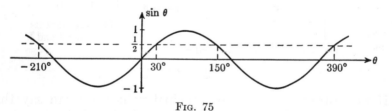

FIG. 75

Similarly, arc cos u denotes an angle whose cosine is u, arc tan u denotes an angle whose tangent is u, etc. The six inverse trigonometric functions are arc sin u, arc cos u, arc tan u, arc cot u, arc sec u, and arc csc u. It is to be borne in mind that every inverse trigonometric function is an angle. Thus arc cos $0 = 90°$, arc tan $1 = 45°$.

* Another common form is $\theta = \sin^{-1} u.$

The trigonometric function sin θ is a single-valued function *
of θ because it takes on only one value for each value assigned to θ.
In contrast, the inverse trigonometric function arc sin u is a mul-
tiple-valued function of u because it takes on several values for
each value assigned to u.

73. Principal values of the inverse trigonometric functions.
The symbol arc sin u is ambiguous because it has many values.
We can easily remove this ambiguity by *agreeing* to choose one
particular value. This value, called the **principal value,** lies
between $-90°$ and $90°$, inclusive. For example, the principal
value of arc sin $\frac{1}{2}$ is $30°$ or $\pi/6$ radians. Following are the definitions of the principal values of arc sin u, arc cos u, and arc tan u,
together with curves in which the heavier lines indicate the range
of the principal values.

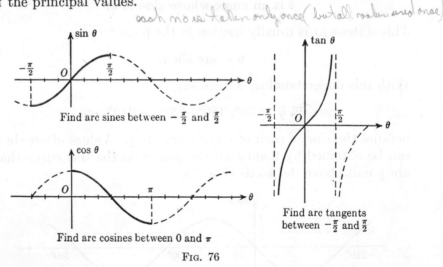

Find arc sines between $-\frac{\pi}{2}$ and $\frac{\pi}{2}$

Find arc cosines between 0 and π

Find arc tangents
between $-\frac{\pi}{2}$ and $\frac{\pi}{2}$

Fig. 76

If we restrict ourselves to principal values, we can say that
arc sin u, arc cos u, and arc tan u are single-valued functions.
Thus arc sin u means *the* angle whose sine is u.

Illustrations. $\text{arc sin}\left(-\frac{\sqrt{3}}{2}\right) = -60° = -\frac{\pi}{3}$,

$\text{arc cos}\left(-\frac{\sqrt{2}}{2}\right) = 135° = \frac{3\pi}{4}$, $\text{arc tan}(-1) = -45° = -\frac{\pi}{4}$.

* See definition of function (Art. 6).

In calculus, frequent use is made of the inverse functions. Whenever arc sin u is encountered, it is understood that *the principal value is to be found and expressed in radians.* We shall follow the same procedure with all inverse trigonometric functions in this text.

The functions arc cot u, arc sec u, and arc csc u are of less importance. They can readily be expressed in terms of arc tan u, arc cos u, and arc sin u, respectively. For example, arc sec u = arc cos $\dfrac{1}{u}$ (the angle whose secant is u is the same angle whose cosine is $1/u$). Thus

$$\text{arc sec } 2 = \text{arc cos } \frac{1}{2} = 60° = \frac{\pi}{3}.$$

EXERCISE 43

Express in radians the principal value of each of the following. Do not use tables.

1. arc sin $(-\frac{1}{2})$.
2. arc sin $\dfrac{\sqrt{2}}{2}$.
3. arc cos 0.
4. arc cos (-1).
5. arc cos $\dfrac{\sqrt{3}}{2}$.
6. arc cos $\left(-\dfrac{\sqrt{3}}{2}\right)$.
7. arc sin $\left(-\dfrac{\sqrt{2}}{2}\right)$.
8. arc sin $\left(\dfrac{\sqrt{3}}{2}\right)$.
9. arc sin 0.
10. arc sin (-1).
11. arc cos $(-\frac{1}{2})$.
12. arc cos $\dfrac{\sqrt{2}}{2}$.
13. arc sec $(-\sqrt{2})$.
14. arc sec 1.
15. arc csc $\dfrac{2}{\sqrt{3}}$.
16. arc csc (-2).
17. arc tan $\left(\dfrac{1}{\sqrt{3}}\right)$.
18. arc tan $(-\sqrt{3})$.
19. arc tan 1.
20. arc tan 0.
21. arc sin 1.

Use Table I to express in radians the principal value of each of the following.

22. arc sin $(-.1248)$.
23. arc sin .9171.
24. arc cos .8004.
25. arc cos $(-.1908)$.
26. arc tan .3121.
27. arc tan (-5.066).

28. Explain why the principal value of arc cos u could not be taken in the interval $-\pi/2$ to $\pi/2$.

74. Operations involving inverse trigonometric functions. Since every inverse trigonometric function is an angle, it is frequently convenient to place this angle in standard position and label its triangle of reference in accordance with the inverse function (Example 1). Sometimes it is advisable to replace the inverse functions with angle symbols, such as θ, A, B, and then try to express the problem in terms of ordinary functions.

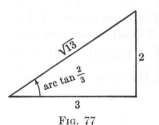

Fig. 77

Example 1. Evaluate cos (arc tan $\frac{2}{3}$).

Solution. We are asked to find the cosine of the angle whose tangent is $\frac{2}{3}$. Draw a right triangle with legs 2 and 3. The acute angle opposite the side 2 has a tangent of $\frac{2}{3}$. It can be labeled arc tan $\frac{2}{3}$. After finding the hypotenuse is $\sqrt{13}$, we see (Fig. 77) that

$$\cos\left(\text{arc tan }\frac{2}{3}\right) = \frac{3}{\sqrt{13}}.$$

Example 2. Find the value of

$$\sin(\text{arc sin } u + \text{arc cos } v).$$

Solution. Since arc sin u and arc cos v are angles, we have the sine of the sum of two angles. Let $A = $ arc sin u and $B = $ arc cos v. Using

$$\sin(A + B) = \sin A \cos B + \cos A \sin B,$$

we have

$$\sin(\text{arc sin } u + \text{arc cos } v) = \sin(\text{arc sin } u)\cos(\text{arc cos } v)$$
$$+ \cos(\text{arc sin } u)\sin(\text{arc cos } v)$$
$$= uv + \sqrt{1 - u^2}\sqrt{1 - v^2}.$$

The value of cos (arc sin u) is found by use of the triangle in Fig. 78. Notice that if u is negative, arc sin u is in Q IV (its principal value lies between $-\pi/2$ and 0) but cos (arc sin u) is still positive. Explain why sin (arc cos v) is always the positive radical $\sqrt{1 - v^2}$.

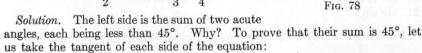

Fig. 78

Example 3. Prove that

$$\text{arc tan }\frac{1}{2} + \text{arc tan }\frac{1}{3} = \frac{\pi}{4}.$$

Solution. The left side is the sum of two acute angles, each being less than 45°. Why? To prove that their sum is 45°, let us take the tangent of each side of the equation:

$$\tan\left(\text{arc tan }\tfrac{1}{2} + \text{arc tan }\tfrac{1}{3}\right)$$
$$= \frac{\tan(\text{arc tan }\tfrac{1}{2}) + \tan(\text{arc tan }\tfrac{1}{3})}{1 - \tan(\text{arc tan }\tfrac{1}{2})\tan(\text{arc tan }\tfrac{1}{3})}$$
$$= \frac{\tfrac{1}{2} + \tfrac{1}{3}}{1 - \tfrac{1}{2}\cdot\tfrac{1}{3}} = \frac{\tfrac{5}{6}}{\tfrac{5}{6}} = 1.$$

$$\tan\frac{\pi}{4}$$
$$= 1$$

The proof is complete if we recall that two acute angles having the same tangent are equal. Notice that the formula for tan $(A + B)$ was used in evaluating the left side.

EXERCISE 44

Find the value of the following without using tables. (Remember that the principal value is implied in each inverse function.)

1. $\sin (\text{arc tan } u)$.
2. $\tan (\text{arc cos } u)$.
3. $\sin (\text{arc csc } u)$.
4. $\cot (\text{arc cot } u)$.
5. $\tan \text{arc sin } \frac{24}{25}$.
6. $\cos \text{arc sin } (-\frac{3}{4})$.
7. $\cos \text{arc tan } \frac{8}{15}$.
8. $\sin \text{arc cos } (-\frac{1}{3})$.
9. $\sin (\text{arc sin } u - \text{arc cos } v)$.
10. $\cos (\text{arc cos } u + \text{arc sin } v)$.
11. $\cos (\text{arc cos } u - \text{arc cos } v)$.
12. $\sin (\text{arc sin } u + \text{arc sin } v)$
13. $\cos (\pi + \text{arc sin } \frac{6}{7})$.
14. $\sin (2\pi - \text{arc cos } \frac{1}{4})$.
15. $\sin \left(\frac{\pi}{2} + \text{arc sin } \frac{2}{5} \right)$.
16. $\cos \left(\frac{3\pi}{2} - \text{arc cos } \frac{1}{6} \right)$
17. $\sin (2 \text{ arc sin } v)$.   *Hint:* Let $A = \text{arc sin } v$. We seek $\sin 2A$.
18. $\cos (2 \text{ arc cos } v)$.
19. $\cos (2 \text{ arc sin } u)$.
20. $\sin (2 \text{ arc cos } 3u)$.
21. $\cos (\text{arc cos } 2v)$.
22. $\sin (\text{arc sin } 6u)$.
23. $\text{arc sin } \left(\sin \frac{\pi}{8} \right)$.
24. $\text{arc sin } \left(\sin \frac{8\pi}{9} \right)$.
25. $\text{arc cos } \left[\cos \left(-\frac{\pi}{10} \right) \right]$.
26. $\text{arc tan } (\tan 170°)$.
27. $\text{arc tan } \left(\cot \frac{3\pi}{10} \right)$.
28. $\text{arc tan } (\sec \pi)$.
29. $\text{arc sin } (\cos^3 \pi)$.
30. $\text{arc cos } (\tan 0)$.

Assume $u > 0$. Copy the following and fill in the blanks.

31. $\text{arc sin } \dfrac{\sqrt{9 - u^2}}{3} = \text{arc cos } \underline{\quad} = \text{arc tan } \underline{\quad}$.

32. $\text{arc sin } \underline{\quad} = \text{arc cos } \dfrac{5u}{\sqrt{25u^2 + 1}} = \text{arc cot } \underline{\quad}$.

33. $\text{arc sin } \underline{\quad} = \text{arc cos } \underline{\quad} = \text{arc tan } \dfrac{4}{\sqrt{u^2 - 16}}$.

34. $\text{arc sin } \dfrac{\sqrt{u^4 - 36}}{u^2} = \text{arc tan } \underline{\quad} = \text{arc sec } \underline{\quad}$.

35. $\text{arc cos } u - \text{arc sin } u = \text{arc tan } \underline{\quad}$.

Prove each of the following without using tables.

36. $\sin \left(\frac{1}{2} \text{ arc cos } u \right) = \sqrt{\dfrac{1 - u}{2}}$.

37. $\cos (\frac{1}{2} \text{ arc cos } 2u) = \sqrt{\frac{1}{2} + u}$.

38. $\cos \left(\frac{1}{2} \text{ arc sin } u \right) = \sqrt{\dfrac{1 + \sqrt{1 - u^2}}{2}}$.

39. $\sin\left(\dfrac{1}{2}\text{ arc sin }a\right) = \pm\sqrt{\dfrac{1 - \sqrt{1 - a^2}}{2}}$.

40. $\text{arc tan }5 - \text{arc tan }\tfrac{1}{8} = \text{arc tan }3$.

41. $\text{arc tan }\dfrac{1}{10} + \text{arc tan }\dfrac{9}{11} = \dfrac{\pi}{4}$.

42. $\text{arc cos }\dfrac{1}{7} - \text{arc cos }\dfrac{13}{14} = \dfrac{\pi}{3}$.

43. $2\text{ arc cos }\tfrac{1}{4} + \text{arc cos }\tfrac{7}{8} = \pi$.

44. $\tfrac{1}{2}\text{ arc cos }\left(-\tfrac{17}{49}\right) - \text{arc sin }\tfrac{16}{17} = \text{arc sin }\left(-\tfrac{31}{119}\right)$.

45. $\text{arc sin }\tfrac{1}{6} + \text{arc cos }\tfrac{17}{18} = \text{arc sin }\tfrac{13}{27}$.

Identify as true or false and give reasons. (Consider all permissible values, positive and negative, of the letters involved.)

46. $\text{arc csc }u = \dfrac{1}{\text{arc sin }u}$.

47. $\text{arc cos }u = \text{arc sin }\sqrt{1 - u^2}$.

48. $\cos(\text{arc csc }a) = \dfrac{1}{a}$.

49. $\text{arc sin }(-u) + \text{arc sin }u = 0$.

50. $\text{arc cos }u = \dfrac{\pi}{2} - \text{arc sin }u$.

51. $\text{arc cos }u + \text{arc cos }(-u) = \pi$.

52. $\text{arc sin }\left(2\sin\dfrac{\theta}{2}\right) = \theta$.

53. $\cos(\tfrac{1}{2}\text{ arc cos }2u) = u$.

54. $\text{arc tan }u = \dfrac{1}{2}\text{ arc cos }\dfrac{1 - u^2}{1 + u^2}$.

55. $\text{arc tan }\infty = \dfrac{\pi}{2}$.

56. $\text{arc cos }\left(-\dfrac{\sqrt{3}}{2}\right) = \dfrac{7\pi}{6} + \text{arc sin }\left(-\dfrac{\sqrt{3}}{2}\right)$.

75. Inverse functions. If the equation $y = f(x)$ is equivalent to the equation $x = g(y)$, then the functions $f(u)$ and $g(u)$ are said to be inverses of each other. To find the inverse of the function $2u + 7$, let $y = 2x + 7$,* solve for x: $x = \tfrac{1}{2}(y - 7)$. Hence the inverse of the function $2u + 7$ is $\tfrac{1}{2}(u - 7)$. Likewise, if $y = \sin x$, then $x = \text{arc sin }y$. Hence the functions $\sin u$ and $\text{arc sin }u$ are inverses. What is the inverse of the function 10^u? Of the function $u^2 - 2u - 5$?

---

* The quantity $2x + 7$ is a function of x. The expression $2u + 7$ is the *same* function of u. In either case the independent variable is doubled and added to **7.**

CHAPTER 13

COMPLEX NUMBERS

76. Complex numbers. In solving the quadratic equation $x^2 + 1 = 0$, we obtain as one of the roots $x = \sqrt{-1}$. Since the square of every positive or negative real number is always positive, it is apparent that $\sqrt{-1}$ is not a real number. Let us use the letter i to represent $\sqrt{-1}$. Then i is a number having the single property: $i^2 = -1$. With this understanding, we can say that the roots of $x^2 + 1 = 0$ are $x = \pm i$. Similarly, the roots of $x^2 + 7 = 0$ are $x = \pm \sqrt{-7} = \pm \sqrt{7} \cdot \sqrt{-1} = \pm i \sqrt{7}$. Such numbers as $\sqrt{-1}$ and $\sqrt{-7}$ are called pure imaginary numbers. In general,

1. *A* **pure imaginary number** *is a square root of a negative number.*

In solving the equation $x^2 - 4x + 13 = 0$, we find the roots to be $x = 2 \pm \sqrt{-9}$. Remembering that $i = \sqrt{-1}$, we have $x = 2 \pm 3i$. Notice that if $2 + 3i$ is substituted for x in the equation $x^2 - 4x + 13 = 0$, we get

$$4 + 12i + 9i^2 - 8 - 12i + 13 = 0.$$

If i^2 is replaced by -1, we obtain $17 + 12i - 12i - 17 = 0$. This shows that $2 + 3i$ is a perfectly good root of the equation, provided we understand that i is a number whose square is -1. A number (such as $2 + 3i$) that is the sum of a real number and a pure imaginary number is called a complex number. In general,

2. *A* **complex number** *is a number of the form $a + bi$, where a and b are real numbers and $i = \sqrt{-1}$.* If $a = 0$, the complex number $a + bi$ becomes bi, a pure imaginary number. If $b = 0$, the complex number $a + bi$ becomes a, a real number. Hence we see that real numbers and pure imaginary numbers are special cases of complex numbers. If $b \neq 0$, the complex number $a + bi$ is called an **imaginary number.**

3. *The complex numbers $a + bi$ and $a - bi$ are said to be* **conjugates** *of each other.* Notice that the roots of the equation $x^2 - 4x$

135

$+ 13 = 0$ are the conjugate imaginary numbers $2 + 3i$ and $2 - 3i$. It can be shown that if an imaginary number $(a + bi)$ is a root of an equation with real coefficients, then the conjugate imaginary $(a - bi)$ is also a root of this equation.

4. *Two complex numbers are said to be equal provided their real parts are equal and their imaginary parts are equal.* This means that *if* $a + bi = c + di$, *then* $a = c$ *and* $b = d$. As a consequence of this definition, we see that if $a + bi = 0$, then $a = 0$ and $b = 0$.

Since $\sqrt{a} \cdot \sqrt{a} = a$ (by the definition of square root), we must conclude that if $i = \sqrt{-1}$, then $i^2 = -1$. Moreover, $i^3 = i^2 \cdot i = -i$, $i^4 = 1$, $i^5 = i$, $i^6 = -1$, etc.

The ordinary algebraic operations on complex numbers yield the following results.

(1) $\qquad (a + bi) + (c + di) = (a + c) + (b + d)i.$

(2) $\qquad (a + bi)(c + di) = (ac - bd) + (ad + bc)i.$

(3) $\qquad \dfrac{a + bi}{c + di} = \dfrac{(a + bi)(c - di)}{(c + di)(c - di)} = \dfrac{(ac + bd) + (bc - ad)i}{c^2 + d^2}.$

Since i is a number whose square is -1, the best procedure in handling complex numbers is to perform all operations as if i were an ordinary letter and then replace i^2 with -1. It is to be noted that the quotient of two complex numbers is obtained by multiplying numerator and denominator by the conjugate of the denominator. For example,

$$\frac{7 + 5i}{3 - i} = \frac{(7 + 5i)(3 + i)}{(3 - i)(3 + i)} = \frac{21 + 7i + 15i + 5i^2}{9 - i^2}$$

$$= \frac{16 + 22i}{10} = \frac{8}{5} + \frac{11}{5} i.$$

This result can be checked by multiplying $\frac{8}{5} + \frac{11}{5}i$ by $3 - i$. What should the result be?

All complex numbers should first be written in the form $a + bi$. Thus $3 + \sqrt{-49} = 3 + \sqrt{49}\sqrt{-1} = 3 + 7i$. This procedure is suggested to avoid mistakes such as $\sqrt{-5} \cdot \sqrt{-5} = \sqrt{(-5)(-5)} = \sqrt{25} = 5$. This is obviously incorrect because, by the definition of square root, $\sqrt{-5}$ is a number which when multiplied by itself becomes -5. The correct way of handling this is $\sqrt{-5}\cdot\sqrt{-5} = i\sqrt{5}\cdot i\sqrt{5} = 5i^2 = -5$. This result agrees with the definition of square root.

EXERCISE 45

Perform each of the indicated operations and express the result in the form $a + bi$.

1. $(2 + 7i) + (4 - 6i)$.
2. $(3 - 5i) + (-1 + 2i)$.
3. $(-9 - 7i) - (5 - 4i)$.
4. $(4 + 3i) - (7 - 5i)$.
5. $(6 - 5i)(-2 + 9i)$.
6. $(2 + i\sqrt{7})(3 - i\sqrt{7})$.
7. $(4 - \sqrt{-2})(5 - \sqrt{-2})$.
8. $(8 + 3i)(2 + 5i)$.
9. $(5 + 8i)^2$.
10. $(4 - 3i)^2$.
11. i^{13}.
12. i^{14}.
13. i^{1960}.
14. i^{23}.
15. $\dfrac{8 - i}{2 + 3i}$.
16. $\dfrac{2 - 23i}{4 - 5i}$.
17. $\dfrac{2 - i\sqrt{5}}{1 - i\sqrt{5}}$.
18. $\dfrac{8 + 7i}{6 + 5i}$.

Find the values of the real numbers x and y.

19. $4x + 7yi = 12 - 35i$.
20. $18 - 5iy = 9x - 40i$.
21. $(3 + iy)(5 + 2i) = x + 26i$.
22. $(2 + xi)(y - 4i) = 38 + 37i$.

23. Find the value of $x^2 - 8x + 25$ if $x = 4 - 3i$.

24. Show by substitution that $-\frac{1}{2} + 5i$ is a root of the equation $4x^2 + 4x + 101 = 0$.

77. Graphical representation of complex numbers.

Let us represent (as in the case of the x-axis of a rectangular coordinate

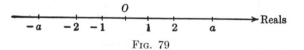

O

$-a$ -2 -1 1 2 a $\rightarrow$ Reals

Fig. 79

system) the real numbers by points on a horizontal directed line (Fig. 79). Let the vector V represent the directed segment connecting the origin O to the point corresponding to the real number a. Since $ai^2 = -a$, it can be said that multiplying a by $i \cdot i$ is geometrically equivalent to rotating V through $180°$ about O. Consequently, it is logical to represent the multiplication of a by i as a rotation of V through $90°$ about O. Accordingly, the number ai will be represented as a point a units above O on the *vertical* line through O. We shall refer to the horizontal axis as the **axis of reals** and the vertical axis as the **axis of (pure) imaginaries.**

This system of axes defines a region called the **complex plane.**
It is to be noted that, while the unit on the axis of reals is the
number 1, the unit on the axis of imaginaries is the imaginary
number i. Hence the complex number $(a + bi)$ is represented
by the point a units from the axis of imaginaries and b units from
the axis of reals. Figure 80 illus-
trates the graphical representa-
tion of complex numbers in the
complex plane.

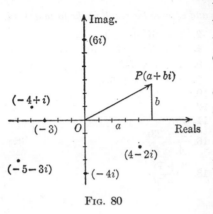

FIG. 80

It is often convenient to think
of the complex number $(a + bi)$
as representing the vector OP
(Fig. 80).

**78. Graphical addition of com-
plex numbers.** Since the sum of
$(a + bi)$ and $(c + di)$ is $(a + c)$
$+ (b + d)i$, we can add the numbers graphically by adding the
real parts, a and c, to get the real part of the sum, and adding the
imaginary coefficients, b and d, to get the imaginary coefficient.
This is illustrated in Fig. 81. The result is exactly the same as

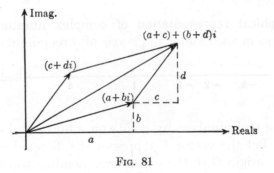

FIG. 81

if we had applied the parallelogram law to the vectors representing the numbers $(a + bi)$ and $(c + di)$. Three complex numbers
can be added graphically by first obtaining the sum of two of
them and then adding this to the third.

We can subtract $(c + di)$ from $(a + bi)$ graphically by adding
$(a + bi)$ to $(-c - di)$.

79. Trigonometric form of a complex number. Let point P in the complex plane represent the complex number $a + bi$. The **absolute value** * of $a + bi$ is the distance r from O to P. It is <u>always considered positive.</u> The **amplitude** * of $a + bi$ is the angle measured from the positive axis of reals to the line OP. From Fig. 82, it is obvious that

Fig. 82

$$(1) \quad r = \sqrt{a^2 + b^2}, \qquad \tan\theta = \frac{b}{a},$$

and

$$(2) \quad a = r\cos\theta, \qquad b = r\sin\theta.$$

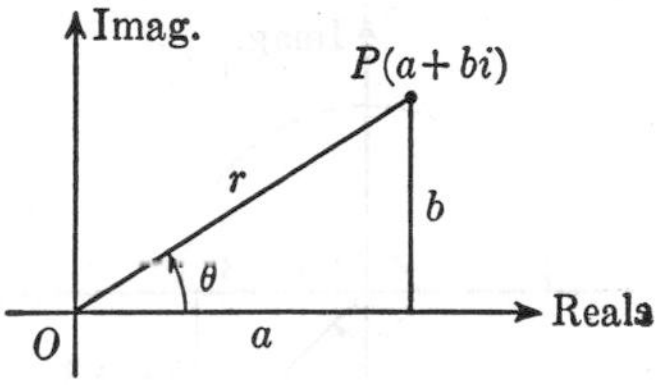

These equations hold regardless of the quadrant in which P lies. If the last equation is multiplied by i and added to the preceding one, we get

$$[3] \qquad\qquad a + bi = r(\cos\theta + i\sin\theta).$$

The expression $r(\cos\theta + i\sin\theta)$ is called the **trigonometric†** form of a complex number. The expression $a + bi$ is called the **algebraic form** of a complex number. The trigonometric form is useful in finding powers and roots of complex numbers.

Any complex number in algebraic form can be expressed in trigonometric form by use of equations (1). After the value of $\tan\theta$ has been obtained, θ can be found by use of a table of trigonometric functions. In general, there are two angles between 0° and 360° having the same tangent. In order to be certain to get the correct angle, we should *always plot the complex number* ‡ in the complex plane. The amplitude of a real number or a pure imaginary number can be obtained by inspection of its location in the complex plane. For example, the amplitude of $-4i$ is 270° (Fig. 80).

Any complex number in trigonometric form can be expressed in algebraic form by use of equations (2).

---

* Absolute value is also called *modulus*: amplitude is sometimes called *argument*.

† Also called the *polar* form. It is sometimes written in the abbreviated form $r \operatorname{cis} \theta$.

‡ The expression *plot the complex number* is an abbreviation we shall use for the more rigorous statement, *plot the point corresponding to the complex number*.

Example. Express each of the following in trigonometric form:

$$(a)\ 3 - 3i, \qquad (b)\ -4.$$

Solution. (a) Plot the number in the complex plane. Equations (1) give us $r = \sqrt{18} = 3\sqrt{2}$, $\tan \theta = -3/3 = -1$. From the last equation, θ could be 135° or 315°. From Fig. 83 we see that θ must be 315°. Hence

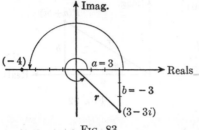

FIG. 83

$$3 - 3i = 3\sqrt{2}\,(\cos 315° + i \sin 315°).$$

This result can be checked by replacing $\cos 315°$ and $\sin 315°$ with $\sqrt{2}/2$ and $-\sqrt{2}/2$, respectively, and then demonstrating that the right side is actually equal to the left side.

(b) After plotting the number, Fig. 83, we find by inspection that $r = 4$ and $\theta = 180°$. Hence we can see immediately that

$$-4 = 4(\cos 180° + i \sin 180°).$$

It is to be carefully noted that, regardless of the signs of a and b, r is always positive, and the signs in front of $\cos \theta$ and $i \sin \theta$ are always positive.

EXERCISE 46

Perform the indicated operations graphically and check the results algebraically.

1. $(4 + i) + (2 - 5i)$.   2. $(1 - 2i) + (-3 - 5i)$.
3. $(7 + 3i) + (2 - 9i)$.   4. $(3 + i) + (-5 + 4i)$.
5. $(-2 + 5i) - (4 + 7i)$.   6. $(5 - 6i) - (2 - 9i)$.
7. $(6 + 3i) + (-2 + 5i) + (1 - 6i)$.   8. $(8 - 5i) + (1 + 7i) - (4 + 3i)$.

Plot each of the following complex numbers and then express it in trigonometric form.

9. $-5 - 5i$.   10. $\sqrt{2} - i\sqrt{2}$.
11. $-3 + 3i$.   12. $4 + 4i$.
13. $-7i$.   14. -3.
15. 6.   16. $8i$.
17. $\sqrt{3} + i$.   18. $-15 - 8i$.
19. $6 - 8i$.   20. $-2 + 2i\sqrt{3}$.

Plot each of the following complex numbers and then express it in algebraic form.

21. $5(\cos 340° + i \sin 340°)$.   22. $6(\cos 150° + i \sin 150°)$.
23. $4(\cos 60° + i \sin 60°)$.   24. $10(\cos 200° + i \sin 200°)$.

25. On one system of coordinates, plot and label the number $2 + 5i$, its conjugate, and its negative.

26. What is the amplitude (a) of a positive real number? (b) of a negative real number? (c) of bi if $b > 0$? (d) of bi if $b < 0$?

27. Show that the conjugate of $r(\cos \theta + i \sin \theta)$ is $r(\cos [-\theta] + i \sin [-\theta])$.

80. Multiplication of complex numbers in trigonometric form.
Theorem. The absolute value of the product of two complex numbers is the product of their absolute values; the amplitude of the product is the sum of their amplitudes;

$$r_1(\cos \theta_1 + i \sin \theta_1) \cdot r_2(\cos \theta_2 + i \sin \theta_2)$$
$$= r_1 r_2[\cos (\theta_1 + \theta_2) + i \sin (\theta_1 + \theta_2)].$$

Proof. Let $r_1(\cos \theta_1 + i \sin \theta_1)$ and $r_2(\cos \theta_2 + i \sin \theta_2)$ be any two complex numbers in trigonometric form. Their product is

$$r_1(\cos \theta_1 + i \sin \theta_1) \cdot r_2(\cos \theta_2 + i \sin \theta_2)$$
$$= r_1 r_2(\cos \theta_1 \cos \theta_2 + i \sin \theta_1 \cos \theta_2 + i \cos \theta_1 \sin \theta_2$$
$$+ i^2 \sin \theta_1 \sin \theta_2)$$
$$= r_1 r_2[(\cos \theta_1 \cos \theta_2 - \sin \theta_1 \sin \theta_2) + i(\sin \theta_1 \cos \theta_2$$
$$+ \cos \theta_1 \sin \theta_2)]$$
$$= r_1 r_2[\cos (\theta_1 + \theta_2) + i \sin (\theta_1 + \theta_2)].$$

Illustration.

$$2(\cos 130° + i \sin 130°) \cdot 3(\cos 50° + i \sin 50°)$$
$$= 2 \cdot 3[\cos (130° + 50°) + i \sin (130° + 50°)]$$
$$= 6(\cos 180° + i \sin 180°) = 6(-1 + i \cdot 0) = -6.$$

This theorem can be extended to include the product of any number of complex numbers:

$$r_1(\cos \theta_1 + i \sin \theta_1) \cdot r_2(\cos \theta_2 + i \sin \theta_2) \cdots r_n(\cos \theta_n + i \sin \theta_n)$$
$$= r_1 r_2 \cdots r_n[\cos(\theta_1 + \theta_2 + \cdots + \theta_n) + i \sin(\theta_1 + \theta_2 + \cdots + \theta_n)].$$

81. De Moivre's theorem. *If n is any real number,*

$$[r(\cos \theta + i \sin \theta)]^n = r^n(\cos n\theta + i \sin n\theta).$$

This theorem can be proved for positive integral values of n by using the last formula of Art. 80 with each factor of the left side set equal to $r(\cos \theta + i \sin \theta)$.

It can be shown that De Moivre's theorem is true for all real values of n. We shall use it for only two cases: (1) when n is a positive integer and (2) when n is the reciprocal of a positive integer. The proof of the latter case is omitted in this text.

Example.   Use De Moivre's theorem to find the value of $(-1 + i)^{10}$.

Solution.   After plotting $(-1 + i)$ and putting it in trigonometric form, we have

$$-1 + i = \sqrt{2}(\cos 135° + i \sin 135°).$$

Apply De Moivre's theorem:

$$(-1 + i)^{10} = [\sqrt{2}(\cos 135° + i \sin 135°)]^{10}$$
$$= (\sqrt{2})^{10}(\cos 10 \cdot 135° + i \sin 10 \cdot 135°)$$
$$= 32(\cos 1350° + i \sin 1350°)$$
$$= 32(\cos 270° + i \sin 270°)$$
$$= -32i.$$

82. Roots of complex numbers.

Theorem.   *The n nth roots of $r(\cos \theta + i \sin \theta)$ are given by the formula*

$$\sqrt[n]{r} \left(\cos \frac{\theta + k \cdot 360°}{n} + i \; \sin \frac{\theta + k \cdot 360°}{n} \right),$$

where $k = 0, 1, 2, \ldots, n - 1$.

Proof.   Assuming De Moivre's theorem is true when n is the reciprocal of a positive integer, we have

$$\sqrt[n]{r(\cos \theta + i \sin \theta)} = [r(\cos \theta + i \sin \theta)]^{\frac{1}{n}}$$
$$= r^{\frac{1}{n}} \left(\cos \frac{\theta}{n} + i \sin \frac{\theta}{n} \right).$$

Since $\cos \theta$ and $\sin \theta$ are periodic functions (Art. 31) with a period of 360°, we can say that $\cos \theta = \cos (\theta + k \cdot 360°)$ and $\sin \theta = \sin (\theta + k \cdot 360°)$.   Hence

$$\sqrt[n]{r(\cos \theta + i \sin \theta)} = \sqrt[n]{r} \left(\cos \frac{\theta + k \cdot 360°}{n} + i \sin \frac{\theta + k \cdot 360°}{n} \right).$$

It is easy to show that the right side of this equation takes on n distinct values when k takes on the values 0, 1, 2, $\ldots$, $n - 1$. But if k takes on a value larger than $(n - 1)$, the result is merely a duplication of one of the n roots already found.

Example.   Find the three cube roots of $-8i$.

Solution.   After plotting the number and putting it in trigonometric form, we have

$$-8i = 8(\cos 270° + i \sin 270°).$$

Apply the theorem on roots.   The three cube roots of $-8i$ are

$$\sqrt[3]{8}\left(\cos\frac{270° + k\cdot 360°}{3} + i\sin\frac{270° + k\cdot 360°}{3}\right)$$
$$=2[\cos(90° + k\cdot 120°) + i\sin(90° + k\cdot 120°)].$$

Let the three roots be r_1, r_2, r_3.   Then

$$r_1 = 2(\cos 90° + i\sin 90°) = 2i, \qquad (k = 0),$$
$$r_2 = 2(\cos 210° + i\sin 210°) = -\sqrt{3} - i, \quad (k = 1),$$
$$r_3 = 2(\cos 330° + i\sin 330°) = \sqrt{3} - i, \quad (k = 2).$$

The three roots are equally spaced on a circle with radius 2 and center at the origin (Fig. 84).   Notice that for $k = 3$, we obtain r_1 again.

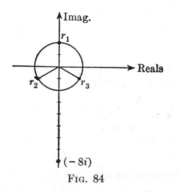

Fig. 84

EXERCISE 47

Perform the indicated multiplications and then express the results in algebraic form.

1. $4(\cos 50° + i\sin 50°) \cdot 5(\cos 70° + i\sin 70°)$.
2. $6(\cos 12° + i\sin 12°) \cdot 2(\cos 48° + i\sin 48°)$.
3. $9(\cos 350° + i\sin 350°) \cdot 7(\cos 280° + i\sin 280°)$.
4. $3(\cos 290° + i\sin 290°) \cdot 10(\cos 250° + i\sin 250°)$.

For each of the following products, (a) express the factors in trigonometric form, (b) find their product trigonometrically, (c) check your result by finding the product algebraically.

5. $2i(3 - 3i)$.
6. $-4i(-2 + 2i\sqrt{3})$.
7. $(-4\sqrt{3} - 4i)(-\sqrt{3} + 3i)$.
8. $(2 - 2i)(-6 - 6i)$.

For each of the following products, (a) express the factors in algebraic form, (b) find their product algebraically, (c) check your result by finding the product trigonometrically.

9. $(\cos 240° + i\sin 240°) \cdot 8(\cos 150° + i\sin 150°)$.
10. $3(\cos 80° + i\sin 80°) \cdot 4(\cos 190° + i\sin 190°)$.
11. $6(\cos 45° + i\sin 45°) \cdot 2(\cos 315° + i\sin 315°)$.
12. $2(\cos 150° + i\sin 150°) \cdot (\cos 330° + i\sin 330°)$.

Use De Moivre's theorem to find the value of each of the following. Express results in algebraic form.

13. $[\sqrt{3}(\cos 63° + i \sin 63°)]^{10}$.   **14.** $[2(\cos 108° + i \sin 108°)]^5$.

15. $(1 - i)^{12}$.   **16.** $(-2 + 2i)^6$.   **17.** $(\sqrt{2} + i \sqrt{2})^5$.

18. $(-1 - i)^7$.   **19.** $\left(-\dfrac{1}{2} - \dfrac{i\sqrt{3}}{2}\right)^{30}$.   **20.** $(1 + i \sqrt{3})^8$.

21. $(- \sqrt{3} + i)^3$.   **22.** $(1 - 3i)^6$.

Find all the indicated roots of the following complex numbers. Express results in algebraic form.

23. The cube roots of $125(\cos 18° + i \sin 18°)$.

24. The fourth roots of $81(\cos 40° + i \sin 40°)$.

25. The square roots of $-18i$.

26. The square roots of $8i$.

27. The square roots of $2 + 2i \sqrt{3}$.

28. The cube roots of $64i$.

29. The cube roots of 8.

30. The cube roots of $-4 \sqrt{2} + 4i \sqrt{2}$.

31. The fourth roots of $-16i$.

32. The fifth roots of $16 \sqrt{2} + 16i \sqrt{2}$.

33. The fourth roots of $-8 + 8i \sqrt{3}$.

34. The fourth roots of -256.

35. The fifth roots of 1.

Find all the roots of the following equations.

36. $x^8 - 256 = 0$. *Hint:* The roots of the equation $x^8 - 256 = 0$ are the eight eighth roots of 256.

37. $x^5 + 32 = 0$.   **38.** $x^6 = 1,000,000$.   **39.** $x^3 = -1000$.

40. Prove that

$$\frac{r_1(\cos \theta_1 + i \sin \theta_1)}{r_2(\cos \theta_2 + i \sin \theta_2)} = \frac{r_1}{r_2} [\cos (\theta_1 - \theta_2) + i \sin (\theta_1 - \theta_2)].$$

APPENDIX

83. Sketching curves by composition of y-coordinates. If the graphs of $y = f(x)$ and $y = g(x)$ are drawn to the same scale on the same set of axes, the graph of

$$y = f(x) + g(x)$$

can be sketched by the process of *composition of y-coordinates*. For any value of x, we can determine the y of the equation $y = f(x) + g(x)$ by finding graphically the *algebraic* sum of the y's of the two equations $y = f(x)$ and $y = g(x)$. After a suitable number of points have been located by "adding the heights of the given curves," we connect them with a smooth curve to get the required graph.

Example 1. Graph the equation $y = x + \sin x$.
Solution. First draw the graphs of $y = x$ and $y = \sin x$ on the same axes (x being measured in radians). Place a straightedge parallel to the y-axis at

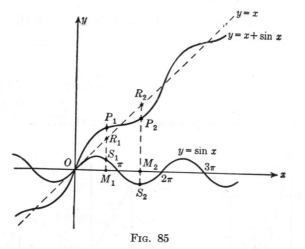

Fig. 85

M_1. Use compasses to add the segments M_1S_1 and M_1R_1. The sum is M_1P_1, thus locating P_1. To get point P_2, add the negative segment M_2S_2 to the positive segment M_2R_2; their *algebraic* sum is M_2P_2.

145

Example 2.   Graph the equation $y = \sin x + \sin 2x$.

Solution.   After graphing the equations $y = \sin x$ and $y = \sin 2x$, we use the process of composition of y-coordinates (Fig. 86).

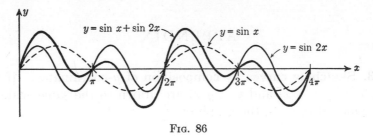

Fig. 86

EXERCISE 48

Graph the following equations in the interval from $x = 0$ to $x = 4\pi$.

1. $y = 4 \sin x$.   **2.** $y = \sin 4x$.   **3.** $y = \cos 3x$.

4. $y = \cos \frac{1}{2}x$.   **5.** $y = 1 + \cos x$.   **6.** $y = \dfrac{x}{2} + \sin x$.

7. $y = x - \sin x$.   **8.** $y = x^2 + \sin x$.   **9.** $y = \sin x + \frac{1}{2} \sin 2x$.

10. $y = 4 \sin x + 3 \cos x$.   *Hint:* Compare Prob. 10 with Prob. 35, page 70.

11. $y = \sin^4 x$.   **12.** $y = \cos^2 x$.

84. The extension of the addition formulas to general angles. We shall outline a proof of the formulas

(1) $\sin (A + B) = \sin A \cos B + \cos A \sin B,$

(2) $\cos (A + B) = \cos A \cos B - \sin A \sin B,$

where A and B are any angles.

(I) If A, B, and $(A + B)$ are acute, the formulas hold (Art. 37).

(II) If A and B are acute, and $(A + B)$ is obtuse (Fig. 87); the proof follows, step by step, exactly as in Art. 37.

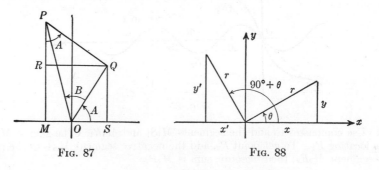

Fig. 87   Fig. 88

(III) If $A = 90° +$ an acute angle, and if B is acute, the formulas hold.

Proof. From Fig. 88, we see that $\dfrac{y'}{r} = \dfrac{x}{r}$ and $\dfrac{x'}{r} = -\dfrac{y}{r}$.

Hence

$$\sin (90° + \theta) = \cos \theta,$$
$$\cos (90° + \theta) = - \sin \theta.$$

Let A_1 and B_1 be acute angles and let $A_2 = 90° + A_1$. Then

$$\sin (A_2 + B_1)$$
$$= \sin (90° + A_1 + B_1)$$
$$= \cos (A_1 + B_1)$$
$$= \cos A_1 \cos B_1 - \sin A_1 \sin B_1$$
$$= \cos (A_2 - 90°) \cos B_1 - \sin (A_2 - 90°) \sin B_1$$
$$= \cos (90° - A_2) \cos B_1 - [- \sin (90° - A_2) \sin B_1]$$
$$= \sin A_2 \cos B_1 + \cos A_2 \sin B_1.$$

Similarly,

$$\cos (A_2 + B_1) = \cos A_2 \cos B_1 - \sin A_2 \sin B_1.$$

Hence we have proved that formulas (1) and (2) are true when A is an angle between 90° and 180°, and B is acute.

Notice that formulas (1) and (2) are symmetric in A and B (if A and B are interchanged, the formulas are unaltered). Consequently, any result proved for A must apply to B. Therefore (1) and (2) hold when one angle is acute and the other is between 90° and 180°.

(IV) If A is 0° or 90° and B is acute, or 0° or 90°, the formulas hold. This can be established by direct substitution for the various cases.

(V) If A and B are any two positive angles, the formulas hold. By repeated additions of 90°, any positive angle may be obtained from an angle between 0° and 90° inclusive. The method exemplified in (III) can be applied repeatedly to establish the formulas for all positive angles.

(VI) If A and B are any two angles, positive or negative, the formulas hold. This follows immediately if we recall that any negative angle can be considered as coterminal with some positive angle.

85. Exponential equations. An exponential equation is an equation in which the unknown appears in an exponent. Such an equation can usually be solved by equating the logarithms of the two sides and then finding the roots of the resulting algebraic equation.

Example. Solve for x: $(9.55)^x = .0345$.
Solution. Take the logarithm of each side:

$$\log (9.55)^x = \log .0345$$
$$x \log 9.55 = \log .0345$$
$$x = \frac{\log .0345}{\log 9.55}$$
$$x = \frac{8.53782 - 10}{0.98000}$$
$$x = \frac{-1.46218}{.98} = -1.49.$$

In this case it is easier to perform the division without logs. Had logs been used, we should first have computed the value of the fraction $\dfrac{1.46218}{.98}$ and then attached a minus sign to the result.

86. Change of base of logarithms. In making numerical computations, the most convenient system of logarithms is the *common*, or *Briggs*, system, which employs the base 10. If we know the logarithm of a number to the base a, we can find the logarithm of that number to the base b by using

(1) $$\log_b N = \frac{\log_a N}{\log_a b} = (\log_b a)(\log_a N).$$

To prove this, let $\log_b N = y$. Then
$$N = b^y.$$

Take the logarithm of each side to the base a:

$$\log_a N = \log_a b^y.$$
$$= y \log_a b.$$
$$\log_a N = \log_b N \log_a b.$$

Hence $$\log_b N = \frac{\log_a N}{\log_a b}.$$

If $N = a$,
$$\log_b a = \frac{1}{\log_a b}.$$

Therefore $\log_b N = (\log_b a)(\log_a N).$

In calculus and higher mathematics, the most suitable system of logarithms is the *natural*, or *Napierian*, system which employs the base e, where e is approximately 2.71828. If $a = 10$ and $b = e$, equation (1) becomes

$$\log_e N = \frac{\log_{10} N}{0.43429} = 2.3026 \log_{10} N.$$

Thus the natural logarithm of a number can be obtained by multiplying its common logarithm by 2.3026.

EXERCISE 49

Solve the following equations.

1. $(6.310)^x = 0.7268.$
2. $(25.12)^x = 0.03946.$
3. $(0.9120)^x = 34.55.$
4. $(0.07741)^x = 0.6352.$
5. $(0.1574)^x = 0.02560.$
6. $(0.07925)^x = 108.3.$
7. $(39.82)^x = 1600.$
8. $(8091)^x = 20.00.$
9. $(6.000)^{2x-1} = (50.00)^{x+3}.$
10. $(3.000)^x(1.024)^{x+1} = 100.0.$

Find the natural logarithm of each of the following numbers.

11. 0.1363.   12. 2981.   13. 20.09.   14. 0.0302.

Evaluate the following logarithms.

15. $\log_2 260.0.$ 16. $\log_5 1000.$

87. The mil as a unit of angular measure. Certain branches of the United States Army employ the mil system for measuring angles. The unit in this sytem is the **mil,** which is defined as $\frac{1}{1600}$ of a right angle.

The mil is a convenient unit for certain kinds of rapid calculation. The reason lies in the fact that one mil subtends an arc equal to approximately $\frac{1}{1000}$ of the radius. If the angle is small, the arc and chord are almost equal and we have the approximation

[1] $c = \frac{r\theta}{1000}$ (θ *in* mils),

where the chord c and the radius r are measured in the same units.

The following relationships exist among the three units of angular measure.

$$90° = 1600 \text{ mils,}$$

$$
\begin{array}{ll}
1° = 17.778 \text{ mils,} & 1 \text{ mil} = 0.056250°, \\
1' = 0.29630 \text{ mil,} & 1 \text{ mil} = 3.3750', \\
1 \text{ radian} = 1018.6 \text{ mils,} & 1 \text{ mil} = 0.00098175 \text{ radian.}
\end{array}
$$

Example 1. An automobile of standard width (5.5 ft.) is facing an observer. How far away is the auto if it subtends a horizontal angle of 5 mils?

Solution. Using $c = \dfrac{r\theta}{1000}$, we have $5.5 = \dfrac{r \cdot 5}{1000}$. Hence $r = 1100$ ft.

Example 2. A circular pill box 300 yd. from an observer subtends a horizontal angle of 16 mils. Find the diameter of the pill box.

Solution. Using $c = \dfrac{r\theta}{1000}$, we get $c = \dfrac{300 \cdot 16}{1000} = 4.8$ yd.

EXERCISE 50

Express in degrees and minutes.
1. 40 mils.   **2.** 25 mils.   **3.** 10.2 mils.   **4.** 55 mils.

Express in mils.
5. 4°.   **6.** 3° 30'.   **7.** 2° 20'.   **8.** 6°.

Express in radians.
9. 200 mils.   **10.** 160 mils.   **11.** 110 mils.   **12.** 300 mils.

Express in mils.
13. 0.07 radian.   **14.** 0.13 radian.   **15.** 0.21 radian.   **16.** 0.067 radian.

Use formula [1] *to obtain approximate solutions of the following problems.*

17. At a distance of 12,040 ft., the San Francisco City Hall subtends an angle of 25 mils. How high is the building?

18. The dirigible Hindenburg was 804 ft. long. How high would it be when directly overhead and subtending an angle of 201 mils at the surface of the earth?

19. Find in mils the angle subtended at a distance of 60 ft. by a regulation baseball having a diameter of 2.90 in.

20. Find the height of the Transit Tower in San Antonio, Tex., if it subtends an angle of 40 mils at a distance of 13,625 ft.

21. A water tower known to be 100 ft. high subtends an angle of 50 mils at the eye of an observer on level ground. How far is the tower from the observer?

22. Find in mils the angle subtended by a circular target 4 ft. in diameter at a distance of 50 ft.

23. How high is a hill if it subtends an angle of 140 mils at a distance of 1500 ft.?

24. A space traveler observes that the angle subtended by the earth is 100 mils. If the diameter of the earth is 7927 miles, how far is the traveler from our planet?

ANSWERS TO PROBLEMS *

Ex. 1, Page 3

1. 5, 8, $\sqrt{53}$, 4.   **2.** 17, 3, $\sqrt{5}$, 3.   **3.** 13, 6, $\sqrt{13}$, 4.
5. -8, $\sqrt{17}$, -4.   **6.** -4, 3, -2.   **7.** -24, $-2\sqrt{6}$, 0.
9. (b) I and IV.   **10.** (c) II and IV.   **11.** 0, 0.

Ex. 2, Pages 4–5

1. $45°$, $-315°$.   **2.** $620°$, $-100°$.   **3.** $460°$, $-260°$.   **5.** $560°$, $-160°$.
6. $510°$, $-210°$.   **7.** $660°$, $-60°$.   **9.** $121°$.   **10.** $315°$.
11. $39°$.   **13.** $346°$.   **14.** $82°$.   **15.** $236°$.
17. $7200°$.

Ex. 3, Page 10

1. .34, .94, .36.   **2.** .98, $-.17$, -5.7.   **3.** $-.34$, $-.94$, .36.
5. .64, $-.77$, $-.84$.   **6.** $-.77$, $-.64$, 1.2.   **7.** $-.77$, .64, -1.2.
9. $-.94$, $-.34$, 2.7.   **10.** $-.17$, .98, $-.18$.   **11.** .98, .17, 5.7.

13. 0, .17, .34, .50, .64, .77, .87, .94, .98, 1.
14. 1, .98, .94, .87, .77, .64, .50, .34, .17, 0.
15. 0, 1, 0, *does not exist*, 1, *does not exist*.
17. -1, 0, *does not exist*, 0, *does not exist*, -1.
18. 0, -1, 0, *does not exist*, -1, *does not exist*.

19. $-\dfrac{3}{5}$, $-\dfrac{4}{5}$, $\dfrac{3}{4}$, $\dfrac{4}{3}$, $-\dfrac{5}{4}$, $-\dfrac{5}{3}$.

21. $-\dfrac{12}{13}$, $\dfrac{5}{13}$, $-\dfrac{12}{5}$, $-\dfrac{5}{12}$, $\dfrac{13}{5}$, $-\dfrac{13}{12}$.

22. $\dfrac{7}{25}$, $\dfrac{24}{25}$, $\dfrac{7}{24}$, $\dfrac{24}{7}$, $\dfrac{25}{24}$, $\dfrac{25}{7}$.

23. $-\dfrac{\sqrt{5}}{5}$, $\dfrac{2\sqrt{5}}{5}$, $-\dfrac{1}{2}$, -2, $\dfrac{\sqrt{5}}{2}$, $-\sqrt{5}$.

25. $-\dfrac{5\sqrt{29}}{29}$, $-\dfrac{2\sqrt{29}}{29}$, $\dfrac{5}{2}$, $\dfrac{2}{5}$, $-\dfrac{\sqrt{29}}{2}$, $-\dfrac{\sqrt{29}}{5}$.

26. $\dfrac{4\sqrt{41}}{41}$, $-\dfrac{5\sqrt{41}}{41}$, $-\dfrac{4}{5}$, $-\dfrac{5}{4}$, $-\dfrac{\sqrt{41}}{5}$, $\dfrac{\sqrt{41}}{4}$.

27. $\dfrac{2\sqrt{2}}{3}$, $\dfrac{1}{3}$, $2\sqrt{2}$, $\dfrac{\sqrt{2}}{4}$, 3, $\dfrac{3\sqrt{2}}{4}$.

29. $\dfrac{\sqrt{7}}{3}$, $-\dfrac{\sqrt{2}}{3}$, $-\dfrac{\sqrt{14}}{2}$, $-\dfrac{\sqrt{14}}{7}$, $-\dfrac{3\sqrt{2}}{2}$, $\dfrac{3\sqrt{7}}{7}$.

30. $-\dfrac{\sqrt{3}}{4}$, $-\dfrac{\sqrt{13}}{4}$, $\dfrac{\sqrt{39}}{13}$, $\dfrac{\sqrt{39}}{3}$, $\dfrac{4\sqrt{13}}{13}$, $-\dfrac{4\sqrt{3}}{3}$.

* Answers are given to all problems except those whose numbers are multiples of four.

31. III.   **33.** II.   **34.** III.   **35.** IV.
37. III.   **38.** II.   **39.** Possible.   **41.** Possible.
42. Possible.   **43.** Impossible.   **45.** Impossible.   **46.** Impossible.
47. Close to 0°.   **49.** Close to 0°.   **50.** Close to 90°.   **51.** Close to 90°.

Ex. 4, Pages 11–12

1. $\cos \theta = \dfrac{\sqrt{5}}{3}$, $\tan \theta = \dfrac{2\sqrt{5}}{5}$, $\cot \theta = \dfrac{\sqrt{5}}{2}$, $\sec \theta = \dfrac{3\sqrt{5}}{5}$, $\csc \theta = \dfrac{3}{2}$.

2. $\sin \theta = \dfrac{\sqrt{13}}{7}$, $\tan \theta = -\dfrac{\sqrt{13}}{6}$, $\cot \theta = -\dfrac{6\sqrt{13}}{13}$, $\sec \theta = -\dfrac{7}{6}$,

$\csc \theta = \dfrac{7\sqrt{13}}{13}$.

3. $\sin \theta = -\dfrac{\sqrt{17}}{17}$, $\cos \theta = \dfrac{4\sqrt{17}}{17}$, $\cot \theta = -4$, $\sec \theta = \dfrac{\sqrt{17}}{4}$, $\csc \theta = -\sqrt{17}$.

5. $\sin \theta = -\dfrac{7}{25}$, $\tan \theta = -\dfrac{7}{24}$, $\cot \theta = -\dfrac{24}{7}$, $\sec \theta = \dfrac{25}{24}$, $\csc \theta = -\dfrac{25}{7}$.

6. $\sin \theta = \dfrac{12}{13}$, $\cos \theta = \dfrac{5}{13}$, $\cot \theta = \dfrac{5}{12}$, $\sec \theta = \dfrac{13}{5}$, $\csc \theta = \dfrac{13}{12}$.

7. $\cos \theta = -\dfrac{8}{17}$, $\tan \theta = -\dfrac{15}{8}$, $\cot \theta = -\dfrac{8}{15}$, $\sec \theta = -\dfrac{17}{8}$, $\csc \theta = \dfrac{17}{15}$.

9. $\sin \theta = -\dfrac{3\sqrt{34}}{34}$, $\cos \theta = -\dfrac{5\sqrt{34}}{34}$, $\cot \theta = \dfrac{5}{3}$, $\sec \theta = -\dfrac{\sqrt{34}}{5}$,

$\csc \theta = -\dfrac{\sqrt{34}}{3}$.

10. $\cos \theta = \dfrac{1}{3}$, $\tan \theta = -2\sqrt{2}$, $\cot \theta = -\dfrac{\sqrt{2}}{4}$, $\sec \theta = 3$, $\csc \theta = -\dfrac{3\sqrt{2}}{4}$.

11. $\sin \theta = -\dfrac{3}{4}$, $\tan \theta = \dfrac{3\sqrt{7}}{7}$, $\cot \theta = \dfrac{\sqrt{7}}{3}$, $\sec \theta = -\dfrac{4\sqrt{7}}{7}$, $\csc \theta = -\dfrac{4}{3}$.

13. $\sin \theta = \dfrac{2\sqrt{2}}{3}$, $\cos \theta = -\dfrac{1}{3}$, $\tan \theta = -2\sqrt{2}$, $\cot \theta = -\dfrac{\sqrt{2}}{4}$, $\csc \theta = \dfrac{3\sqrt{2}}{4}$.

14. $\sin \theta = -\dfrac{\sqrt{5}}{3}$, $\cos \theta = -\dfrac{2}{3}$, $\tan \theta = \dfrac{\sqrt{5}}{2}$, $\sec \theta = -\dfrac{3}{2}$, $\csc \theta = -\dfrac{3\sqrt{5}}{5}$.

15. $\sin \theta = \dfrac{1}{a}$, $\cos \theta = \dfrac{\sqrt{a^2-1}}{a}$, $\tan \theta = \dfrac{\sqrt{a^2-1}}{a^2-1}$, $\cot \theta = \sqrt{a^2-1}$,

$\sec \theta = \dfrac{a\sqrt{a^2-1}}{a^2-1}$.

Ex. 6, Page 16

1. $\dfrac{3}{4}$.   **2.** $\dfrac{9}{32}$.   **3.** $2\sqrt{3}$.   **5.** 5.

6. $2\sqrt{6}$.   **7.** $\sqrt{2}$.   **9.** False.   **10.** True.
11. True.   **13.** True.   **14.** False.   **15.** True.

Ex. 7, Page 18

1. .4383. **2.** 5.396. **3.** .2221. **5.** .6536.
6. 1.036. **7.** .6756. **9.** .9971. **10.** .5783.
11. 5.671. **13.** 73° 0′. **14.** 51° 40′. **15.** 22° 20′.
17. 38° 30′. **18.** 43° 50′. **19.** 88° 10′. **21.** 67° 30′.
22. 78° 10′. **23.** 44° 20′.

Ex. 8, Page 20

1. .5195. **2.** .8787. **3.** .3775. **5.** .5042.
6. .9532. **7.** .7432. **9.** 1.097. **10.** .1254.
11. .7927. **13.** 2.204. **14.** .6437. **15.** .0518.
17. 61° 14′. **18.** 48° 24′. **19.** 39° 1′. **21.** 16° 32′.
22. 20° 8′. **23.** 52° 48′. **25.** 68° 6′. **26.** 75° 13′.
27. 4° 27′. **29.** 30° 40′. **30.** 41° 57′. **31.** 59° 33′.

Ex. 9, Page 22

1. (a) .7835, (b) .783, (c) .78. **2.** (a) .08176, (b) .0818, (c) .082.
3. (a) 19.28, (b) 19.3, (c) 19. **5.** (a) 18° 44′, (b) 18° 40′, (c) 19°.
6. (a) 42° 35′, (b) 42° 30′, (c) 43°. **7.** (a) 7° 28′, (b) 7° 30′, (c) 7°.
9. 4.275 to 4.285, inclusive. **10.** 91.25 to 91.35, exclusive.
11. 69.05 to 69.15, exclusive. **13.** 82.345 to 82.355, exclusive.
14. 1.8755 to 1.8765, inclusive. **15.** 3.0795 to 3.0805, inclusive.

Ex. 10, Page 24

1. $B = 23° 30′, a = 642, b = 279$. **2.** $A = 46° 20′, a = 43.4, b = 41.4$.
3. $B = 70° 0′, b = 4.70, c = 5.00$. **5.** $A = 42° 50′, B = 47° 10′, a = 0.408$.
6. $A = 57° 30′, B = 32° 30′, c = 372$. **7.** $A = 27° 50′, B = 62° 10′, c = 283$.
9. $A = 64°, B = 26°, c = 46$. **10.** $A = 27°, B = 63°, a = 25$.
11. $A = 70° 36′, B = 19° 24′, b = 1363$ (or 1364, depending upon the method used).
13. $A = 78° 32′, b = 1423, c = 7157$. **14.** $B = 34° 45′, a = 6097, c = 7418$.
15. $A = 9°, a = 14, b = 89$. **17.** $B = 24° 30′, b = 338, c = 815$.
18. $A = 22° 20′, B = 67° 40′, b = 740$. **19.** $B = 51° 20′, a = 444, c = 711$.

Ex. 11, Pages 26–28

1. N 49° W; S 49° E. **2.** 270 miles; 110 miles. **3.** 150 miles; 180 miles.
5. 469 ft. **6.** 464 ft. **7.** 308 ft.
9. Only 78 ft., but to him it may seem like worlds.
10. 625 ft. **11.** 9:17 A.M. **14.** S 78° E.
15. 1:48 P.M. **17.** 6.282; 6.283. **18.** 9.2 miles.
19. 6° 50′. **21.** N 16° 10′ W. **22.** 35° 16′.
23. 39.0 in.; 20.9 in. **25.** 69 miles; 74 miles. **26.** 690 ft.

Ex. 12, Page 32

1. tan 200°. **2.** tan B. **3.** $\csc \dfrac{B}{2}$. **5.** cot 25°.

6. cos 130°. **7.** sin 40°. **9.** tan 170°. **10.** sin 400°.
11. False. **13.** False. **14.** False. **15.** False.

17. True.   **18.** True.   **19.** True.   **21.** True.
22. True.   **23.** True.   **25.** False.   **26.** False.
27. False.   **29.** False.   **30.** True.   **31.** True.

Ex. 13, Pages 34–35

1. $\sec^2 \theta + \sec \theta \tan \theta + \tan^2 \theta$.   **2.** 1.

3. $\dfrac{\tan^2 \theta}{6}$.   **5.** 1.   **6.** 3.   **7.** $\sin \theta$.

9. $\sin \theta = \pm \sqrt{1 - \cos^2 \theta}$, $\tan \theta = \pm \dfrac{\sqrt{1 - \cos^2 \theta}}{\cos \theta}$,

$\cot \theta = \pm \dfrac{\cos \theta}{\sqrt{1 - \cos^2 \theta}}$, $\sec \theta = \dfrac{1}{\cos \theta}$, $\csc \theta = \dfrac{\pm 1}{\sqrt{1 - \cos^2 \theta}}$.

10. $\sin \theta = \pm \dfrac{\tan \theta}{\sqrt{1 + \tan^2 \theta}}$, $\cos \theta = \pm \dfrac{1}{\sqrt{1 + \tan^2 \theta}}$, $\cot \theta = \dfrac{1}{\tan \theta}$,

$\sec \theta = \pm \sqrt{1 + \tan^2 \theta}$, $\csc \theta = \pm \dfrac{\sqrt{1 + \tan^2 \theta}}{\tan \theta}$.

11. $\cos 111° = - \sqrt{1 - \sin^2 111°}$.   **13.** $\cot 234° = \sqrt{\csc^2 234° - 1}$.

14. $\tan 25° = \sqrt{\sec^2 25° - 1}$.   **15.** $\sec 4\theta = \pm \sqrt{1 + \tan^2 4\theta}$.

Ex. 15, Page 42

1. 70°.   **2.** 83°.   **3.** 40°.
5. 74°.   **6.** 88° 45′.   **7.** 53° 10′.
9. 75°.   **10.** 20°.   **11.** 5°.

Ex. 16, Page 44

1. $\sin 225° = - \dfrac{\sqrt{2}}{2}$, $\cos 225° = - \dfrac{\sqrt{2}}{2}$.

2. $\sin 315° = - \dfrac{\sqrt{2}}{2}$, $\cos 315° = \dfrac{\sqrt{2}}{2}$.

3. $\sin 135° = \dfrac{\sqrt{2}}{2}$, $\cos 135° = - \dfrac{\sqrt{2}}{2}$.

5. $\sin 330° = - \dfrac{1}{2}$, $\cos 330° = \dfrac{\sqrt{3}}{2}$.

6. $\sin 150° = \dfrac{1}{2}$, $\cos 150° = - \dfrac{\sqrt{3}}{2}$.

7. $\sin 240° = - \dfrac{\sqrt{3}}{2}$, $\cos 240° = - \dfrac{1}{2}$.

9. $\sin 1200° = \dfrac{\sqrt{3}}{2}$, $\cos 1200° = - \dfrac{1}{2}$.

10. $\sin 600° = - \dfrac{\sqrt{3}}{2}$, $\cos 600° = - \dfrac{1}{2}$.

11. $\sin 1050° = - \dfrac{1}{2}$, $\cos 1050° = \dfrac{\sqrt{3}}{2}$.

13. −.9004. **14.** −.9744. **15.** −.3249. **17.** −.2756.
18. −.9744. **19.** .7046. **21.** .9853. **22.** .8268.
23. .9906. **25.** False. **26.** False. **27.** False.
29. True. **30.** True. **31.** True.
33. 72°, 108°, 288°. **34.** 15°, 165°, 195°. **35.** 154°, 206°, 334°.

Ex. 17, Page 46

1. $\sin(-45°) = -\dfrac{\sqrt{2}}{2}$, $\cos(-45°) = \dfrac{\sqrt{2}}{2}$, $\tan(-45°) = -1$.

2. $\sin(-30°) = -\dfrac{1}{2}$, $\cos(-30°) = \dfrac{\sqrt{3}}{2}$, $\tan(-30°) = -\dfrac{\sqrt{3}}{3}$.

3. $\sin(-60°) = -\dfrac{\sqrt{3}}{2}$, $\cos(-60°) = \dfrac{1}{2}$, $\tan(-60°) = -\sqrt{3}$.

5. False. **6.** True. **7.** True. **9.** False.
10. True. **11.** False. **13.** True. **14.** False.

Ex. 18, Pages 49–50

1. 36°. **2.** 54°. **3.** 150°. **5.** 315°.
6. 300°. **7.** 63°. **9.** −110°. **10.** 210°.

11. 1000°. **13.** $\dfrac{1080°}{\pi} \rightarrow 343°\,46'$. **14.** $\dfrac{558°}{\pi} \rightarrow 177°\,37'$.

15. $\dfrac{270°}{\pi} \rightarrow 85°\,57'$. **17.** $\dfrac{\pi}{3}$. **18.** $\dfrac{\pi}{4}$.

19. $\dfrac{3\pi}{4}$. **21.** $\dfrac{3\pi}{2}$. **22.** $\dfrac{11\pi}{6}$. **23.** $\dfrac{4\pi}{3}$.

25. $\dfrac{\pi}{8}$. **26.** $\dfrac{2\pi}{9}$. **27.** $\dfrac{3\pi}{5}$. **29.** $\dfrac{17\pi}{6}$.

30. $\dfrac{13\pi}{18}$. **31.** 5π. **33.** 0.6036. **34.** 1.0806.

35. 1.4561. **37.** $-\dfrac{\sqrt{3}}{2}$. **38.** $-\dfrac{\sqrt{2}}{2}$. **39.** $\dfrac{\sqrt{2}}{2}$.

41. 1. **42.** $\dfrac{1}{2}$. **43.** $-\dfrac{1}{2}$. **45.** −2.

46. *Does not exist.* **47.** 0. **49.** $\dfrac{\sqrt{3}}{3}$. **50.** $-\dfrac{\sqrt{3}}{2}$.

51. $-\dfrac{\sqrt{2}}{2}$. **53.** .8418. **54.** .8241. **55.** .1524.

57. $\dfrac{2\pi}{3}$; $\dfrac{3\pi}{4}$. **58.** $\dfrac{5\pi}{9}$. **59.** $\dfrac{5\pi}{3}$; 16π.

Ex. 19, Pages 51–52

1. 251 ft. **2.** $\dfrac{1}{5}$ radian; 11° 30′. **3.** 200 ft.

5. 86° 0′. **6.** 600 ft. **7.** 2000 miles; 4300 miles. **9.** 1400 miles.
10. 60° N. **11.** 42° N. **13.** 370 ft. **14.** 42 ft.

15. Angle subtended by moon is 31′; angle subtended by sun is 32′.

17. 26.5 in. **18.** 251 in. **19.** 4.92.

Ex. 20, Pages 53–54

1. 21π mph $\to$ 66.0 mph. **2.** 2.00 ft.

3. $\dfrac{50}{\pi}$ rpm $\to$ 15.9 rpm; $\dfrac{200}{3\pi}$ rpm $\to$ 21.2 rpm.

5. $\dfrac{2000}{\pi}$ rpm $\to$ 637 rpm. **6.** 5π mph $\to$ 15.7 mph.

7. $\dfrac{20}{\pi}$ in. $\to$ 6.37 in.

Ex. 21, Pages 61–62

11. 45°, 315°. **13.** 150°, 210°. **14.** 120°, 240°. **15.** 210°, 330°.
17. 30°, 150°. **18.** 45°, 135°. **19.** 60°, 120°. **21.** 135°, 315°.

22. 150°, 330°. **23.** 0, π. **25.** $\dfrac{4\pi}{3}, \dfrac{5\pi}{3}$. **26.** $\dfrac{3\pi}{2}$.

27. π. **29.** $\dfrac{\pi}{2}, \dfrac{3\pi}{2}$. **30.** No solution. **31.** 143°, 217°.

33. 190°, 350°. **34.** 76°, 284°. **35.** 84°, 264°. **37.** 55°, 235°.
38. 178°, 358°. **39.** 1; π. **41.** 1; 2π.

Ex. 22, Pages 66–67

1. $\sin 195° = \dfrac{-\sqrt{6}+\sqrt{2}}{4} \to -.259.$

2. $\cos 255° = \dfrac{-\sqrt{6}+\sqrt{2}}{4} \to -.259.$

3. $\cos 285° = \dfrac{\sqrt{6}-\sqrt{2}}{4} \to .259.$

6. -1. **7.** $\sin \theta$. **9.** 1.

17. $\cos 82° = \cos 50° \cos 32° - \sin 50° \sin 32°.$
18. $\sin 33° = \sin 11° \cos 22° + \cos 11° \sin 22°.$

21. $\dfrac{\sqrt{5}+4\sqrt{2}}{9} \to .8770.$

22. $\dfrac{117}{125}$. **23.** (a) $-\dfrac{156}{205}$, (b) $\dfrac{133}{205}$, (c) Q IV.

Ex. 23, Pages 68–70

1. $\dfrac{\sqrt{3}+1}{\sqrt{3}-1} = 2+\sqrt{3} \to 3.732.$ **2.** $\dfrac{1-\sqrt{3}}{1+\sqrt{3}} = -2+\sqrt{3} \to -0.268.$

3. $\dfrac{\sqrt{2}-\sqrt{6}}{4} \to -0.259.$ **5.** $\cos 7\theta$.

6. $\dfrac{1}{2}$. **7.** $\sqrt{3}$.

13. (a) $-\dfrac{77}{85}$, (b) $\dfrac{36}{85}$, (c) $\dfrac{13}{84}$, (d) $-\dfrac{77}{36}$.

14. (a) $\dfrac{204}{325}$, (b) $-\dfrac{253}{325}$, (c) $-\dfrac{36}{323}$, (d) $-\dfrac{204}{253}$.

17. False.   **18.** True.   **19.** False.

21. $\tan 40° = \dfrac{\tan 50° - \tan 10°}{1 + \tan 50° \tan 10°}$.   **22.** $\tan 85° = \dfrac{\tan 20° + \tan 65°}{1 - \tan 20° \tan 65°}$.

23. $\sin 11° = \sin 77° \cos 66° - \cos 77° \sin 66°$.

37. $\sqrt{2} \sin (\theta + 45°)$.   **38.** $13 \sin (\theta - 67° 23')$.

Ex. 24, Pages 73–75

3. $\sin 22\frac{1}{2}° = \frac{1}{2} \sqrt{2 - \sqrt{2}}$, $\cos 22\frac{1}{2}° = \frac{1}{2} \sqrt{2 + \sqrt{2}}$.

5. $\cos 12\theta$.   **6.** $5 \cos 32°$.   **7.** $\sin \dfrac{2\theta}{3}$.

9. $\pm \sin 5\theta$.   **10.** $\cos 115°$.   **11.** $\cos^2 7B$.

13. $\sin 2A = \dfrac{120}{169}$, $\sin \dfrac{A}{2} = \sqrt{\dfrac{4}{13}} = \dfrac{2\sqrt{13}}{13}$.

14. $\cos 2B = -\dfrac{17}{18}$, $\cos \dfrac{B}{2} = \sqrt{\dfrac{5}{12}} = \dfrac{\sqrt{15}}{6}$.

15. $\cos 20A = -\dfrac{7}{32}$, $\cos 5A = -\dfrac{\sqrt{13}}{4}$.

17. $\cos 140° = -\sqrt{\dfrac{1 + \cos 280°}{2}}$.   **18.** $\sin 10° = \sqrt{\dfrac{1 - \cos 20°}{2}}$.

19. $\sin 200° = 2 \sin 100° \cos 100°$.   **21.** $\cos 8\theta = 1 - 2 \sin^2 4\theta$.

22. $\sin 7\theta = 2 \sin \dfrac{7\theta}{2} \cos \dfrac{7\theta}{2}$.   **23.** $\sin^2 2\theta = \dfrac{1 - \cos 4\theta}{2}$.

25. True.   **26.** True.   **27.** True.
29. True.   **30.** True.   **31.** True.
33. False.   **34.** True.   **35.** False.

Ex. 25, Page 77

1. $\cos 2\theta - \cos 8\theta$.   **2.** $5 \sin 7\theta + 5 \sin 5\theta$.

3. $\dfrac{1}{2} \cos 90° + \dfrac{1}{2} \cos 60° = \dfrac{1}{4}$.   **5.** $2 \sin 45° + 2 \sin 30° = \sqrt{2} + 1$.

6. $3 \cos 7\theta + 3 \cos 3\theta$.   **7.** $-2 \sin \dfrac{3\theta}{2} \sin \dfrac{\theta}{2}$.

9. $\sqrt{3} \cos (A + 30°)$.   **10.** $\cos 6°$.

Ex. 26, Pages 81–82

1. $50°, 110°$.   **2.** $155°, 215°$.   **3.** $60°, 120°, 240°, 300°$.
5. $60°, 120°, 240°, 300°$.   **6.** $90°, 270°$.   **7.** $30°, 225°, 315°, 330°$.

9. $0°, 90°, 180°, 270°$.   **10.** $30°, 90°, 150°, 210°, 270°, 330°$.

11. 90°, 180°, 210°, 330°.   **13.** 45°, 135°.   **14.** 0°, 180°, 240°, 300°.

15. 45°, 90°, 135°, 225°, 270°, 315°.   **17.** 0°, 45°, 180°, 225°.

18. 210°, 330°.   **19.** 30°, 150°.   **21.** 60°, 300°.   **22.** 120°, 300°.

23. 0°, 120°, 240°.   **25.** 0°, 120°, 180°, 240°.   **26.** 0°, 30°, 150°, 180°.

27. 0°, 20°, 60°, 100°, 120°, 140°, 180°, 220°, 240°, 260°, 300°, 340°.

29. 30°, 150°, 210°, 330°.   **30.** 120°, 180°, 240°.

31. 90°.   **33.** 330°.   **34.** 0°, 240°.

35. 45°, 75° 58′, 225°, 255° 58′.   **37.** 105° 3′, 254° 57′.

38. 189° 20′, 350° 40′.   **39.** 131° 36′, 334° 40′.   **41.** 5° 43′, 185° 43′.

42. 90°, 106° 16′.   **43.** No solution.   **45.** 315°.

46. 240°, 300°.   **47.** 120°, 240°.   **49.** No solution

50. No solution.   **51.** 15°, 105°, 195°, 285°.

53. 30°, 90°, 150°, 210°, 270°, 330°.   **54.** 0°, 90°, 120°, 180°, 240°, 270°.

55. 45°, 135°, 225°, 315°.   **57.** 60°, 300°.

58. 30°, 150°, 210°, 330°.   **59.** 10°, 70°, 100°, 190°, 250°, 280°.

Ex. 27, Pages 84–85

1. 2.   **2.** −1.   **3.** 1.   **5.** 0.

6. $\dfrac{1}{2}$.   **7.** −1.   **9.** $\dfrac{2}{3}$.   **10.** $-\dfrac{1}{3}$.

11. $-\dfrac{1}{2}$.   **13.** −6.   **14.** 6.   **15.** $\dfrac{5}{4}$.

17. $\dfrac{1}{27}$.   **18.** 64.   **19.** 3.   **21.** $\dfrac{1}{5}$.

22. −2.   **23.** 1.   **25.** 8.   **26.** 2.

27. 10.   **29.** $\log_{12} \dfrac{1}{12} = -1$.   **30.** $\log_{10} \dfrac{1}{100{,}000} = -5$.

31. $\log_{125} 625 = \dfrac{4}{3}$.   **33.** $b^c = a$.   **34.** $6^0 = 1$.

35. $2^{-10} = \dfrac{1}{1024}$.   **37.** True.   **38.** True.   **39.** True.

Ex. 28, Pages 86–87

1. 1.15.   **2.** 0.18.   **3.** −0.55.   **5.** 0.12.

6. 0.42.   **7.** 2.40.   **9.** 0.42.   **10.** 2.40.

11. 0.05.   **13.** 4.85.   **14.** −0.51.   **15.** 2.33.

17. $\log (5x - x^2)$.   **18.** $\log \dfrac{x}{yz}$.   **19.** $\log P(1 + i)^n$.

21. $\log \dfrac{ac^7}{\sqrt[5]{b}}$.   **22.** $\log s^8 \sqrt[6]{r}$.   **23.** $\log \dfrac{\sqrt[3]{\pi}}{2}$.

25. True.   **26.** True.   **27.** True.

29. False.   **30.** False.   **31.** False.

33. True.   **34.** False.   **35.** True.

Ex. 29, Pages 90–91

1. 4.55775.   **2.** 8.55775 − 10.   **3.** 7.89081 − 10.   **5.** 9.89081 − 10.
6. 3.89081.   **7.** 1.55775.   **9.** 5.89081 − 10.   **10.** 6.55775.
11. 7.89081.   **13.** 0.6428.   **14.** 6.428.   **15.** 33,330.
17. 333,300.   **18.** 0.03333.   **19.** 0.006428.   **21.** 0.000 003333.
22. 642.8.   **23.** 0.000 000 000 003333.
25. 0.0006428.   **26.** 0.003333.   **27.** 0.06428.

Ex. 30, Page 92

1. 0.75921.   **2.** 1.63225.   **3.** 3.92681.   **5.** 7.59051 − 10.
6. 6.79007 − 10.   **7.** 9.42062 − 10.   **9.** 5.86688.   **10.** 2.96759.
11. 5.83385 − 10.   **13.** 2977.   **14.** 0.1163.   **15.** 1.258.
17. 0.06026.   **18.** 77660.   **19.** 43.67.   **21.** 8,341,000.
22. 0.000 08690.   **23.** 0.0009540.

Ex. 31, Page 94

1. 8.61823 − 10.   **2.** 0.76793.   **3.** 6.52247 − 10.   **5.** 3.91738.
6. 9.48912 − 10.   **7.** 0.24112.   **9.** 3.83044 − 10.   **10.** 4.86009.
11. 5.70013.   **13.** 2.10697.   **14.** 1.40309 − 10.   **15.** 4.98847 − 10.
17. 1.0104.   **18.** 4931.5.   **19.** 0.70419.   **21.** 183,720,000.
22. 0.00027248.   **23.** 592.38.   **25.** 0.0091254.   **26.** 23,456,000.
27. 3,098,600.   **29.** 20.140.   **30.** 0.000 0014260.   **31.** 0.000 035093.

Ex. 32, Pages 97–98

1. 0.4520.   **2.** 21.19.   **3.** 20.51.   **5.** 0.001362.
6. 0.0002470.   **7.** 511.0.   **9.** 4,302,000.   **10.** 9,991,000,000.
11. 0.2871.   **13.** 3247.   **14.** 0.3036.   **15.** 0.007166.
17. 0.09052.   **18.** 0.09045.   **19.** 0.6985.   **21.** −24.70.
22. 831,700.   **23.** −5.230.   **25.** 23.92.   **26.** 6214.
27. 2.268.   **29.** 8.001.   **30.** 0.0002066.   **31.** 0.0009507.
33. 1.6220.   **34.** 0.014465.   **35.** 16114.   **37.** 0.44359.
38. 0.36435.   **39.** 0.042315.   **41.** 528.79.   **42.** 241.12.
43. 0.000 000 036681.   **45.** 0.000 00871.   **46.** 3.3666.
47. 6,463,000.   **49.** 1.1087.   **50.** 0.00880.   **51.** 0.010912.
53. 0.0001014.   **54.** 312.9.   **55.** 1140.   **57.** $26,877.

Ex. 33, Page 100

1. 9.52951 − 10.   **2.** 0.69283.   **3.** 9.05778 − 10.   **5.** 9.78824 − 10.
6. 0.39417.   **7.** 9.99611 − 10.   **9.** 0.05138.   **10.** 9.52934 − 10.
11. 9.96188 − 10.   **13.** 1.23891.   **14.** 9.77555 − 10.   **15.** 9.98432 − 10.
17. 63° 21′.   **18.** 34° 17′.   **19.** 11° 36′.   **21.** 44° 50.6′.
22. 45° 8.7′.   **23.** 15° 44.5′.   **25.** 48° 19.2′.   **26.** 8° 45.8′.
27. 33° 40.8′.   **29.** 14° 4.3′.   **30.** 82° 23.4′.   **31.** 51° 58.9′.
33. 22° 7.0′.   **34.** Impossible.   **35.** 4° 29.0′.

Ex. 34, Page 102

5. $B = 11° 1′, b = 13.35, c = 69.86.$
6. $A = 61° 18′, a = 3405, b = 1866.$

7. $B = 49° 58'$, $a = 1.492$, $b = 1.776$.

9. $A = 38° 22'$, $B = 51° 38'$, $c = 9.483$.

10. $A = 16° 6'$, $B = 73° 54'$, $a = 261.7$.

11. $A = 50° 13'$, $B = 39° 47'$, $b = 0.04028$.

13. $A = 74° 11.1'$, $B = 15° 48.9'$, $a = 28271$ or 28273, depending upon the method used.

14. $A = 28° 41.4'$, $B = 61° 18.6'$, $c = 6.1524$.

15. $A = 44° 1.7'$, $a = 356.80$, $c = 513.37$.

17. $A = 50° 19.3'$, $a = 427.28$, $b = 354.45$.

18. $B = 9° 46.8'$, $a = 80.780$, $c = 81.972$.

19. $A = 69° 47.4'$, $B = 20° 12.6'$, $c = 76433$.

Ex. 35, Pages 104–106

1. 1612 ft.　　　**2.** 555 ft.　　　**3.** 512 ft.

5. 1:26 P.M.　　　**6.** 3.1426; 3.1416.　　　**7.** 18° 10'.

9. S 6° 50' W; 273 mph.　　　**10.** N 6° 40' E; 151 mph.

11. 164 mph; 162 mph.　　**13.** 4952 lb.　　　**14.** 34° 50'.

15. 869.1 lb.　　**17.** 29.78 ft.　　　**18.** 47.0 lb.; 135 lb.

19. 481 ft. 4.0 in.; 755 ft. 8.8 in.　　**22.** $C = 41° 49'$, $a = 80.40$, $c = 63.33$.

23. $B = 75° 48'$, $C = 55° 39'$, $a = 515.2$.

25. $C = 29° 59'$, $b = 4841$, $c = 3642$.　　**26.** $B = 25° 21'$, $C = 29° 26'$, $a = 8599$.

Ex. 36, Pages 109–110

1. 113°.　　**2.** 96°.　　**3.** 82° 50'.　　**5.** 25.

6. 388.　　**7.** 31.　　**9.** 2.9.　　**10.** 7.7.

11. $A = 22°$, $B = 60°$, $C = 98°$.　　**13.** S 37° 10' E.

14. N 55° E, N 65° E or N 55° W, N 65° W.

15. 5.6 miles.

Ex. 37, Pages 112–113

1. $B = 24° 50'$, $a = 708$, $c = 683$.　　**2.** $B = 20°$, $a = 59$, $b = 21$.

7. $A = 42° 10'$, $b = 3987$, $c = 4343$.　　**9.** $B = 70° 1'$, $b = 5.427$, $c = 5.714$.

10. $B = 64° 33'$, $a = 0.03957$, $c = 0.05159$.

11. $B = 59° 30'$, $a = 248$, $b = 433$.　　**13.** $C = 104° 2.0'$, $a = 36894$, $b = 17171$.

14. $C = 50° 30.0'$, $b = 40131$, $c = 45265$.

15. $A = 43° 39.0'$, $a = 0.56488$, $c = 0.68490$.

17. $b = 159$.　　　**18.** 1572 ft.　　　**19.** 260 mph; 270 mph.

Ex. 38, Pages 115–116

1. No triangle.

2. $B = 74° 30'$, $C = 52° 19'$, $c = 586.0$; $B' = 105° 30'$, $C' = 21° 19'$, $c = 269.2$.

3. $B = 46° 57'$, $C = 110° 6'$, $c = 4482$; $B' = 133° 3'$, $C' = 24° 0'$, $c' = 1941$.

5. $B = 53° 40'$, $C = 50° 42'$, $c = 0.02319$.

6. $B = 30° 39'$, $C = 25° 36'$, $c = 1536$.

7. No triangle.

9. $B = 114° 27.2'$, $C = 47° 59.0'$, $b = 91722$; $B' = 30° 25.2'$, $C' = 132° 1.0'$. $b' = 51016$.

10. No triangle.

11. $A = 41° 20.0'$, $B = 90° 0.0'$, $a = 50.689$.

13. There are two Washingtons that satisfy the conditions of the problem. Washington, Pa., is 100 miles from Wooster; Washington, D.C., is 280 miles from Wooster.

14. 63,000,000 miles or 117,000,000 miles.

15. 15° or 79°.

Ex. 39, Pages 119–120

5. $A = 70° 0'$, $B = 30° 0'$, $c = 5472$.

6. $A = 54° 0'$, $B = 10° 0'$, $c = 849.9$.

7. $A = 60° 0'$, $B = 32° 0'$, $c = 44.81$.

9. $A = 22° 10'$, $C = 119° 56'$, $b = 0.3103$.

10. $B = 58° 26'$, $C = 74° 56'$, $a = 6.871$.

11. $B = 54° 31.4'$, $C = 29° 46.8'$, $a = 113,700$.

13. $A = 17° 24.6'$, $B = 32° 7.8'$, $c = 53.086$ or 53.088, depending upon the method used.

14. $A = 42° 55.9'$, $B = 62° 53.1'$, $c = 4961.8$ or 4961.7, depending upon the method used.

15. 511 ft., 429 ft., 193 ft.   17. N 77° E; 230 mph.   18. S 83° E; 340 miles.

Ex. 40, Page 123

2. $A = 30° 0'$, $B = 59° 50'$, $C = 90° 10'$.

3. $A = 45° 36'$, $B = 77° 29'$, $C = 56° 55'$.

5. $A = 42° 20'$, $B = 88° 24'$, $C = 49° 15'$.

6. $A = 110° 53'$, $B = 50° 15'$, $C = 18° 52'$.

7. $A = 15° 38'$, $B = 13° 44'$, $C = 150° 38'$.

9. $A = 101° 46.6'$, $B = 34° 25.0'$, $C = 43° 48.4'$.

10. $A = 52° 42.6'$, $B = 73° 11.6'$, $C = 54° 5.8'$.

11. $A = 81° 0.0'$, $B = 58° 20.4'$, $C = 40° 39.6'$.

13. 596 in.; 427 in.; 326 in.

14. N 81° E, S 23° E or S 81° E, N 23° E.

15. S 9° E; S 15° W.

Ex. 41, Page 125

1. 98.   2. 591.   3. 48.   5. 252.

6. 61.   7. 2689.   9. 151.6.   10. 37.17.

11. 24.05.   15. 1.39 acres.

Ex. 42, Pages 125–128

1. $A = 79°$.   2. $a = 86$.

3. $B = 30° 41'$.   5. $B = 20° 2'$, $C = 83° 44'$.

6. $B = 79° 15'$.   7. $b = 4.54$.

9. $a = 3010$.   10. $C = 70° 22'$ or $109° 38'$.

11. $A = 50° 50'$.   13. 87 miles.   14. 180 ft.

15. 792 ft.   17. 45 ft.   18. 49°.

19. 44°, 57°, 78°.   21. S 45° W; N 19° W.   22. 170 miles; 320 miles.

23. S 58° E; 210 miles.   25. 324 ft. per min.; 939 ft. per min.

26. Wind blows toward N 65° E at 46 mph.

27. N 54° E, 140 mph or S 34° E, 97 mph.

29. N 57° 54′ W or S 57° 54′ W.   **30.** S 51° 12′ W; 1123 lb.

31. 15.91 in.; 20.64 in.   **33.** S 71° E.   **34.** 7811.
35. 38 mph.   **42.** 3413 ft.   **43.** $20\sqrt{86}$ ft. $\rightarrow$ 185 ft.
45. Approximately 77.14.   **46.** 2 ft.   **47.** 6; 14; 16.

Ex. 43, Page 131

1. $-\dfrac{\pi}{6}$.   **2.** $\dfrac{\pi}{4}$.   **3.** $\dfrac{\pi}{2}$.   **5.** $\dfrac{\pi}{6}$.

6. $\dfrac{5\pi}{6}$.   **7.** $-\dfrac{\pi}{4}$.   **9.** 0.   **10.** $-\dfrac{\pi}{2}$.

11. $\dfrac{2\pi}{3}$.   **13.** $\dfrac{3\pi}{4}$.   **14.** 0.   **15.** $\dfrac{\pi}{3}$.

17. $\dfrac{\pi}{6}$.   **18.** $-\dfrac{\pi}{3}$.   **19.** $\dfrac{\pi}{4}$.   **21.** $\dfrac{\pi}{2}$.

22. $-.1251$.   **23.** 1.1606.   **25.** 1.7628.   **26.** .3025.
27. -1.3759.

Ex. 44, Pages 133–134

1. $\dfrac{u}{\sqrt{u^2+1}}$.   **2.** $\dfrac{\sqrt{1-u^2}}{u}$.   **3.** $\dfrac{1}{u}$.

5. $\dfrac{24}{7}$.   **6.** $\dfrac{\sqrt{7}}{4}$.   **7.** $\dfrac{15}{17}$.

9. $uv - \sqrt{1-u^2}\,\sqrt{1-v^2}$.   **10.** $u\,\sqrt{1-v^2} - v\,\sqrt{1-u^2}$.

11. $uv + \sqrt{1-u^2}\,\sqrt{1-v^2}$.   **13.** $-\dfrac{\sqrt{13}}{7}$.

14. $-\dfrac{\sqrt{15}}{4}$.   **15.** $\dfrac{\sqrt{21}}{5}$.   **17.** $2v\,\sqrt{1-v^2}$.   **18.** $2v^2 - 1$.

19. $1 - 2u^2$.   **21.** $2v$.   **22.** $6u$.   **23.** $\dfrac{\pi}{8}$.

25. $\dfrac{\pi}{10}$.   **26.** $-\dfrac{\pi}{18}$.   **27.** $\dfrac{\pi}{5}$.   **29.** $-\dfrac{\pi}{2}$.

30. $\dfrac{\pi}{2}$.   **31.** $\dfrac{u}{3}$; $\dfrac{\sqrt{9-u^2}}{u}$.   **33.** $\dfrac{4}{u}$; $\dfrac{\sqrt{u^2-16}}{u}$.

34. $\dfrac{\sqrt{u^4-36}}{6}$; $\dfrac{u^2}{6}$.   **35.** $\dfrac{1-2u^2}{2u\,\sqrt{1-u^2}}$.   **46.** False.

47. False if $u < 0$.   **49.** True.   **50.** True.

51. True.   **53.** False.
54. True if $u \geqq 0$; false if $u < 0$.   **55.** True.

Ex. 45, Page 137

1. $6 + i$.   **2.** $2 - 3i$.   **3.** $-14 - 3i$.   **5.** $33 + 64i$.
6. $13 + i\sqrt{7}$.   **7.** $18 - 9i\sqrt{2}$.   **9.** $-39 + 80i$.   **10.** $7 - 24i$.
11. i.   **13.** 1.   **14.** $-i$.   **15.** $1 - 2i$.

17. $\dfrac{7}{6} + \dfrac{\sqrt{5}}{6}\, i.$

18. $\dfrac{83}{61} + \dfrac{2}{61}\, i.$

19. $x = 3,\ y = -5.$

21. $x = 7,\ y = 4.$

22. $x = 5,\ y = 9;\ x = \dfrac{9}{2},\ y = 10.$

23. $0.$

Ex. 46, Page 140

9. $5\sqrt{2}(\cos 225° + i \sin 225°).$

10. $2(\cos 315° + i \sin 315°).$

11. $3\sqrt{2}(\cos 135° + i \sin 135°).$

13. $7(\cos 270° + i \sin 270°).$

14. $3(\cos 180° + i \sin 180°).$

15. $6(\cos 0° + i \sin 0°).$

17. $2(\cos 30° + i \sin 30°).$

18. $17(\cos 208° 4' + i \sin 208° 4').$

19. $10(\cos 306° 52' + i \sin 306° 52').$

21. $4.6985 - 1.7100i.$

22. $-3\sqrt{3} + 3i.$

23. $2 + 2i\sqrt{3}.$

Ex. 47, Pages 143–144

1. $-10 + 10i\sqrt{3}.$

2. $6 + 6i\sqrt{3}.$

3. $-63i.$

5. $6 + 6i.$

6. $8\sqrt{3} + 8i.$

7. $24 - 8i\sqrt{3}.$

9. $4\sqrt{3} + 4i.$

10. $-12i.$

11. $12.$

13. $-243i.$

14. $-32.$

15. $-64.$

17. $-16\sqrt{2} - 16i\sqrt{2}.$

18. $-8 + 8i.$

19. $1.$

21. $8i.$

22. $351.8 - 936.0i,$ using four-place tables. The correct value is $352 - 936i.$

23. $4.9725 + 0.5225i;\ -2.9390 + 4.0450i;\ -2.0335 - 4.5675i.$

25. $-3 + 3i;\ 3 - 3i.$

26. $2 + 2i;\ -2 - 2i.$

27. $\sqrt{3} + i;\ -\sqrt{3} - i.$

29. $2;\ -1 + i\sqrt{3};\ -1 - i\sqrt{3}.$

30. $\sqrt{2} + i\sqrt{2};\ -1.9318 + 0.5176i;\ 0.5176 - 1.9318i.$

31. $0.7654 + 1.8478i;\ -1.8478 + 0.7654i;\ -0.7654 - 1.8478i;\ 1.8478 - 0.7654i.$

33. $\sqrt{3} + i;\ -1 + i\sqrt{3};\ -\sqrt{3} - i;\ 1 - i\sqrt{3}.$

34. $2\sqrt{2} + 2i\sqrt{2};\ -2\sqrt{2} + 2i\sqrt{2};\ -2\sqrt{2} - 2i\sqrt{2};\ 2\sqrt{2} - 2i\sqrt{2}.$

35. $1;\ 0.3090 + 0.9511i;\ -0.8090 + 0.5878i;\ -0.8090 - 0.5878i;\ 0.3090 - 0.9511i.$

37. $1.6180 + 1.1756i;\ -0.6180 + 1.9022i;\ -2;\ -0.6180 - 1.9022i;$
$1.6180 - 1.1756i.$

38. $10;\ 5 + 5i\sqrt{3};\ -5 + 5i\sqrt{3};\ -10;\ -5 - 5i\sqrt{3};\ 5 - 5i\sqrt{3}.$

39. $5 + 5i\sqrt{3};\ -10;\ 5 - 5i\sqrt{3}.$

Ex. 49, Page 149

1. $-0.1732.$

2. $-1.003.$

3. $-38.45.$

5. $1.982.$

6. $-1.848.$

7. $2.002.$

9. $-41.18.$

10. $4.082.$

11. $-1.993.$

13. $3.000.$

14. $-3.500.$

15. $8.022.$

Ex. 50, Page 150

1. $2° 15'.$

2. $1° 24'.$

3. $0° 34'.$

5. 71 mils.

6. 62 mils.

7. 41 mils.

9. 0.1964 radian.

10. 0.1571 radian.

11. 0.1080 radian.

13. 71 mils.

14. 132 mils.

15. 214 mils.

17. 301 ft.

18. 4000 ft.

19. 4.03 mils.

21. 2000 ft.

22. 80 mils.

23. 210 ft.

INDEX

165

LOGARITHMIC AND
TRIGONOMETRIC TABLES

BY

E. RICHARD HEINEMAN

Professor of Mathematics
Texas Technological College

McGRAW-HILL BOOK COMPANY, INC.

New York   Toronto   London

1942

LOGARITHMIC AND TRIGONOMETRIC TABLES

XXIV

CONTENTS

CONTENTS

2.3026

TABLE I

*Values of the Trigonometric Functions
to Four Places*

TABLE I

Radians	Degrees	Sin	Tan	Cot	Cos		
.0000	0° 00′	.0000	.0000	———	1.0000	90° 00′	1.5708
029	10	029	029	343.8	000	89° 50′	679
058	20	058	058	171.9	000	40	650
.0087	30	.0087	.0087	114.6	1.0000	30	1.5621
116	40	116	116	85.94	.9999	20	592
145	50	145	145	68.75	999	10	563
.0175	1° 00′	.0175	.0175	57.29	.9998	89° 00′	1.5533
204	10	204	204	49.10	998	88° 50′	504
233	20	233	233	42.96	997	40	475
.0262	30	.0262	.0262	38.19	.9997	30	1.5446
291	40	291	291	34.37	996	20	417
320	50	320	320	31.24	995	10	388
.0349	2° 00′	.0349	.0349	28.64	.9994	88° 00′	1.5359
378	10	378	378	26.43	993	87° 50′	330
407	20	407	407	24.54	992	40	301
.0436	30	.0436	.0437	22.90	.9990	30	1.5272
465	40	465	466	21.47	989	20	243
495	50	494	495	20.21	988	10	213
.0524	3° 00′	.0523	.0524	19.08	.9986	87° 00′	1.5184
553	10	552	553	18.07	985	86° 50′	155
582	20	581	582	17.17	983	40	126
.0611	30	.0610	.0612	16.35	.9981	30	1.5097
640	40	640	641	15.60	980	20	068
669	50	669	670	14.92	978	10	039
.0698	4° 00′	.0698	.0699	14.30	.9976	86° 00′	1.5010
727	10	727	729	13.73	974	85° 50′	981
756	20	756	758	13.20	971	40	952
.0785	30	.0785	.0787	12.71	.9969	30	1.4923
814	40	814	816	12.25	967	20	893
844	50	843	846	11.83	964	10	864
.0873	5° 00′	.0872	.0875	11.43	.9962	85° 00′	1.4835
902	10	901	904	11.06	959	84° 50′	806
931	20	929	934	10.71	957	40	777
.0960	30	.0958	.0963	10.39	.9954	30	1.4748
989	40	987	992	10.08	951	20	719
.1018	50	.1016	.1022	9.788	948	10	690
.1047	6° 00′	.1045	.1051	9.514	.9945	84° 00′	1.4661
076	10	074	080	9.255	942	83° 50′	632
105	20	103	110	9.010	939	40	603
.1134	30	.1132	.1139	8.777	.9936	30	1.4573
164	40	161	169	8.556	932	20	544
193	50	190	198	8.345	929	10	515
.1222	7° 00′	.1219	.1228	8.144	.9925	83° 00′	1.4486
251	10	248	257	7.953	922	82° 50′	457
280	20	276	287	7.770	918	40	428
.1309	30	.1305	.1317	7.596	.9914	30	1.4399
338	40	334	346	7.429	911	20	370
367	50	363	376	7.269	907	10	341
.1396	8° 00′	.1392	.1405	7.115	.9903	82° 00′	1.4312
425	10	421	435	6.968	899	81° 50′	283
454	20	449	465	6.827	894	40	254
.1484	30	.1478	.1495	6.691	.9890	30	1.4224
513	40	507	524	6.561	886	20	195
542	50	536	554	6.435	881	10	166
.1571	9° 00′	.1564	.1584	6.314	.9877	81° 00′	1.4137
		Cos	Cot	Tan	Sin	Degrees	Radians

TABLE I

Radians	Degrees	Sin	Tan	Cot	Cos		
.1571	9° 00′	.1564	.1584	6.314	.9877	81° 00′	1.4137
600	10	593	614	197	872	80° 50	108
629	20	622	644	084	868	40	079
.1658	30	.1650	.1673	5.976	.9863	30	1.4050
687	40	679	703	871	858	20	1.4021
716	50	708	733	769	853	10	992
.1745	10° 00′	.1736	.1763	5.671	.9848	80° 00′	1.3963
774	10	765	793	576	843	79° 50′	934
804	20	794	823	485	838	40	904
.1833	30	.1822	.1853	5.396	.9833	30	1.3875
862	40	851	883	309	827	20	846
891	50	880	914	226	822	10	817
.1920	11° 00′	.1908	.1944	5.145	.9816	79° 00′	1.3788
949	10	937	974	066	811	78° 50′	759
978	20	965	.2004	4.989	805	40	730
.2007	30	.1994	.2035	4.915	.9799	30	1.3701
036	40	.2022	065	843	793	20	672
065	50	051	095	773	787	10	643
.2094	12° 00′	.2079	.2126	4.705	.9781	78° 00′	1.3614
123	10	108	156	638	775	77° 50′	584
153	20	136	186	574	769	40	555
.2182	30	.2164	.2217	4.511	.9763	30	1.3526
211	40	193	247	449	757	20	497
240	50	221	278	390	750	10	468
.2269	13° 00′	.2250	.2309	4.331	.9744	77° 00′	1.3439
298	10	278	339	275	737	76° 50′	410
327	20	306	370	219	730	40	381
.2356	30	.2334	.2401	4.165	.9724	30	1.3352
385	40	363	432	113	717	20	323
414	50	391	462	061	710	10	294
.2443	14° 00′	.2419	.2493	4.011	.9703	76° 00′	1.3265
473	10	447	524	3.962	696	75° 50′	235
502	20	476	555	914	689	40	206
.2531	30	.2504	.2586	3.867	.9681	30	1.3177
560	40	532	617	821	674	20	148
589	50	560	648	776	667	10	119
.2618	15° 00′	.2588	.2679	3.732	.9659	75° 00′	1.3090
647	10	616	711	689	652	74° 50′	061
676	20	644	742	647	644	40	032
.2705	30	.2672	.2773	3.606	.9636	30	1.3003
734	40	700	805	566	628	20	974
763	50	728	836	526	621	10	945
.2793	16° 00′	.2756	.2867	3.487	.9613	74° 00′	1.2915
822	10	784	899	450	605	73° 50′	886
851	20	812	931	412	596	40	857
.2880	30	.2840	.2962	3.376	.9588	30	1.2828
909	40	868	994	340	580	20	799
938	50	896	.3026	305	572	10	770
.2967	17° 00′	.2924	.3057	3.271	.9563	73° 00′	1.2741
996	10	952	089	237	555	72° 50′	712
.3025	20	979	121	204	546	40	683
.3054	30	.3007	.3153	3.172	.9537	30	1.2654
083	40	035	185	140	528	20	625
113	50	062	217	108	520	10	595
.3142	18° 00′	.3090	.3249	3.078	.9511	72° 00′	1.2566
		Cos	Cot	Tan	Sin	Degrees	Radians

TABLE I

Radians	Degrees	Sin	Tan	Cot	Cos		
.3142	18° 00'	.3090	.3249	3.078	.9511	72° 00'	1.2566
171	10	118	281	047	502	71° 50'	537
200	20	145	314	018	492	40	508
.3229	30	.3173	.3346	2.989	.9483	30	1.2479
258	40	201	378	960	474	20	450
287	50	228	411	932	465	10	421
.3316	19° 00'	.3256	.3443	2.904	.9455	71° 00'	1.2392
345	10	283	476	877	446	70° 50'	363
374	20	311	508	850	436	40	334
.3403	30	.3338	.3541	2.824	.9426	30	1.2305
432	40	365	574	798	417	20	275
462	50	393	607	773	407	10	246
.3491	20° 00'	.3420	.3640	2.747	.9397	70° 00'	1.2217
520	10	448	673	723	387	69° 50'	188
549	20	475	706	699	377	40	159
.3578	30	.3502	.3739	2.675	.9367	30	1.2130
607	40	529	772	651	356	20	101
636	50	557	805	628	346	10	072
.3665	21° 00'	.3584	.3839	2.605	.9336	69° 00'	1.2043
694	10	611	872	583	325	68° 50'	1.2014
723	20	638	906	560	315	40	985
.3752	30	.3665	.3939	2.539	.9304	30	1.1956
782	40	692	973	517	293	20	926
811	50	719	.4006	496	283	10	897
.3840	22° 00'	.3746	.4040	2.475	.9272	68° 00'	1.1868
869	10	773	074	455	261	67° 50'	839
898	20	800	108	434	250	40	810
.3927	30	.3827	.4142	2.414	.9239	30	1.1781
956	40	854	176	394	228	20	752
985	50	881	210	375	216	10	723
.4014	23° 00'	.3907	.4245	2.356	.9205	67° 00'	1.1694
043	10	934	279	337	194	66° 50'	665
072	20	961	314	318	182	40	636
.4102	30	.3987	.4348	2.300	.9171	30	1.1606
131	40	.4014	383	282	159	20	577
160	50	041	417	264	147	10	548
.4189	24° 00'	.4067	.4452	2.246	.9135	66° 00'	1.1519
218	10	094	487	229	124	65° 50'	490
247	20	120	522	211	112	40	461
.4276	30	.4147	.4557	2.194	.9100	30	1.1432
305	40	173	592	177	088	20	403
334	50	200	628	161	075	10	374
.4363	25° 00'	.4226	.4663	2.145	.9063	65° 00'	1.1345
392	10	253	699	128	051	64° 50'	316
422	20	279	734	112	038	40	286
.4451	30	.4305	.4770	2.097	.9026	30	1.1257
480	40	331	806	081	013	20	228
509	50	358	841	066	001	10	199
.4538	26° 00'	.4384	.4877	2.050	.8988	64° 00'	1.1170
567	10	410	913	035	975	63° 50'	141
596	20	436	950	020	962	40	112
.4625	30	.4462	.4986	2.006	.8949	30	1.1083
654	40	488	.5022	1.991	936	20	054
683	50	514	059	977	923	10	1.1025
.4712	27° 00'	.4540	.5095	1.963	.8910	63° 00'	1.0996
		Cos	Cot	Tan	Sin	Degrees	Radians

TABLE I

Radians	Degrees	Sin	Tan	Cot	Cos		
.4712	27° 00′	.4540	.5095	1.963	.8910	63° 00′	1.0996
741	10	566	132	949	897	62° 50′	966
771	20	592	169	935	884	40	937
.4800	30	.4617	.5206	1.921	.8870	30	1.0908
829	40	643	243	907	857	20	879
858	50	669	280	894	843	10	850
.4887	28° 00′	.4695	.5317	1.881	.8829	62° 00′	1.0821
916	10	720	354	868	816	61° 50′	792
945	20	746	392	855	802	40	763
.4974	30	.4772	.5430	1.842	.8788	30	1.0734
.5003	40	797	467	829	774	20	705
032	50	823	505	816	760	10	676
.5061	29° 00′	.4848	.5543	1.804	.8746	61° 00′	1.0647
091	10	874	581	792	732	60° 50′	617
120	20	899	619	780	718	40	588
.5149	30	.4924	.5658	1.767	.8704	30	1.0559
178	40	950	696	756	689	20	530
207	50	975	735	744	675	10	501
.5236	30° 00′	.5000	.5774	1.732	.8660	60° 00′	1.0472
265	10	025	812	720	646	59° 50′	443
294	20	050	851	709	631	40	414
.5323	30	.5075	.5890	1.698	.8616	30	1.0385
352	40	100	930	686	601	20	356
381	50	125	969	675	587	10	327
.5411	31° 00′	.5150	.6009	1.664	.8572	59° 00′	1.0297
440	10	175	048	653	557	58° 50′	268
469	20	200	088	643	542	40	239
.5498	30	.5225	.6128	1.632	.8526	30	1.0210
527	40	250	168	621	511	20	181
556	50	275	208	611	496	10	152
.5585	32° 00′	.5299	.6249	1.600	.8480	58° 00′	1.0123
614	10	324	289	590	465	57° 50′	094
643	20	348	330	580	450	40	065
.5672	30	.5373	.6371	1.570	.8434	30	1.0036
701	40	398	412	560	418	20	1.0007
730	50	422	453	550	403	10	977
.5760	33° 00′	.5446	.6494	1.540	.8387	57° 00′	.9948
789	10	471	536	530	371	56° 50′	919
818	20	495	577	520	355	40	890
.5847	30	.5519	.6619	1.511	.8339	30	.9861
876	40	544	661	501	323	20	832
905	50	568	703	1.492	307	10	803
.5934	34° 00′	.5592	.6745	1.483	.8290	56° 00′	.9774
963	10	616	787	473	274	55° 50′	745
992	20	640	830	464	258	40	716
.6021	30	.5664	.6873	1.455	.8241	30	.9687
050	40	688	916	446	225	20	657
080	50	712	959	437	208	10	628
.6109	35° 00′	.5736	.7002	1.428	.8192	55° 00′	.9599
138	10	760	046	419	175	54° 50′	570
167	20	783	089	411	158	40	541
.6196	30	.5807	.7133	1.402	.8141	30	.9512
225	40	831	177	393	124	20	483
254	50	854	221	385	107	10	454
.6283	36° 00′	.5878	.7265	1.376	.8090	54° 00′	.9425
		Cos	Cot	Tan	Sin	Degrees	Radians

TABLE I

Radians	Degrees	Sin	Tan	Cot	Cos		
.6283	36° 00′	.5878	.7265	1.376	.8090	54° 00′	.9425
312	10	901	310	368	073	53° 50′	396
341	20	925	355	360	056	40	367
.6370	30	.5948	.7400	1.351	.8039	30	.9338
400	40	972	445	343	021	20	308
429	50	995	490	335	004	10	279
.6458	37° 00′	.6018	.7536	1.327	.7986	53° 00′	.9250
487	10	041	581	319	969	52° 50′	221
516	20	065	627	311	951	40	192
.6545	30	.6088	.7673	1.303	.7934	30	.9163
574	40	111	720	295	916	20	134
603	50	134	766	288	898	10	105
.6632	38° 00′	.6157	.7813	1.280	.7880	52° 00′	.9076
661	10	180	860	272	862	51° 50′	047
690	20	202	907	265	844	40	.9018
.6720	30	.6225	.7954	1.257	.7826	30	.8988
749	40	248	.8002	250	808	20	959
778	50	271	050	242	790	10	930
.6807	39° 00′	.6293	.8098	1.235	.7771	51° 00′	.8901
836	10	316	146	228	753	50° 50′	872
865	20	338	195	220	735	40	843
.6894	30	.6361	.8243	1.213	.7716	30	.8814
923	40	383	292	206	698	20	785
952	50	406	342	199	679	10	756
.6981	40° 00′	.6428	.8391	1.192	.7660	50° 00′	.8727
.7010	10	450	441	185	642	49° 50′	698
039	20	472	491	178	623	40	668
.7069	30	.6494	.8541	1.171	.7604	30	.8639
098	40	517	591	164	585	20	610
127	50	539	642	157	566	10	581
.7156	41° 00′	.6561	.8693	1.150	.7547	49° 00′	.8552
185	10	583	744	144	528	48° 50′	523
214	20	604	796	137	509	40	494
.7243	30	.6626	.8847	1.130	.7490	30	.8465
272	40	648	899	124	470	20	436
301	50	670	952	117	451	10	407
.7330	42° 00′	.6691	.9004	1.111	.7431	48° 00′	.8378
359	10	713	057	104	412	47° 50′	348
389	20	734	110	098	392	40	319
.7418	30	.6756	.9163	1.091	.7373	30	.8290
447	40	777	217	085	353	20	261
476	50	799	271	079	333	10	232
.7505	43° 00′	.6820	.9325	1.072	.7314	47° 00′	.8203
534	10	841	380	066	294	46° 50′	174
563	20	862	435	060	274	40	145
.7592	30	.6884	.9490	1.054	.7254	30	.8116
621	40	905	545	048	234	20	087
650	50	926	601	042	214	10	058
.7679	44° 00′	.6947	.9657	1.036	.7193	46° 00′	.8029
709	10	967	713	030	173	45° 50′	999
738	20	988	770	024	153	40	970
.7767	30	.7009	.9827	1.018	.7133	30	.7941
796	40	030	884	012	112	20	912
825	50	050	942	006	092	10	883
.7854	45° 00′	.7071	1.000	1.000	.7071	45° 00′	.7854
		Cos	Cot	Tan	Sin	Degrees	Radians

TABLE II

Mantissas of Common Logarithms of Numbers to Five Decimal Places

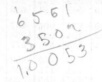

100 = 1.00

TABLE II   100-150

N.	0	1	2	3	4	5	6	7	8	9
100	00 000	043	087	130	173	217	260	303	346	389
101	432	475	518	561	604	647	689	732	775	817
102	860	903	945	988	*030	*072	*115	*157	*199	*242
103	01 284	326	368	410	452	494	536	578	620	662
104	703	745	787	828	870	912	953	995	*036	*078
105	02 119	160	202	243	284	325	366	407	449	490
106	531	572	612	653	694	735	776	816	857	898
107	938	979	*019	*060	*100	*141	*181	*222	*262	*302
108	03 342	383	423	463	503	543	583	623	663	703
109	743	782	822	862	902	941	981	*021	*060	*100
110	04 139	179	218	258	297	336	376	415	454	493
111	532	571	610	650	689	727	766	805	844	883
112	922	961	999	*038	*077	*115	*154	*192	*231	*269
113	05 308	346	385	423	461	500	538	576	614	652
114	690	729	767	805	843	881	918	956	994	*032
115	06 070	108	145	183	221	258	296	333	371	408
116	446	483	521	558	595	633	670	707	744	781
117	819	856	893	930	967	*004	*041	*078	*115	*151
118	07 188	225	262	298	335	372	408	445	482	518
119	555	591	628	664	700	737	773	809	846	882
120	918	954	990	*027	*063	*099	*135	*171	*207	*243
121	08 279	314	350	386	422	458	493	529	565	600
122	636	672	707	743	778	814	849	884	920	955
123	991	*026	*061	*096	*132	*167	*202	*237	*272	*307
124	09 342	377	412	447	482	517	552	587	621	656
125	691	726	760	795	830	864	899	934	968	*003
126	10 037	072	106	140	175	209	243	278	312	346
127	380	415	449	483	517	551	585	619	653	687
128	721	755	789	823	857	890	924	958	992	*025
129	11 059	093	126	160	193	227	261	294	327	361
130	394	428	461	494	528	561	594	628	661	694
131	727	760	793	826	860	893	926	959	992	*024
132	12 057	090	123	156	189	222	254	287	320	352
133	385	418	450	483	516	548	581	613	646	678
134	710	743	775	808	840	872	905	937	969	*001
135	13 033	066	098	130	162	194	226	258	290	322
136	354	386	418	450	481	513	545	577	609	640
137	672	704	735	767	799	830	862	893	925	956
138	988	*019	*051	*082	*114	*145	*176	*208	*239	*270
139	14 301	333	364	395	426	457	489	520	551	582
140	613	644	675	706	737	768	799	829	860	891
141	922	953	983	*014	*045	*076	*106	*137	*168	*198
142	15 229	259	290	320	351	381	412	442	473	503
143	534	564	594	625	655	685	715	746	776	806
144	836	866	897	927	957	987	*017	*047	*077	*107
145	16 137	167	197	227	256	286	316	346	376	406
146	435	465	495	524	554	584	613	643	673	702
147	732	761	791	820	850	879	909	938	967	997
148	17 026	056	085	114	143	173	202	231	260	289
149	319	348	377	406	435	464	493	522	551	580
150	609	638	667	696	725	754	782	811	840	869

Prop. Pts.

	44	43	42
1	4.4	4.3	4.2
2	8.8	8.6	8.4
3	13.2	12.9	12.6
4	17.6	17.2	16.8
5	22.0	21.5	21.0
6	26.4	25.8	25.2
7	30.8	30.1	29.4
8	35.2	34.4	33.6
9	39.6	38.7	37.8

	41	40	39
1	4.1	4.0	3.9
2	8.2	8.0	7.8
3	12.3	12.0	11.7
4	16.4	16.0	15.6
5	20.5	20.0	19.5
6	24.6	24.0	23.4
7	28.7	28.0	27.3
8	32.8	32.0	31.2
9	36.9	36.0	35.1

	38	37	36
1	3.8	3.7	3.6
2	7.6	7.4	7.2
3	11.4	11.1	10.8
4	15.2	14.8	14.4
5	19.0	18.5	18.0
6	22.8	22.2	21.6
7	26.6	25.9	25.2
8	30.4	29.6	28.8
9	34.2	33.3	32.4

	35	34	33
1	3.5	3.4	3.3
2	7.0	6.8	6.6
3	10.5	10.2	9.9
4	14.0	13.6	13.2
5	17.5	17.0	16.5
6	21.0	20.4	19.8
7	24.5	23.8	23.1
8	28.0	27.2	26.4
9	31.5	30.6	29.7

	32	31	30
1	3.2	3.1	3.0
2	6.4	6.2	6.0
3	9.6	9.3	9.0
4	12.8	12.4	12.0
5	16.0	15.5	15.0
6	19.2	18.6	18.0
7	22.4	21.7	21.0
8	25.6	24.8	24.0
9	28.8	27.9	27.0

N.	0	1	2	3	4	5	6	7	8	9	Prop. Pts.

N.	0	1	2	3	4	5	6	7	8	9	Prop. Pts.
150	17 609	638	667	696	725	754	782	811	840	869	
151	898	926	955	984	*013	*041	*070	*099	*127	*156	
152	18 184	213	241	270	298	327	355	384	412	441	
153	469	498	526	554	583	611	639	667	696	724	
154	752	780	808	837	865	893	921	949	977	*005	
155	19 033	061	089	117	145	173	201	229	257	285	
156	312	340	368	396	424	451	479	507	535	562	
157	590	618	645	673	700	728	756	783	811	838	
158	866	893	921	948	976	*003	*030	*058	*085	*112	
159	20 140	167	194	222	249	276	303	330	358	385	
160	412	439	466	493	520	548	575	602	629	656	
161	683	710	737	763	790	817	844	871	898	925	
162	952	978	*005	*032	*059	*085	*112	*139	*165	*192	
163	21 219	245	272	299	325	352	378	405	431	458	
164	484	511	537	564	590	617	643	669	696	722	
165	748	775	801	827	854	880	906	932	958	985	
166	22 011	037	063	089	115	141	167	194	220	246	
167	272	298	324	350	376	401	427	453	479	505	
168	531	557	583	608	634	660	686	712	737	763	
169	789	814	840	866	891	917	943	968	994	*019	
170	23 045	070	096	121	147	172	198	223	249	274	
171	300	325	350	376	401	426	452	477	502	528	
172	553	578	603	629	654	679	704	729	754	779	
173	805	830	855	880	905	930	955	980	*005	*030	
174	24 055	080	105	130	155	180	204	229	254	279	
175	304	329	353	378	403	428	452	477	502	527	
176	551	576	601	625	650	674	699	724	748	773	
177	797	822	846	871	895	920	944	969	993	*018	
178	25 042	066	091	115	139	164	188	212	237	261	
179	285	310	334	358	382	406	431	455	479	503	
180	527	551	575	600	624	648	672	696	720	744	
181	768	792	816	840	864	888	912	935	959	983	
182	26 007	031	055	079	102	126	150	174	198	221	
183	245	269	293	316	340	364	387	411	435	458	
184	482	505	529	553	576	600	623	647	670	694	
185	717	741	764	788	811	834	858	881	905	928	
186	951	975	998	*021	*045	*068	*091	*114	*138	*161	
187	27 184	207	231	254	277	300	323	346	370	393	
188	416	439	462	485	508	531	554	577	600	623	
189	646	669	692	715	738	761	784	807	830	852	
190	875	898	921	944	967	989	*012	*035	*058	*081	
191	28 103	126	149	171	194	217	240	262	285	307	
192	330	353	375	398	421	443	466	488	511	533	
193	556	578	601	623	646	668	691	713	735	758	
194	780	803	825	847	870	892	914	937	959	981	
195	29 003	026	048	070	092	115	137	159	181	203	
196	226	248	270	292	314	336	358	380	403	425	
197	447	469	491	513	535	557	579	601	623	645	
198	667	688	710	732	754	776	798	820	842	863	
199	885	907	929	951	973	994	*016	*038	*060	*081	
200	30 103	125	146	168	190	211	233	255	276	298	
N.	0	1	2	3	4	5	6	7	8	9	Prop. Pts.

Prop. Pts.

	29	28
1	2.9	2.8
2	5.8	5.6
3	8.7	8.4
4	11.6	11.2
5	14.5	14.0
6	17.4	16.8
7	20.3	19.6
8	23.2	22.4
9	26.1	25.2

	27	26
1	2.7	2.6
2	5.4	5.2
3	8.1	7.8
4	10.8	10.4
5	13.5	13.0
6	16.2	15.6
7	18.9	18.2
8	21.6	20.8
9	24.3	23.4

	25
1	2.5
2	5.0
3	7.5
4	10.0
5	12.5
6	15.0
7	17.5
8	20.0
9	22.5

	24	23
1	2.4	2.3
2	4.8	4.6
3	7.2	6.9
4	9.6	9.2
5	12.0	11.5
6	14.4	13.8
7	16.8	16.1
8	19.2	18.4
9	21.6	20.7

	22	21
1	2.2	2.1
2	4.4	4.2
3	6.6	6.3
4	8.8	8.4
5	11.0	10.5
6	13.2	12.6
7	15.4	14.7
8	17.6	16.8
9	19.8	18.9

TABLE II   200-250

N.	0	1	2	3	4	5	6	7	8	9
200	30 103	125	146	168	190	211	233	255	276	298
201	320	341	363	384	406	428	449	471	492	514
202	535	557	578	600	621	643	664	685	707	728
203	750	771	792	814	835	856	878	899	920	942
204	963	984	*006	*027	*048	*069	*091	*112	*133	*154
205	31 175	197	218	239	260	281	302	323	345	366
206	387	408	429	450	471	492	513	534	555	576
207	597	618	639	660	681	702	723	744	765	785
208	806	827	848	869	890	911	931	952	973	994
209	32 015	035	056	077	098	118	139	160	181	201
210	222	243	263	284	305	325	346	366	387	408
211	428	449	469	490	510	531	552	572	593	613
212	634	654	675	695	715	736	756	777	797	818
213	838	858	879	899	919	940	960	980	*001	*021
214	33 041	062	082	102	122	143	163	183	203	224
215	244	264	284	304	325	345	365	385	405	425
216	445	465	486	506	526	546	566	586	606	626
217	646	666	686	706	726	746	766	786	806	826
218	846	866	885	905	925	945	965	985	*005	*025
219	34 044	064	084	104	124	143	163	183	203	223
220	242	262	282	301	321	341	361	380	400	420
221	439	459	479	498	518	537	557	577	596	616
222	635	655	674	694	713	733	753	772	792	811
223	830	850	869	889	908	928	947	967	986	*005
224	35 025	044	064	083	102	122	141	160	180	199
225	218	238	257	276	295	315	334	353	372	392
226	411	430	449	468	488	507	526	545	564	583
227	603	622	641	660	679	698	717	736	755	774
228	793	813	832	851	870	889	908	927	946	965
229	984	*003	*021	*040	*059	*078	*097	*116	*135	*154
230	36 173	192	211	229	248	267	286	305	324	342
231	361	380	399	418	436	455	474	493	511	530
232	549	568	586	605	624	642	661	680	698	717
233	736	754	773	791	810	829	847	866	884	903
234	922	940	959	977	996	*014	*033	*051	*070	*088
235	37 107	125	144	162	181	199	218	236	254	273
236	291	310	328	346	365	383	401	420	438	457
237	475	493	511	530	548	566	585	603	621	639
238	658	676	694	712	731	749	767	785	803	822
239	840	858	876	894	912	931	949	967	985	*003
240	38 021	039	057	075	093	112	130	148	166	184
241	202	220	238	256	274	292	310	328	346	364
242	382	399	417	435	453	471	489	507	525	543
243	561	578	596	614	632	650	668	686	703	721
244	739	757	775	792	810	828	846	863	881	899
245	917	934	952	970	987	*005	*023	*041	*058	*076
246	39 094	111	129	146	164	182	199	217	235	252
247	270	287	305	322	340	358	375	393	410	428
248	445	463	480	498	515	533	550	568	585	602
249	620	637	655	672	690	707	724	742	759	777
250	794	811	829	846	863	881	898	915	933	950
N.	0	1	2	3	4	5	6	7	8	9

Prop. Pts.

	22	21
1	2.2	2.1
2	4.4	4.2
3	6.6	6.3
4	8.8	8.4
5	11.0	10.5
6	13.2	12.6
7	15.4	14.7
8	17.6	16.8
9	19.8	18.9

	20
1	2.0
2	4.0
3	6.0
4	8.0
5	10.0
6	12.0
7	14.0
8	16.0
9	18.0

	19
1	1.9
2	3.8
3	5.7
4	7.6
5	9.5
6	11.4
7	13.3
8	15.2
9	17.1

	18
1	1.8
2	3.6
3	5.4
4	7.2
5	9.0
6	10.8
7	12.6
8	14.4
9	16.2

	17
1	1.7
2	3.4
3	5.1
4	6.8
5	8.5
6	10.2
7	11.9
8	13.6
9	15.3

N.	0	1	2	3	4	5	6	7	8	9
250	39 794	811	829	846	863	881	898	915	933	950
251	967	985	*002	*019	*037	*054	*071	*088	*106	*123
252	40 140	157	175	192	209	226	243	261	278	295
253	312	329	346	364	381	398	415	432	449	466
254	483	500	518	535	552	569	586	603	620	637
255	654	671	688	705	722	739	756	773	790	807
256	824	841	858	875	892	909	926	943	960	976
257	993	*010	*027	*044	*061	*078	*095	*111	*128	*145
258	41 162	179	196	212	229	246	263	280	296	313
259	330	347	363	380	397	414	430	447	464	481
260	497	514	531	547	564	581	597	614	631	647
261	664	681	697	714	731	747	764	780	797	814
262	830	847	863	880	896	913	929	946	963	979
263	996	*012	*029	*045	*062	*078	*095	*111	*127	*144
264	42 160	177	193	210	226	243	259	275	292	308
265	325	341	357	374	390	406	423	439	455	472
266	488	504	521	537	553	570	586	602	619	635
267	651	667	684	700	716	732	749	765	781	797
268	813	830	846	862	878	894	911	927	943	959
269	975	991	*008	*024	*040	*056	*072	*088	*104	*120
270	43 136	152	169	185	201	217	233	249	265	281
271	297	313	329	345	361	377	393	409	425	441
272	457	473	489	505	521	537	553	569	584	600
273	616	632	648	664	680	696	712	727	743	759
274	775	791	807	823	838	854	870	886	902	917
275	933	949	965	981	996	*012	*028	*044	*059	*075
276	44 091	107	122	138	154	170	185	201	217	232
277	248	264	279	295	311	326	342	358	373	389
278	404	420	436	451	467	483	498	514	529	545
279	560	576	592	607	623	638	654	669	685	700
280	716	731	747	762	778	793	809	824	840	855
281	871	886	902	917	932	948	963	979	994	*010
282	45 025	040	056	071	086	102	117	133	148	163
283	179	194	209	225	240	255	271	286	301	317
284	332	347	362	378	393	408	423	439	454	469
285	484	500	515	530	545	561	576	591	606	021
286	637	652	667	682	697	712	728	743	758	773
287	788	803	818	834	849	864	879	894	909	924
288	939	954	969	984	*000	*015	*030	*045	*060	*075
289	46 090	105	120	135	150	165	180	195	210	225
290	240	255	270	285	300	315	330	345	359	374
291	389	404	419	434	449	464	479	494	509	523
292	538	553	568	583	598	613	627	642	657	672
293	687	702	716	731	746	761	776	790	805	820
294	835	850	864	879	894	909	923	938	953	967
295	982	997	*012	*026	*041	*056	*070	*085	*100	*114
296	47 129	144	159	173	188	202	217	232	246	261
297	276	290	305	319	334	349	363	378	392	407
298	422	436	451	465	480	494	509	524	538	553
299	567	582	596	611	625	640	654	669	683	698
300	712	727	741	756	770	784	799	813	828	842
N.	0	1	2	3	4	5	6	7	8	9

Prop. Pts.

	18		17		16		15		14
1	1.8	1	1.7	1	1.6	1	1.5	1	1.4
2	3.6	2	3.4	2	3.2	2	3.0	2	2.8
3	5.4	3	5.1	3	4.8	3	4.5	3	4.2
4	7.2	4	6.8	4	6.4	4	6.0	4	5.6
5	9.0	5	8.5	5	8.0	5	7.5	5	7.0
6	10.8	6	10.2	6	9.6	6	9.0	6	8.4
7	12.6	7	11.9	7	11.2	7	10.5	7	9.8
8	14.4	8	13.6	8	12.8	8	12.0	8	11.2
9	16.2	9	15.3	9	14.4	9	13.5	9	12.6

$\log e = 0.43429$

11

TABLE II   **300-350**

N.	0	1	2	3	4	5	6	7	8	9
300	47 712	727	741	756	770	784	799	813	828	842
301	857	871	885	900	914	929	943	958	972	986
302	48 001	015	029	044	058	073	087	101	116	130
303	144	159	173	187	202	216	230	244	259	273
304	287	302	316	330	344	359	373	387	401	416
305	430	444	458	473	487	501	515	530	544	558
306	572	586	601	615	629	643	657	671	686	700
307	714	728	742	756	770	785	799	813	827	841
308	855	869	883	897	911	926	940	954	968	982
309	996	*010	*024	*038	*052	*066	*080	*094	*108	*122
310	49 136	150	164	178	192	206	220	234	248	262
311	276	290	304	318	332	346	360	374	388	402
312	415	429	443	457	471	485	499	513	527	541
313	554	568	582	596	610	624	638	651	665	679
314	693	707	721	734	748	762	776	790	803	817
315	831	845	859	872	886	900	914	927	941	955
316	969	982	996	*010	*024	*037	*051	*065	*079	*092
317	50 106	120	133	147	161	174	188	202	215	229
318	243	256	270	284	297	311	325	338	352	365
319	379	393	406	420	433	447	461	474	488	501
320	515	529	542	556	569	583	596	610	623	637
321	651	664	678	691	705	718	732	745	759	772
322	786	799	813	826	840	853	866	880	893	907
323	920	934	947	961	974	987	*001	*014	*028	*041
324	51 055	068	081	095	108	121	135	148	162	175
325	188	202	215	228	242	255	268	282	295	308
326	322	335	348	362	375	388	402	415	428	441
327	455	468	481	495	508	521	534	548	561	574
328	587	601	614	627	640	654	667	680	693	706
329	720	733	746	759	772	786	799	812	825	838
330	851	865	878	891	904	917	930	943	957	970
331	983	996	*009	*022	*035	*048	*061	*075	*088	*101
332	52 114	127	140	153	166	179	192	205	218	231
333	244	257	270	284	297	310	323	336	349	362
334	375	388	401	414	427	440	453	466	479	492
335	504	517	530	543	556	569	582	595	608	621
336	634	647	660	673	686	699	711	724	737	750
337	763	776	789	802	815	827	840	853	866	879
338	892	905	917	930	943	956	969	982	994	*007
339	53 020	033	046	058	071	084	097	110	122	135
340	148	161	173	186	199	212	224	237	250	263
341	275	288	301	314	326	339	352	364	377	390
342	403	415	428	441	453	466	479	491	504	517
343	529	542	555	567	580	593	605	618	631	643
344	656	668	681	694	706	719	732	744	757	769
345	782	794	807	820	832	845	857	870	882	895
346	908	920	933	945	958	970	983	995	*008	*020
347	54 033	045	058	070	083	095	108	120	133	145
348	158	170	183	195	208	220	233	245	258	270
349	283	295	307	320	332	345	357	370	382	394
350	407	419	432	444	456	469	481	494	506	518
N.	0	1	2	3	4	5	6	7	8	9

Prop. Pts.

15
1	1.5
2	3.0
3	4.5
4	6.0
5	7.5
6	9.0
7	10.5
8	12.0
9	13.5

$\log \pi = 0.49715$

14
1	1.4
2	2.8
3	4.2
4	5.6
5	7.0
6	8.4
7	9.8
8	11.2
9	12.6

13
1	1.3
2	2.6
3	3.9
4	5.2
5	6.5
6	7.8
7	9.1
8	10.4
9	11.7

12
1	1.2
2	2.4
3	3.6
4	4.8
5	6.0
6	7.2
7	8.4
8	9.6
9	10.8

N.	0	1	2	3	4	5	6	7	8	9
350	54 407	419	432	444	456	469	481	494	506	518
351	531	543	555	568	580	593	605	617	630	642
352	654	667	679	691	704	716	728	741	753	765
353	777	790	802	814	827	839	851	864	876	888
354	900	913	925	937	949	962	974	986	998	*011
355	55 023	035	047	060	072	084	096	108	121	133
356	145	157	169	182	194	206	218	230	242	255
357	267	279	291	303	315	328	340	352	364	376
358	388	400	413	425	437	449	461	473	485	497
359	509	522	534	546	558	570	582	594	606	618
360	630	642	654	666	678	691	703	715	727	739
361	751	763	775	787	799	811	823	835	847	859
362	871	883	895	907	919	931	943	955	967	979
363	991	*003	*015	*027	*038	*050	*062	*074	*086	*098
364	56 110	122	134	146	158	170	182	194	205	217
365	229	241	253	265	277	289	301	312	324	336
366	348	360	372	384	396	407	419	431	443	455
367	467	478	490	502	514	526	538	549	561	573
368	585	597	608	620	632	644	656	667	679	691
369	703	714	726	738	750	761	773	785	797	808
370	820	832	844	855	867	879	891	902	914	926
371	937	949	961	972	984	996	*008	*019	*031	*043
372	57 054	066	078	089	101	113	124	136	148	159
373	171	183	194	206	217	229	241	252	264	276
374	287	299	310	322	334	345	357	368	380	392
375	403	415	426	438	449	461	473	484	496	507
376	519	530	542	553	565	576	588	600	611	623
377	634	646	657	669	680	692	703	715	726	738
378	749	761	772	784	795	807	818	830	841	852
379	864	875	887	898	910	921	933	944	955	967
380	978	990	*001	*013	*024	*035	*047	*058	*070	*081
381	58 092	104	115	127	138	149	161	172	184	195
382	206	218	229	240	252	263	274	286	297	309
383	320	331	343	354	365	377	388	399	410	422
384	433	444	456	467	478	490	501	512	524	535
385	546	557	569	580	591	602	614	625	636	647
386	659	670	681	692	704	715	726	737	749	760
387	771	782	794	805	816	827	838	850	861	872
388	883	894	906	917	928	939	950	961	973	984
389	995	*006	*017	*028	*040	*051	*062	*073	*084	*095
390	59 106	118	129	140	151	162	173	184	195	207
391	218	229	240	251	262	273	284	295	306	318
392	329	340	351	362	373	384	395	406	417	428
393	439	450	461	472	483	494	506	517	528	539
394	550	561	572	583	594	605	616	627	638	649
395	660	671	682	693	704	715	726	737	748	759
396	770	780	791	802	813	824	835	846	857	868
397	879	890	901	912	923	934	945	956	966	977
398	988	999	*010	*021	*032	*043	*054	*065	*076	*086
399	60 097	108	119	130	141	152	163	173	184	195
400	206	217	228	239	249	260	271	282	293	304
N.	0	1	2	3	4	5	6	7	8	9

Prop. Pts.

13		12		11		10	
1	1.3	1	1.2	1	1.1	1	1.0
2	2.6	2	2.4	2	2.2	2	2.0
3	3.9	3	3.6	3	3.3	3	3.0
4	5.2	4	4.8	4	4.4	4	4.0
5	6.5	5	6.0	5	5.5	5	5.0
6	7.8	6	7.2	6	6.6	6	6.0
7	9.1	7	8.4	7	7.7	7	7.0
8	10.4	8	9.6	8	8.8	8	8.0
9	11.7	9	10.8	9	9.9	9	9.0

TABLE II   **400-450**

N.	0	1	2	3	4	5	6	7	8	9	Prop. Pts.
400	60 206	217	228	239	249	260	271	282	293	304	
401	314	325	336	347	358	369	379	390	401	412	
402	423	433	444	455	466	477	487	498	509	520	
403	531	541	552	563	574	584	595	606	617	627	
404	638	649	660	670	681	692	703	713	724	735	
405	746	756	767	778	788	799	810	821	831	842	
406	853	863	874	885	895	906	917	927	938	949	
407	959	970	981	991	*002	*013	*023	*034	*045	*055	
408	61 066	077	087	098	109	119	130	140	151	162	
409	172	183	194	204	215	225	236	247	257	268	
410	278	289	300	310	321	331	342	352	363	374	
411	384	395	405	416	426	437	448	458	469	479	
412	490	500	511	521	532	542	553	563	574	584	
413	595	606	616	627	637	648	658	669	679	690	
414	700	711	721	731	742	752	763	773	784	794	
415	805	815	826	836	847	857	868	878	888	899	
416	909	920	930	941	951	962	972	982	993	*003	
417	62 014	024	034	045	055	066	076	086	097	107	
418	118	128	138	149	159	170	180	190	201	211	
419	221	232	242	252	263	273	284	294	304	315	
420	325	335	346	356	366	377	387	397	408	418	
421	428	439	449	459	469	480	490	500	511	521	
422	531	542	552	562	572	583	593	603	613	624	
423	634	644	655	665	675	685	696	706	716	726	
424	737	747	757	767	778	788	798	808	818	829	
425	839	849	859	870	880	890	900	910	921	931	
426	941	951	961	972	982	992	*002	*012	*022	*033	
427	63 043	053	063	073	083	094	104	114	124	134	
428	144	155	165	175	185	195	205	215	225	236	
429	246	256	266	276	286	296	306	317	327	337	
430	347	357	367	377	387	397	407	417	428	438	
431	448	458	468	478	488	498	508	518	528	538	
432	548	558	568	579	589	599	609	619	629	639	
433	649	659	669	679	689	699	709	719	729	739	
434	749	759	769	779	789	799	809	819	829	839	
435	849	859	869	879	889	899	909	919	929	939	
436	949	959	969	979	988	998	*008	*018	*028	*038	
437	64 048	058	068	078	088	098	108	118	128	137	
438	147	157	167	177	187	197	207	217	227	237	
439	246	256	266	276	286	296	306	316	326	335	
440	345	355	365	375	385	395	404	414	424	434	
441	444	454	464	473	483	493	503	513	523	532	
442	542	552	562	572	582	591	601	611	621	631	
443	640	650	660	670	680	689	699	709	719	729	
444	738	748	758	768	777	787	797	807	816	826	
445	836	846	856	865	875	885	895	904	914	924	
446	933	943	953	963	972	982	992	*002	*011	*021	
447	65 031	040	050	060	070	079	089	099	108	118	
448	128	137	147	157	167	176	186	196	205	215	
449	225	234	244	254	263	273	283	292	302	312	
450	321	331	341	350	360	369	379	389	398	408	
N.	0	1	2	3	4	5	6	7	8	9	Prop. Pts.

Prop. Pts.

11		10		9	
1	1.1	1	1.0	1	0.9
2	2.2	2	2.0	2	1.8
3	3.3	3	3.0	3	2.7
4	4.4	4	4.0	4	3.6
5	5.5	5	5.0	5	4.5
6	6.6	6	6.0	6	5.4
7	7.7	7	7.0	7	6.3
8	8.8	8	8.0	8	7.2
9	9.9	9	9.0	9	8.1

N.	0	1	2	3	4	5	6	7	8	9
450	65 321	331	341	350	360	369	379	389	398	408
451	418	427	437	447	456	466	475	485	495	504
452	514	523	533	543	552	562	571	581	591	600
453	610	619	629	639	648	658	667	677	686	696
454	706	715	725	734	744	753	763	772	782	792
455	801	811	820	830	839	849	858	868	877	887
456	896	906	916	925	935	944	954	963	973	982
457	992	*001	*011	*020	*030	*039	*049	*058	*068	*077
458	66 087	096	106	115	124	134	143	153	162	172
459	181	191	200	210	219	229	238	247	257	266
460	276	285	295	304	314	323	332	342	351	361
461	370	380	389	398	408	417	427	436	445	455
462	464	474	483	492	502	511	521	530	539	549
463	558	567	577	586	596	605	614	624	633	642
464	652	661	671	680	689	699	708	717	727	736
465	745	755	764	773	783	792	801	811	820	829
466	839	848	857	867	876	885	894	904	913	922
467	932	941	950	960	969	978	987	997	*006	*015
468	67 025	034	043	052	062	071	080	089	099	108
469	117	127	136	145	154	164	173	182	191	201
470	210	219	228	237	247	256	265	274	284	293
471	302	311	321	330	339	348	357	367	376	385
472	394	403	413	422	431	440	449	459	468	477
473	486	495	504	514	523	532	541	550	560	569
474	578	587	596	605	614	624	633	642	651	660
475	669	679	688	697	706	715	724	733	742	752
476	761	770	779	788	797	806	815	825	834	843
477	852	861	870	879	888	897	906	916	925	934
478	943	952	961	970	979	988	997	*006	*015	*024
479	68 034	043	052	061	070	079	088	097	106	115
480	124	133	142	151	160	169	178	187	196	205
481	215	224	233	242	251	260	269	278	287	296
482	305	314	323	332	341	350	359	368	377	386
483	395	404	413	422	431	440	449	458	467	476
484	485	494	502	511	520	529	538	547	556	565
485	574	583	592	601	610	619	628	637	646	655
486	664	673	681	690	699	708	717	726	735	744
487	753	762	771	780	789	797	806	815	824	833
488	842	851	860	869	878	886	895	904	913	922
489	931	940	949	958	966	975	984	993	*002	*011
490	69 020	028	037	046	055	064	073	082	090	099
491	108	117	126	135	144	152	161	170	179	188
492	197	205	214	223	232	241	249	258	267	276
493	285	294	302	311	320	329	338	346	355	364
494	373	381	390	399	408	417	425	434	443	452
495	461	469	478	487	496	504	513	522	531	539
496	548	557	566	574	583	592	601	609	618	627
497	636	644	653	662	671	679	688	697	705	714
498	723	732	740	749	758	767	775	784	793	801
499	810	819	827	836	845	854	862	871	880	888
500	897	906	914	923	932	940	949	958	966	975
N.	0	1	2	3	4	5	6	7	8	9

Prop. Pts.

10	
1	1.0
2	2.0
3	3.0
4	4.0
5	5.0
6	6.0
7	7.0
8	8.0
9	9.0

9	
1	0.9
2	1.8
3	2.7
4	3.6
5	4.5
6	5.4
7	6.3
8	7.2
9	8.1

8	
1	0.8
2	1.6
3	2.4
4	3.2
5	4.0
6	4.8
7	5.6
8	6.4
9	7.2

TABLE II   500-550

N.	0	1	2	3	4	5	6	7	8	9
500	69 897	906	914	923	932	940	949	958	966	975
501	984	992	*001	*010	*018	*027	*036	*044	*053	*062
502	70 070	079	088	096	105	114	122	131	140	148
503	157	165	174	183	191	200	209	217	226	234
504	243	252	260	269	278	286	295	303	312	321
505	329	338	346	355	364	372	381	389	398	406
506	415	424	432	441	449	458	467	475	484	492
507	501	509	518	526	535	544	552	561	569	578
508	586	595	603	612	621	629	638	646	655	663
509	672	680	689	697	706	714	723	731	740	749
510	757	766	774	783	791	800	808	817	825	834
511	842	851	859	868	876	885	893	902	910	919
512	927	935	944	952	961	969	978	986	995	*003
513	71 012	020	029	037	046	054	063	071	079	088
514	096	105	113	122	130	139	147	155	164	172
515	181	189	198	206	214	223	231	240	248	257
516	265	273	282	290	299	307	315	324	332	341
517	349	357	366	374	383	391	399	408	416	425
518	433	441	450	458	466	475	483	492	500	508
519	517	525	533	542	550	559	567	575	584	592
520	600	609	617	625	634	642	650	659	667	675
521	684	692	700	709	717	725	734	742	750	759
522	767	775	784	792	800	809	817	825	834	842
523	850	858	867	875	883	892	900	908	917	925
524	933	941	950	958	966	975	983	991	999	*008
525	72 016	024	032	041	049	057	066	074	082	090
526	099	107	115	123	132	140	148	156	165	173
527	181	189	198	206	214	222	230	239	247	255
528	263	272	280	288	296	304	313	321	329	337
529	346	354	362	370	378	387	395	403	411	419
530	428	436	444	452	460	469	477	485	493	501
531	509	518	526	534	542	550	558	567	575	583
532	591	599	607	616	624	632	640	648	656	665
533	673	681	689	697	705	713	722	730	738	746
534	754	762	770	779	787	795	803	811	819	827
535	835	843	852	860	868	876	884	892	900	908
536	916	925	933	941	949	957	965	973	981	989
537	997	*006	*014	*022	*030	*038	*046	*054	*062	*070
538	73 078	086	094	102	111	119	127	135	143	151
539	159	167	175	183	191	199	207	215	223	231
540	239	247	255	263	272	280	288	296	304	312
541	320	328	336	344	352	360	368	376	384	392
542	400	408	416	424	432	440	448	456	464	472
543	480	488	496	504	512	520	528	536	544	552
544	560	568	576	584	592	600	608	616	624	632
545	640	648	656	664	672	679	687	695	703	711
546	719	727	735	743	751	759	767	775	783	791
547	799	807	815	823	830	838	846	854	862	870
548	878	886	894	902	910	918	926	933	941	949
549	957	965	973	981	989	997	*005	*013	*020	*028
550	74 036	044	052	060	068	076	084	092	099	107
N.	0	1	2	3	4	5	6	7	8	9

Prop. Pts.

9
1 | 0.9
2 | 1.8
3 | 2.7
4 | 3.6
5 | 4.5
6 | 5.4
7 | 6.3
8 | 7.2
9 | 8.1

8
1 | 0.8
2 | 1.6
3 | 2.4
4 | 3.2
5 | 4.0
6 | 4.8
7 | 5.6
8 | 6.4
9 | 7.2

7
1 | 0.7
2 | 1.4
3 | 2.1
4 | 2.8
5 | 3.5
6 | 4.2
7 | 4.9
8 | 5.6
9 | 6.3

N.	0	1	2	3	4	5	6	7	8	9
550	74 036	044	052	060	068	076	084	092	099	107
551	115	123	131	139	147	155	162	170	178	186
552	194	202	210	218	225	233	241	249	257	265
553	273	280	288	296	304	312	320	327	335	343
554	351	359	367	374	382	390	398	406	414	421
555	429	437	445	453	461	468	476	484	492	500
556	507	515	523	531	539	547	554	562	570	578
557	586	593	601	609	617	624	632	640	648	656
558	663	671	679	687	695	702	710	718	726	733
559	741	749	757	764	772	780	788	796	803	811
560	819	827	834	842	850	858	865	873	881	889
561	896	904	912	920	927	935	943	950	958	966
562	974	981	989	997	*005	*012	*020	*028	*035	*043
563	75 051	059	066	074	082	089	097	105	113	120
564	128	136	143	151	159	166	174	182	189	197
565	205	213	220	228	236	243	251	259	266	274
566	282	289	297	305	312	320	328	335	343	351
567	358	366	374	381	389	397	404	412	420	427
568	435	442	450	458	465	473	481	488	496	504
569	511	519	526	534	542	549	557	565	572	580
570	587	595	603	610	618	626	633	641	648	656
571	664	671	679	686	694	702	709	717	724	732
572	740	747	755	762	770	778	785	793	800	808
573	815	823	831	838	846	853	861	868	876	884
574	891	899	906	914	921	929	937	944	952	959
575	967	974	982	989	997	*005	*012	*020	*027	*035
576	76 042	050	057	065	072	080	087	095	103	110
577	118	125	133	140	148	155	163	170	178	185
578	193	200	208	215	223	230	238	245	253	260
579	268	275	283	290	298	305	313	320	328	335
580	343	350	358	365	373	380	388	395	403	410
581	418	425	433	440	448	455	462	470	477	485
582	492	500	507	515	522	530	537	545	552	559
583	567	574	582	589	597	604	612	619	626	634
584	641	649	656	664	671	678	686	693	701	708
585	716	723	730	738	745	753	760	768	775	782
586	790	797	805	812	819	827	834	842	849	856
587	864	871	879	886	893	901	908	916	923	930
588	938	945	953	960	967	975	982	989	997	*004
589	77 012	019	026	034	041	048	056	063	070	078
590	085	093	100	107	115	122	129	137	144	151
591	159	166	173	181	188	195	203	210	217	225
592	232	240	247	254	262	269	276	283	291	298
593	305	313	320	327	335	342	349	357	364	371
594	379	386	393	401	408	415	422	430	437	444
595	452	459	466	474	481	488	495	503	510	517
596	525	532	539	546	554	561	568	576	583	590
597	597	605	612	619	627	634	641	648	656	663
598	670	677	685	692	699	706	714	721	728	735
599	743	750	757	764	772	779	786	793	801	808
600	815	822	830	837	844	851	859	866	873	880
N.	**0**	**1**	**2**	**3**	**4**	**5**	**6**	**7**	**8**	**9**

Prop. Pts.

8
1	0.8
2	1.6
3	2.4
4	3.2
5	4.0
6	4.8
7	5.6
8	6.4
9	7.2

7
1	0.7
2	1.4
3	2.1
4	2.8
5	3.5
6	4.2
7	4.9
8	5.6
9	6.3

TABLE II   600-650

N.	0	1	2	3	4	5	6	7	8	9	Prop. Pts.
600	77 815	822	830	837	844	851	859	866	873	880	
601	887	895	902	909	916	924	931	938	945	952	
602	960	967	974	981	988	996	*003	*010	*017	*025	
603	78 032	039	046	053	061	068	075	082	089	097	
604	104	111	118	125	132	140	147	154	161	168	
605	176	183	190	197	204	211	219	226	233	240	
606	247	254	262	269	276	283	290	297	305	312	
607	319	326	333	340	347	355	362	369	376	383	
608	390	398	405	412	419	426	433	440	447	455	
609	462	469	476	483	490	497	504	512	519	526	
610	533	540	547	554	561	569	576	583	590	597	
611	604	611	618	625	633	640	647	654	661	668	
612	675	682	689	696	704	711	718	725	732	739	
613	746	753	760	767	774	781	789	796	803	810	
614	817	824	831	838	845	852	859	866	873	880	
615	888	895	902	909	916	923	930	937	944	951	
616	958	965	972	979	986	993	*000	*007	*014	*021	
617	79 029	036	043	050	057	064	071	078	085	092	
618	099	106	113	120	127	134	141	148	155	162	
619	169	176	183	190	197	204	211	218	225	232	
620	239	246	253	260	267	274	281	288	295	302	
621	309	316	323	330	337	344	351	358	365	372	
622	379	386	393	400	407	414	421	428	435	442	
623	449	456	463	470	477	484	491	498	505	511	
624	518	525	532	539	546	553	560	567	574	581	
625	588	595	602	609	616	623	630	637	644	650	
626	657	664	671	678	685	692	699	706	713	720	
627	727	734	741	748	754	761	768	775	782	789	
628	796	803	810	817	824	831	837	844	851	858	
629	865	872	879	886	893	900	906	913	920	927	
630	934	941	948	955	962	969	975	982	989	996	
631	80 003	010	017	024	030	037	044	051	058	065	
632	072	079	085	092	099	106	113	120	127	134	
633	140	147	154	161	168	175	182	188	195	202	
634	209	216	223	229	236	243	250	257	264	271	
635	277	284	291	298	305	312	318	325	332	339	
636	346	353	359	366	373	380	387	393	400	407	
637	414	421	428	434	441	448	455	462	468	475	
638	482	489	496	502	509	516	523	530	536	543	
639	550	557	564	570	577	584	591	598	604	611	
640	618	625	632	638	645	652	659	665	672	679	
641	686	693	699	706	713	720	726	733	740	747	
642	754	760	767	774	781	787	794	801	808	814	
643	821	828	835	841	848	855	862	868	875	882	
644	889	895	902	909	916	922	929	936	943	949	
645	956	963	969	976	983	990	996	*003	*010	*017	
646	81 023	030	037	043	050	057	064	070	077	084	
647	090	097	104	111	117	124	131	137	144	151	
648	158	164	171	178	184	191	198	204	211	218	
649	224	231	238	245	251	258	265	271	278	285	
650	291	298	305	311	318	325	331	338	345	351	
N.	0	1	2	3	4	5	6	7	8	9	Prop. Pts.

Prop. Pts.

8
1 | 0.8
2 | 1.6
3 | 2.4
4 | 3.2
5 | 4.0
6 | 4.8
7 | 5.6
8 | 6.4
9 | 7.2

7
1 | 0.7
2 | 1.4
3 | 2.1
4 | 2.8
5 | 3.5
6 | 4.2
7 | 4.9
8 | 5.6
9 | 6.3

6
1 | 0.6
2 | 1.2
3 | 1.8
4 | 2.4
5 | 3.0
6 | 3.6
7 | 4.2
8 | 4.8
9 | 5.4

18

N.	0	1	2	3	4	5	6	7	8	9	Prop. Pts.
650	81 291	298	305	311	318	325	331	338	345	351	
651	358	365	371	378	385	391	398	405	411	418	
652	425	431	438	445	451	458	465	471	478	485	
653	491	498	505	511	518	525	531	538	544	551	
654	558	564	571	578	584	591	598	604	611	617	
655	624	631	637	644	651	657	664	671	677	684	
656	690	697	704	710	717	723	730	737	743	750	
657	757	763	770	776	783	790	796	803	809	816	
658	823	829	836	842	849	856	862	869	875	882	
659	889	895	902	908	915	921	928	935	941	948	**7**
660	954	961	968	974	981	987	994	*000	*007	*014	1 0.7
661	82 020	027	033	040	046	053	060	066	073	079	2 1.4
662	086	092	099	105	112	119	125	132	138	145	3 2.1
663	151	158	164	171	178	184	191	197	204	210	4 2.8
664	217	223	230	236	243	249	256	263	269	276	5 3.5
665	282	289	295	302	308	315	321	328	334	341	6 4.2
666	347	354	360	367	373	380	387	393	400	406	7 4.9
667	413	419	426	432	439	445	452	458	465	471	8 5.6
668	478	484	491	497	504	510	517	523	530	536	9 6.3
669	543	549	556	562	569	575	582	588	595	601	
670	607	614	620	627	633	640	646	653	659	666	
671	672	679	685	692	698	705	711	718	724	730	
672	737	743	750	756	763	769	776	782	789	795	
673	802	808	814	821	827	834	840	847	853	860	
674	866	872	879	885	892	898	905	911	918	924	
675	930	937	943	950	956	963	969	975	982	988	
676	995	*001	*008	*014	*020	*027	*033	*040	*046	*052	
677	83 059	065	072	078	085	091	097	104	110	117	
678	123	129	136	142	149	155	161	168	174	181	
679	187	193	200	206	213	219	225	232	238	245	
680	251	257	264	270	276	283	289	296	302	308	
681	315	321	327	334	340	347	353	359	366	372	**6**
682	378	385	391	398	404	410	417	423	429	436	1 0.6
683	442	448	455	461	467	474	480	487	493	499	2 1.2
684	506	512	518	525	531	537	544	550	556	563	3 1.8
685	569	575	582	588	594	601	607	613	620	626	4 2.4
686	632	639	645	651	658	664	670	677	683	689	5 3.0
687	696	702	708	715	721	727	734	740	746	753	6 3.6
688	759	765	771	778	784	790	797	803	809	816	7 4.2
689	822	828	835	841	847	853	860	866	872	879	8 4.8
690	885	891	897	904	910	916	923	929	935	942	9 5.4
691	948	954	960	967	973	979	985	992	998	*004	
692	84 011	017	023	029	036	042	048	055	061	067	
693	073	080	086	092	098	105	111	117	123	130	
694	136	142	148	155	161	167	173	180	186	192	
695	198	205	211	217	223	230	236	242	248	255	
696	261	267	273	280	286	292	298	305	311	317	
697	323	330	336	342	348	354	361	367	373	379	
698	386	392	398	404	410	417	423	429	435	442	
699	448	454	460	466	473	479	485	491	497	504	
700	510	516	522	528	535	541	547	553	559	566	
N.	**0**	**1**	**2**	**3**	**4**	**5**	**6**	**7**	**8**	**9**	**Prop. Pts.**

19

TABLE II 700-750

N.	0	1	2	3	4	5	6	7	8	9
700	84 510	516	522	528	535	541	547	553	559	566
701	572	578	584	590	597	603	609	615	621	628
702	634	640	646	652	658	665	671	677	683	689
703	696	702	708	714	720	726	733	739	745	751
704	757	763	770	776	782	788	794	800	807	813
705	819	825	831	837	844	850	856	862	868	874
706	880	887	893	899	905	911	917	924	930	936
707	942	948	954	960	967	973	979	985	991	997
708	85 003	009	016	022	028	034	040	046	052	058
709	065	071	077	083	089	095	101	107	114	120
710	126	132	138	144	150	156	163	169	175	181
711	187	193	199	205	211	217	224	230	236	242
712	248	254	260	266	272	278	285	291	297	303
713	309	315	321	327	333	339	345	352	358	364
714	370	376	382	388	394	400	406	412	418	425
715	431	437	443	449	455	461	467	473	479	485
716	491	497	503	509	516	522	528	534	540	546
717	552	558	564	570	576	582	588	594	600	606
718	612	618	625	631	637	643	649	655	661	667
719	673	679	685	691	697	703	709	715	721	727
720	733	739	745	751	757	763	769	775	781	788
721	794	800	806	812	818	824	830	836	842	848
722	854	860	866	872	878	884	890	896	902	908
723	914	920	926	932	938	944	950	956	962	968
724	974	980	986	992	998	*004	*010	*016	*022	*028
725	86 034	040	046	052	058	064	070	076	082	088
726	094	100	106	112	118	124	130	136	141	147
727	153	159	165	171	177	183	189	195	201	207
728	213	219	225	231	237	243	249	255	261	267
729	273	279	285	291	297	303	308	314	320	326
730	332	338	344	350	356	362	368	374	380	386
731	392	398	404	410	415	421	427	433	439	445
732	451	457	463	469	475	481	487	493	499	504
733	510	516	522	528	534	540	546	552	558	564
734	570	576	581	587	593	599	605	611	617	623
735	629	635	641	646	652	658	664	670	676	682
736	688	694	700	705	711	717	723	729	735	741
737	747	753	759	764	770	776	782	788	794	800
738	806	812	817	823	829	835	841	847	853	859
739	864	870	876	882	888	894	900	906	911	917
740	923	929	935	941	947	953	958	964	970	976
741	982	988	994	999	*005	*011	*017	*023	*029	*035
742	87 040	046	052	058	064	070	075	081	087	093
743	099	105	111	116	122	128	134	140	146	151
744	157	163	169	175	181	186	192	198	204	210
745	216	221	227	233	239	245	251	256	262	268
746	274	280	286	291	297	303	309	315	320	326
747	332	338	344	349	355	361	367	373	379	384
748	390	396	402	408	413	419	425	431	437	442
749	448	454	460	466	471	477	483	489	495	500
750	506	512	518	523	529	535	541	547	552	558
N.	0	1	2	3	4	5	6	7	8	9

Prop. Pts.

7
1|0.7
2|1.4
3|2.1
4|2.8
5|3.5
6|4.2
7|4.9
8|5.6
9|6.3

6
1|0.6
2|1.2
3|1.8
4|2.4
5|3.0
6|3.6
7|4.2
8|4.8
9|5.4

5
1|0.5
2|1.0
3|1.5
4|2.0
5|2.5
6|3.0
7|3.5
8|4.0
9|4.5

N.	0	1	2	3	4	5	6	7	8	9	Prop. Pts.
750	87 506	512	518	523	529	535	541	547	552	558	
751	564	570	576	581	587	593	599	604	610	616	
752	622	628	633	639	645	651	656	662	668	674	
753	679	685	691	697	703	708	714	720	726	731	
754	737	743	749	754	760	766	772	777	783	789	
755	795	800	806	812	818	823	829	835	841	846	
756	852	858	864	869	875	881	887	892	898	904	
757	910	915	921	927	933	938	944	950	955	961	
758	967	973	978	984	990	996	*001	*007	*013	*018	
759	88 024	030	036	041	047	053	058	064	070	076	
760	081	087	093	098	104	110	116	121	127	133	
761	138	144	150	156	161	167	173	178	184	190	
762	195	201	207	213	218	224	230	235	241	247	
763	252	258	264	270	275	281	287	292	298	304	
764	309	315	321	326	332	338	343	349	355	360	
765	366	372	377	383	389	395	400	406	412	417	
766	423	429	434	440	446	451	457	463	468	474	
767	480	485	491	497	502	508	513	519	525	530	
768	536	542	547	553	559	564	570	576	581	587	
769	593	598	604	610	615	621	627	632	638	643	
770	649	655	660	666	672	677	683	689	694	700	
771	705	711	717	722	728	734	739	745	750	756	
772	762	767	773	779	784	790	795	801	807	812	
773	818	824	829	835	840	846	852	857	863	868	
774	874	880	885	891	897	902	908	913	919	925	
775	930	936	941	947	953	958	964	969	975	981	
776	986	992	997	*003	*009	*014	*020	*025	*031	*037	
777	89 042	048	053	059	064	070	076	081	087	092	
778	098	104	109	115	120	126	131	137	143	148	
779	154	159	165	170	176	182	187	193	198	204	
780	209	215	221	226	232	237	243	248	254	260	
781	265	271	276	282	287	293	298	304	310	315	
782	321	326	332	337	343	348	354	360	365	371	
783	376	382	387	393	398	404	409	415	421	426	
784	432	437	443	448	454	459	465	470	476	481	
785	487	492	498	504	509	515	520	526	531	537	
786	542	548	553	559	564	570	575	581	586	592	
787	597	603	609	614	620	625	631	636	642	647	
788	653	658	664	669	675	680	686	691	697	702	
789	708	713	719	724	730	735	741	746	752	757	
790	763	768	774	779	785	790	796	801	807	812	
791	818	823	829	834	840	845	851	856	862	867	
792	873	878	883	889	894	900	905	911	916	922	
793	927	933	938	944	949	955	960	966	971	977	
794	982	988	993	998	*004	*009	*015	*020	*026	*031	
795	90 037	042	048	053	059	064	069	075	080	086	
796	091	097	102	108	113	119	124	129	135	140	
797	146	151	157	162	168	173	179	184	189	195	
798	200	206	211	217	222	227	233	238	244	249	
799	255	260	266	271	276	282	287	293	298	304	
800	309	314	320	325	331	336	342	347	352	358	
N.	0	1	2	3	4	5	6	7	8	9	Prop. Pts.

6

1	0.6
2	1.2
3	1.8
4	2.4
5	3.0
6	3.6
7	4.2
8	4.8
9	5.4

5

1	0.5
2	1.0
3	1.5
4	2.0
5	2.5
6	3.0
7	3.5
8	4.0
9	4.5

21

TABLE II   800-850

N.	0	1	2	3	4	5	6	7	8	9	Prop. Pts.
800	90 309	314	320	325	331	336	342	347	352	358	
801	363	369	374	380	385	390	396	401	407	412	
802	417	423	428	434	439	445	450	455	461	466	
803	472	477	482	488	493	499	504	509	515	520	
804	526	531	536	542	547	553	558	563	569	574	
805	580	585	590	596	601	607	612	617	623	628	
806	634	639	644	650	655	660	666	671	677	682	
807	687	693	698	703	709	714	720	725	730	736	
808	741	747	752	757	763	768	773	779	784	789	
809	795	800	806	811	816	822	827	832	838	843	
810	849	854	859	865	870	875	881	886	891	897	
811	902	907	913	918	924	929	934	940	945	950	
812	956	961	966	972	977	982	988	993	998	*004	
813	91 009	014	020	025	030	036	041	046	052	057	
814	062	068	073	078	084	089	094	100	105	110	
815	116	121	126	132	137	142	148	153	158	164	
816	169	174	180	185	190	196	201	206	212	217	
817	222	228	233	238	243	249	254	259	265	270	
818	275	281	286	291	297	302	307	312	318	323	
819	328	334	339	344	350	355	360	365	371	376	
820	381	387	392	397	403	408	413	418	424	429	
821	434	440	445	450	455	461	466	471	477	482	
822	487	492	498	503	508	514	519	524	529	535	
823	540	545	551	556	561	566	572	577	582	587	
824	593	598	603	609	614	619	624	630	635	640	
825	645	651	656	661	666	672	677	682	687	693	
826	698	703	709	714	719	724	730	735	740	745	
827	751	756	761	766	772	777	782	787	793	798	
828	803	808	814	819	824	829	834	840	845	850	
829	855	861	866	871	876	882	887	892	897	903	
830	908	913	918	924	929	934	939	944	950	955	
831	960	965	971	976	981	986	991	997	*002	*007	
832	92 012	018	023	028	033	038	044	049	054	059	
833	065	070	075	080	085	091	096	101	106	111	
834	117	122	127	132	137	143	148	153	158	163	
835	169	174	179	184	189	195	200	205	210	215	
836	221	226	231	236	241	247	252	257	262	267	
837	273	278	283	288	293	298	304	309	314	319	
838	324	330	335	340	345	350	355	361	366	371	
839	376	381	387	392	397	402	407	412	418	423	
840	428	433	438	443	449	454	459	464	469	474	
841	480	485	490	495	500	505	511	516	521	526	
842	531	536	542	547	552	557	562	567	572	578	
843	583	588	593	598	603	609	614	619	624	629	
844	634	639	645	650	655	660	665	670	675	681	
845	686	691	696	701	706	711	716	722	727	732	
846	737	742	747	752	758	763	768	773	778	783	
847	788	793	799	804	809	814	819	824	829	834	
848	840	845	850	855	860	865	870	875	881	886	
849	891	896	901	906	911	916	921	927	932	937	
850	942	947	952	957	962	967	973	978	983	988	
N.	0	1	2	3	4	5	6	7	8	9	Prop. Pts.

Prop. Pts.

6
1 | 0.6
2 | 1.2
3 | 1.8
4 | 2.4
5 | 3.0
6 | 3.6
7 | 4.2
8 | 4.8
9 | 5.4

5
1 | 0.5
2 | 1.0
3 | 1.5
4 | 2.0
5 | 2.5
6 | 3.0
7 | 3.5
8 | 4.0
9 | 4.5

N.	0	1	2	3	4	5	6	7	8	9
850	92 942	947	952	957	962	967	973	978	983	988
851	993	998	*003	*008	*013	*018	*024	*029	*034	*039
852	93 044	049	054	059	064	069	075	080	085	090
853	095	100	105	110	115	120	125	131	136	141
854	146	151	156	161	166	171	176	181	186	192
855	197	202	207	212	217	222	227	232	237	242
856	247	252	258	263	268	273	278	283	288	293
857	298	303	308	313	318	323	328	334	339	344
858	349	354	359	364	369	374	379	384	389	394
859	399	404	409	414	420	425	430	435	440	445
860	450	455	460	465	470	475	480	485	490	495
861	500	505	510	515	520	526	531	536	541	546
862	551	556	561	566	571	576	581	586	591	596
863	601	606	611	616	621	626	631	636	641	646
864	651	656	661	666	671	676	682	687	692	697
865	702	707	712	717	722	727	732	737	742	747
866	752	757	762	767	772	777	782	787	792	797
867	802	807	812	817	822	827	832	837	842	847
868	852	857	862	867	872	877	882	887	892	897
869	902	907	912	917	922	927	932	937	942	947
870	952	957	962	967	972	977	982	987	992	997
871	94 002	007	012	017	022	027	032	037	042	047
872	052	057	062	067	072	077	082	086	091	096
873	101	106	111	116	121	126	131	136	141	146
874	151	156	161	166	171	176	181	186	191	196
875	201	206	211	216	221	226	231	236	240	245
876	250	255	260	265	270	275	280	285	290	295
877	300	305	310	315	320	325	330	335	340	345
878	349	354	359	364	369	374	379	384	389	394
879	399	404	409	414	419	424	429	433	438	443
880	448	453	458	463	468	473	478	483	488	493
881	498	503	507	512	517	522	527	532	537	542
882	547	552	557	562	567	571	576	581	586	591
883	596	601	606	611	616	621	626	630	635	640
884	645	650	655	660	665	670	675	680	685	689
885	694	699	704	709	714	719	724	729	734	738
886	743	748	753	758	763	768	773	778	783	787
887	792	797	802	807	812	817	822	827	832	836
888	841	846	851	856	861	866	871	876	880	885
889	890	895	900	905	910	915	919	924	929	934
890	939	944	949	954	959	963	968	973	978	983
891	988	993	998	*002	*007	*012	*017	*022	*027	*032
892	95 036	041	046	051	056	061	066	071	075	080
893	085	090	095	100	105	109	114	119	124	129
894	134	139	143	148	153	158	163	168	173	177
895	182	187	192	197	202	207	211	216	221	226
896	231	236	240	245	250	255	260	265	270	274
897	279	284	289	294	299	303	308	313	318	323
898	328	332	337	342	347	352	357	361	366	371
899	376	381	386	390	395	400	405	410	415	419
900	424	429	434	439	444	448	453	458	463	468
N.	0	1	2	3	4	5	6	7	8	9

Prop. Pts.

6		**5**		**4**	
1	0.6	1	0.5	1	0.4
2	1.2	2	1.0	2	0.8
3	1.8	3	1.5	3	1.2
4	2.4	4	2.0	4	1.6
5	3.0	5	2.5	5	2.0
6	3.6	6	3.0	6	2.4
7	4.2	7	3.5	7	2.8
8	4.8	8	4.0	8	3.2
9	5.4	9	4.5	9	3.6

TABLE II   900-950

N.	0	1	2	3	4	5	6	7	8	9	Prop. Pts.
900	95 424	429	434	439	444	448	453	458	463	468	
901	472	477	482	487	492	497	501	506	511	516	
902	521	525	530	535	540	545	550	554	559	564	
903	569	574	578	583	588	593	598	602	607	612	
904	617	622	626	631	636	641	646	650	655	660	
905	665	670	674	679	684	689	694	698	703	708	
906	713	718	722	727	732	737	742	746	751	756	
907	761	766	770	775	780	785	789	794	799	804	
908	809	813	818	823	828	832	837	842	847	852	
909	856	861	866	871	875	880	885	890	895	899	
910	904	909	914	918	923	928	933	938	942	947	**5**
911	952	957	961	966	971	976	980	985	990	995	1 0.5
912	999	*004	*009	*014	*019	*023	*028	*033	*038	*042	2 1.0
913	96 047	052	057	061	066	071	076	080	085	090	3 1.5
914	095	099	104	109	114	118	123	128	133	137	4 2.0
915	142	147	152	156	161	166	171	175	180	185	5 2.5
916	190	194	199	204	209	213	218	223	227	232	6 3.0
917	237	242	246	251	256	261	265	270	275	280	7 3.5 / 8 4.0
918	284	289	294	298	303	308	313	317	322	327	9 4.5
919	332	336	341	346	350	355	360	365	369	374	
920	379	384	388	393	398	402	407	412	417	421	
921	426	431	435	440	445	450	454	459	464	468	
922	473	478	483	487	492	497	501	506	511	515	
923	520	525	530	534	539	544	548	553	558	562	
924	567	572	577	581	586	591	595	600	605	609	
925	614	619	624	628	633	638	642	647	652	656	
926	661	666	670	675	680	685	689	694	699	703	
927	708	713	717	722	727	731	736	741	745	750	
928	755	759	764	769	774	778	783	788	792	797	
929	802	806	811	816	820	825	830	834	839	844	
930	848	853	858	862	867	872	876	881	886	890	
931	895	900	904	909	914	918	923	928	932	937	**4**
932	942	946	951	956	960	965	970	974	979	984	1 0.4
933	988	993	997	*002	*007	*011	*016	*021	*025	*030	2 0.8
934	97 035	039	044	049	053	058	063	067	072	077	3 1.2
935	081	086	090	095	100	104	109	114	118	123	4 1.6
936	128	132	137	142	146	151	155	160	165	169	5 2.0
937	174	179	183	188	192	197	202	206	211	216	6 2.4 / 7 2.8
938	220	225	230	234	239	243	248	253	257	262	8 3.2
939	267	271	276	280	285	290	294	299	304	308	9 3.6
940	313	317	322	327	331	336	340	345	350	354	
941	359	364	368	373	377	382	387	391	396	400	
942	405	410	414	419	424	428	433	437	442	447	
943	451	456	460	465	470	474	479	483	488	493	
944	497	502	506	511	516	520	525	529	534	539	
945	543	548	552	557	562	566	571	575	580	585	
946	589	594	598	603	607	612	617	621	626	630	
947	635	640	644	649	653	658	663	667	672	676	
948	681	685	690	695	699	704	708	713	717	722	
949	727	731	736	740	745	749	754	759	763	768	
950	772	777	782	786	791	795	800	804	809	813	
N.	0	1	2	3	4	5	6	7	8	9	Prop. Pts.

N.	0	1	2	3	4	5	6	7	8	9	Prop. Pts.
950	97 772	777	782	786	791	795	800	804	809	813	
951	818	823	827	832	836	841	845	850	855	859	
952	864	868	873	877	882	886	891	896	900	905	
953	909	914	918	923	928	932	937	941	946	950	
954	955	959	964	968	973	978	982	987	991	996	
955	98 000	005	009	014	019	023	028	032	037	041	
956	046	050	055	059	064	068	073	078	082	087	
957	091	096	100	105	109	114	118	123	127	132	
958	137	141	146	150	155	159	164	168	173	177	
959	182	186	191	195	200	204	209	214	218	223	
960	227	232	236	241	245	250	254	259	263	268	
961	272	277	281	286	290	295	299	304	308	313	
962	318	322	327	331	336	340	345	349	354	358	**5**
963	363	367	372	376	381	385	390	394	399	403	1 0.5
964	408	412	417	421	426	430	435	439	444	448	2 1.0
965	453	457	462	466	471	475	480	484	489	493	3 1.5
966	498	502	507	511	516	520	525	529	534	538	4 2.0
967	543	547	552	556	561	565	570	574	579	583	5 2.5
968	588	592	597	601	605	610	614	619	623	628	6 3.0
969	632	637	641	646	650	655	659	664	668	673	7 3.5
970	677	682	686	691	695	700	704	709	713	717	8 4.0
971	722	726	731	735	740	744	749	753	758	762	9 4.5
972	767	771	776	780	784	789	793	798	802	807	
973	811	816	820	825	829	834	838	843	847	851	
974	856	860	865	869	874	878	883	887	892	896	
975	900	905	909	914	918	923	927	932	936	941	
976	945	949	954	958	963	967	972	976	981	985	
977	989	994	998	*003	*007	*012	*016	*021	*025	*029	
978	99 034	038	043	047	052	056	061	065	069	074	
979	078	083	087	092	096	100	105	109	114	118	
980	123	127	131	136	140	145	149	154	158	162	
981	167	171	176	180	185	189	193	198	202	207	
982	211	216	220	224	229	233	238	242	247	251	**4**
983	255	260	264	269	273	277	282	286	291	295	1 0.4
984	300	304	308	313	317	322	326	330	335	339	2 0.8
985	344	348	352	357	361	366	370	374	379	383	3 1.2
986	388	392	396	401	405	410	414	419	423	427	4 1.6
987	432	436	441	445	449	454	458	463	467	471	5 2.0
988	476	480	484	489	493	498	502	506	511	515	6 2.4
989	520	524	528	533	537	542	546	550	555	559	7 2.8
990	564	568	572	577	581	585	590	594	599	603	8 3.2
991	607	612	616	621	625	629	634	638	642	647	9 3.6
992	651	656	660	664	669	673	677	682	686	691	
993	695	699	704	708	712	717	721	726	730	734	
994	739	743	747	752	756	760	765	769	774	778	
995	782	787	791	795	800	804	808	813	817	822	
996	826	830	835	839	843	848	852	856	861	865	
997	870	874	878	883	887	891	896	900	904	909	
998	913	917	922	926	930	935	939	944	948	952	
999	957	961	965	970	974	978	983	987	991	996	
1000	00 000	004	009	013	017	022	026	030	035	039	
N.	0	1	2	3	4	5	6	7	8	9	Prop. Pts.

Special interpolation in Table III. In the first three columns on pages 28, 29, and 30, the tabular differences are so large that linear interpolation gives inaccurate results. Since every entry for the logarithm of the cosine of an angle near 90° can be thought of as the logarithm of the sine of an angle near 0°, it is sufficient if we consider only the sines of small angles. In like manner, since the tangent and cotangent are both reciprocals and cofunctions, it is sufficient to consider interpolation for tangents of very small angles, for we have

$$\log \tan A = -\log \cot A = -\log \tan (90° - A)$$
$$= \log \cot (90° - A).$$

If A and B are sufficiently small angles, both expressed in minutes, it can be shown that the following relations are accurate to five places of decimals.

(a) *log sin A = log sin B + log A − log B;*
(b) *log tan A = log tan B + log A − log B.*

In particular, these relations will be reliable to five places of decimals if both A and B are less than 3° and $A - B$ is less than 1′. Since these conditions are true for interpolation problems for the sine and tangent in the first columns on pages 28, 29, and 30, these formulas may be used.

Example 1. Find log cos 89° 27.5′. This is the same as finding

$$\log \sin 0° 32.5'.$$

Let $A = 32.5'$, and let $B = 32'$. Then

$$\log \sin 32.5' = \log \sin 32' + \log 32.5 - \log 32,$$

whence log cos 89° 27.5′ = 7.97560 − 10.

Example 2. Find log tan 1° 15.2′. Let $A = 1° 15.2' = 75.2'$, and let $B = 1° 15' = 75'$. Then

log tan 1° 15.2′ = log tan 1° 15′ + log 75.2 − log 75 = 8.34002 − 10.

NOTE. Ordinary linear interpolation in the first example would have given the result 7.97555 − 10, with an error of 5 in the last place. Linear interpolation in the last example would have given the result 8.34001 − 10, with an error of 1 in the last place.

TABLE III

Logarithms of Trigonometric Functions to Five Decimal Places

(Subtract 10 from Each Entry)

TABLE III   0°

′	L Sin	d	L Tan	c d	L Cot	L Cos	
0	———		———		———	0.00 000	**60**
1	6.46 373		6.46 373		13.53 627	0.00 000	59
2	6.76 476	30103	6.76 476	30103	13.23 524	0.00 000	58
3	6.94 085	17609	6.94 085	17609	13.05 915	0.00 000	57
4	7.06 579	12494	7.06 579	12494	12.93 421	0.00 000	56
5	7.16 270	9691	7.16 270	9691	12.83 730	0.00 000	55
6	7.24 188	7918	7.24 188	7918	12.75 812	0.00 000	54
7	7.30 882	6694	7.30 882	6694	12.69 118	0.00 000	53
8	7.36 682	5800	7 36 682	5800	12.63 318	0.00 000	52
9	7.41 797	5115	7.41 797	5115	12.58 203	0.00 000	51
10	7.46 373	4576	7.46 373	4576	12.53 627	0.00 000	**50**
11	7.50 512	4139	7.50 512	4139	12.49 488	0.00 000	49
12	7.54 291	3779	7.54 291	3779	12.45 709	0.00 000	48
13	7.57 767	3476	7.57 767	3476	12.42 233	0.00 000	47
14	7.60 985	3218	7.60 986	3219	12.39 014	0.00 000	46
15	7.63 982	2997	7.63 982	2996	12.36 018	0.00 000	45
16	7.66 784	2802	7.66 785	2803	12.33 215	0.00 000	44
17	7.69 417	2633	7.69 418	2633	12.30 582	9.99 999	43
18	7.71 900	2483	7.71 900	2482	12.28 100	9.99 999	42
19	7.74 248	2348	7.74 248	2348	12.25 752	9.99 999	41
20	7.76 475	2227	7.76 476	2228	12.23 524	9.99 999	**40**
21	7.78 594	2119	7.78 595	2119	12.21 405	9.99 999	39
22	7.80 615	2021	7.80 615	2020	12.19 385	9.99 999	38
23	7.82 545	1930	7.82 546	1931	12.17 454	9.99 999	37
24	7.84 393	1848	7.84 394	1848	12.15 606	9.99 999	36
25	7.86 166	1773	7.86 167	1773	12.13 833	9.99 999	35
26	7.87 870	1704	7.87 871	1704	12.12 129	9.99 999	34
27	7.89 509	1639	7.89 510	1639	12.10 490	9.99 999	33
28	7.91 088	1579	7.91 089	1579	12.08 911	9.99 999	32
29	7.92 612	1524	7.92 613	1524	12.07 387	9.99 998	31
30	7.94 084	1472	7.94 086	1473	12.05 914	9.99 998	**30**
31	7.95 508	1424	7.95 510	1424	12.04 490	9.99 998	29
32	7.96 887	1379	7.96 889	1379	12.03 111	9.99 998	28
33	7.98 223	1336	7.98 225	1336	12.01 775	9.99 998	27
34	7.99 520	1297	7.99 522	1297	12.00 478	9.99 998	26
35	8.00 779	1259	8.00 781	1259	11.99 219	9.99 998	25
36	8.02 002	1223	8.02 004	1223	11.97 996	9.99 998	24
37	8.03 192	1190	8.03 194	1190	11.96 806	9.99 997	23
38	8.04 350	1158	8.04 353	1159	11.95 647	9.99 997	22
39	8.05 478	1128	8.05 481	1128	11.94 519	9.99 997	21
40	8.06 578	1100	8.06 581	1100	11.93 419	9.99 997	**20**
41	8.07 650	1072	8.07 653	1072	11.92 347	9.99 997	19
42	8.08 696	1046	8.08 700	1047	11.91 300	9.99 997	18
43	8.09 718	1022	8.09 722	1022	11.90 278	9.99 997	17
44	8.10 717	999	8.10 720	998	11.89 280	9.99 996	16
45	8.11 693	976	8.11 696	976	11.88 304	9.99 996	15
46	8.12 647	954	8.12 651	955	11.87 349	9.99 996	14
47	8.13 581	934	8.13 585	934	11.86 415	9.99 996	13
48	8.14 495	914	8.14 500	915	11.85 500	9.99 996	12
49	8.15 391	896	8.15 395	895	11.84 605	9.99 996	11
50	8.16 268	877	8.16 273	878	11.83 727	9.99 995	**10**
51	8.17 128	860	8.17 133	860	11.82 867	9.99 995	9
52	8.17 971	843	8.17 976	843	11.82 024	9.99 995	8
53	8.18 798	827	8.18 804	828	11.81 196	9.99 995	7
54	8.19 610	812	8.19 616	812	11.80 384	9.99 995	6
55	8.20 407	797	8.20 413	797	11.79 587	9.99 994	5
56	8.21 189	782	8.21 195	782	11.78 805	9.99 994	4
57	8.21 958	769	8.21 964	769	11.78 036	9.99 994	3
58	8.22 713	755	8.22 720	756	11.77 280	9.99 994	2
59	8.23 456	743	8.23 462	742	11.76 538	9.99 994	1
60	8.24 186	730	8.24 192	730	11.75 808	9.99 993	**0**
	L Cos	d	L Cot	c d	L Tan	L Sin	′

Since the tabular differences in the first three columns of this page, and on each of the two pages following, are so large and change so rapidly in value that ordinary linear interpolation does not give results accurate to five places of decimals, special methods of interpolation are necessary. A brief account of these special methods is given on page 26 of the tables.

'	L Sin	d	L Tan	c d	L Cot	L Cos	
0	8.24 186	717	8.24 192	718	11.75 808	9.99 993	60
1	8.24 903	706	8.24 910	706	11.75 090	9.99 993	59
2	8.25 609	695	8.25 616	696	11.74 384	9.99 993	58
3	8.26 304	684	8.26 312	684	11.73 688	9.99 993	57
4	8.26 988	673	8.26 996	673	11.73 004	9.99 992	56
5	8.27 661	663	8.27 669	663	11.72 331	9.99 992	55
6	8.28 324	653	8.28 332	654	11.71 668	9.99 992	54
7	8.28 977	644	8.28 986	643	11.71 014	9.99 992	53
8	8.29 621	634	8.29 629	634	11.70 371	9.99 992	52
9	8.30 255	624	8.30 263	625	11.69 737	9.99 991	51
10	8.30 879	616	8.30 888	617	11.69 112	9.99 991	50
11	8.31 495	608	8.31 505	607	11.68 495	9.99 991	49
12	8.32 103	599	8.32 112	599	11.67 888	9.99 990	48
13	8.32 702	590	8.32 711	591	11.67 289	9.99 990	47
14	8.33 292	583	8.33 302	584	11.66 698	9.99 990	46
15	8.33 875	575	8.33 886	575	11.66 114	9.99 990	45
16	8.34 450	568	8.34 461	568	11.65 539	9.99 989	44
17	8.35 018	560	8.35 029	561	11.64 971	9.99 989	43
18	8.35 578	553	8.35 590	553	11.64 410	9.99 989	42
19	8.36 131	547	8.36 143	546	11.63 857	9.99 989	41
20	8.36 678	539	8.36 689	540	11.63 311	9.99 988	40
21	8.37 217	533	8.37 229	533	11.62 771	9.99 988	39
22	8.37 750	526	8.37 762	527	11.62 238	9.99 988	38
23	8.83 276	520	8.38 289	520	11.61 711	9.99 987	37
24	8.38 796	514	8.38 809	514	11.61 191	9.99 987	36
25	8.39 310	508	8.39 323	509	11.60 677	9.99 987	35
26	8.39 818	502	8.39 832	502	11.60 168	9.99 986	34
27	8.40 320	496	8.40 334	496	11.59 666	9.99 986	33
28	8.40 816	491	8.40 830	491	11.59 170	9.99 986	32
29	8.41 307	485	8.41 321	486	11.58 679	9.99 985	31
30	8.41 792	480	8.41 807	480	11.58 193	9.99 985	30
31	8.42 272	474	8.42 287	475	11.57 713	9.99 985	29
32	8.42 746	470	8.42 762	470	11.57 238	9.99 984	28
33	8.43 216	464	8.43 232	464	11.56 768	9.99 984	27
34	8.43 680	459	8.43 696	460	11.56 304	9.99 984	26
35	8.44 139	455	8.44 156	455	11.55 844	9.99 983	25
36	8.44 594	450	8.44 611	450	11.55 389	9.99 983	24
37	8.45 044	445	8.45 061	446	11.54 939	9.99 983	23
38	8.45 489	441	8.45 507	441	11.54 493	9.99 982	22
39	8.45 930	436	8.45 948	437	11.54 052	9.99 982	21
40	8.46 366	433	8.46 385	432	11.53 615	9.99 982	20
41	8.46 799	427	8.46 817	428	11.53 183	9.99 981	19
42	8.47 226	424	8.47 245	424	11.52 755	9.99 981	18
43	8.47 650	419	8.47 669	420	11.52 331	9.99 981	17
44	8.48 069	416	8.48 089	416	11.51 911	9.99 980	16
45	8.48 485	411	8.48 505	412	11.51 495	9.99 980	15
46	8.48 896	408	8.48 917	408	11.51 083	9.99 979	14
47	8.49 304	404	8.49 325	404	11.50 675	9.99 979	13
48	8.49 708	400	8.49 729	401	11.50 271	9.99 979	12
49	8.50 108	396	8.50 130	397	11.49 870	9.99 978	11
50	8.50 504	393	8.50 527	393	11.49 473	9.99 978	10
51	8.50 897	390	8.50 920	390	11.49 080	9.99 977	9
52	8.51 287	386	8.51 310	386	11.48 690	9.99 977	8
53	8.51 673	382	8.51 696	383	11.48 304	9.99 977	7
54	8.52 055	379	8.52 079	380	11.47 921	0.00 076	6
55	8.52 434	376	8.52 459	376	11.47 541	9.99 976	5
56	8.52 810	373	8.52 835	373	11.47 165	9.99 975	4
57	8.53 183	369	8.53 208	370	11.46 792	9.99 975	3
58	8.53 552	367	8.53 578	367	11.46 422	9.99 974	2
59	8.53 919	363	8.53 945	363	11.46 055	9.99 974	1
60	8.54 282		8.54 308		11.45 692	9.99 974	0
	L Cos	d	L Cot	c d	L Tan	L Sin	'

If ordinary linear interpolation is not sufficiently accurate, use the special methods described on page 26 of the tables.

88°

TABLE III   2°

′	L Sin	d	L Tan	c d	L Cot	L Cos	
0	8.54 282		8.54 308		11.45 692	9.99 974	60
		360		361			
1	8.54 642	357	8.54 669	358	11.45 331	9.99 973	59
2	8.54 999	355	8.55 027	355	11.44 973	9.99 973	58
3	8.55 354		8.55 382		11.44 618	9.99 972	57
		351		352			
4	8.55 705	349	8.55 734	349	11.44 266	9.99 972	56
5	8.56 054	346	8.56 083	346	11.43 917	9.99 971	55
6	8.56 400		8.56 429		11.43 571	9.99 971	54
		343		344			
7	8.56 743	341	8.56 773	341	11.43 227	9.99 970	53
8	8.57 084	337	8.57 114	338	11.42 886	9.99 970	52
9	8.57 421		8.57 452		11.42 548	9.99 969	51
		336		336			
10	8.57 757	332	8.57 788		11.42 212	9.99 969	50
11	8.58 089	330	8.58 121	333	11.41 879	9.99 968	49
12	8.58 419	328	8.58 451	330	11.41 549	9.99 968	48
13	8.58 747		8.58 779	328	11.41 221	9.99 967	47
		325		326			
14	8.59 072	323	8.59 105	323	11.40 895	9.99 967	46
15	8.59 395	320	8.59 428	321	11.40 572	9.99 967	45
16	8.59 715		8.59 749		11.40 251	9.99 966	44
		318		319			
17	8.60 033	316	8.60 068	316	11.39 932	9.99 966	43
18	8.60 349	313	8.60 384	314	11.39 616	9.99 965	42
19	8.60 662		8.60 698		11.39 302	9.99 964	41
		311		311			
20	8.60 973	309	8.61 009	310	11.38 991	9.99 964	40
21	8.61 282	307	8.61 319	307	11.38 681	9.99 963	39
22	8.61 589	305	8.61 626	305	11.38 374	9.99 963	38
23	8.61 894		8.61 931		11.38 069	9.99 962	37
		302		303			
24	8.62 196	301	8.62 234	301	11.37 766	9.99 962	36
25	8.62 497	298	8.62 535	299	11.37 465	9.99 961	35
26	8.62 795		8.62 834		11.37 166	9.99 961	34
		296		297			
27	8.63 091	294	8.63 131	295	11.36 869	9.99 960	33
28	8.63 385	293	8.63 426	292	11.36 574	9.99 960	32
29	8.63 678		8.63 718		11.36 282	9.99 959	31
		290		291			
30	8.63 968	288	8.64 009	289	11.35 991	9.99 959	30
31	8.64 256	287	8.64 298	287	11.35 702	9.99 958	29
32	8.64 543	284	8.64 585	285	11.35 415	9.99 958	28
33	8.64 827		8.64 870		11.35 130	9.99 957	27
		283		284			
34	8.65 110	281	8.65 154	281	11.34 846	9.99 956	26
35	8.65 391	279	8.65 435	280	11.34 565	9.99 956	25
36	8.65 670		8.65 715		11.34 285	9.99 955	24
		277		278			
37	8.65 947	276	8.65 993	276	11.34 007	9.99 955	23
38	8 66 223	274	8.66 269	274	11.33 731	9.99 954	22
39	8.66 497		8.66 543		11.33 457	9.99 954	21
		272		273			
40	8.66 769	270	8.66 816	271	11.33 184	9.99 953	20
41	8.67 039	269	8.67 087	269	11.32 913	9.99 952	19
42	8.67 308	267	8.67 356	268	11.32 644	9.99 952	18
43	8.67 575		8.67 624		11.32 376	9.99 951	17
		266		266			
44	8.67 841	263	8.67 890	264	11.32 110	9.99 951	16
45	8.68 104	263	8.68 154	263	11.31 846	9.99 950	15
46	8.68 367		8.68 417		11.31 583	9.99 949	14
		260		261			
47	8.68 627	259	8.68 678	260	11.31 322	9.99 949	13
48	8.68 886	258	8.68 938	258	11.31 062	9.99 948	12
49	8.69 144		8.69 196		11.30 804	9.99 948	11
		256		257			
50	8.69 400	254	8.69 453	255	11.30 547	9.99 947	10
51	8.69 654	253	8.69 708	254	11.30 292	9.99 946	9
52	8.69 907	252	8.69 962	252	11.30 038	9.99 946	8
53	8.70 159		8.70 214		11.29 786	9.99 945	7
		250		251			
54	8.70 409	249	8.70 465	249	11.29 535	9.99 944	6
55	8.70 658	247	8.70 714	248	11.29 286	9.99 944	5
56	8.70 905		8.70 962		11.29 038	9.99 943	4
		246		246			
57	8.71 151	244	8.71 208	245	11.28 792	9.99 942	3
58	8.71 395	243	8.71 453	244	11.28 547	9.99 942	2
59	8.71 638		8.71 697		11.28 303	9.99 941	1
		242		243			
60	8.71 880		8.71 940		11.28 060	9.99 940	0
	L Cos	d	L Cot	c d	L Tan	L Sin	′

If ordinary linear interpolation is not sufficiently accurate, use the special methods described on page 26 of the tables.

′	L Sin	d	L Tan	c d	L Cot	L Cos	′
0	8.71 880		8.71 940		11.28 060	9.99 940	60
1	8.72 120	240	8.72 181	241	11.27 819	9.99 940	59
2	8.72 359	239	8.72 420	239	11.27 580	9.99 939	58
3	8.72 597	238	8.72 659	239	11.27 341	9.99 938	57
4	8.72 834	237	8.72 896	237	11.27 104	9.99 938	56
5	8.73 069	235	8.73 132	236	11.26 868	9.99 937	55
6	8.73 303	234	8.73 366	234	11.26 634	9.99 936	54
7	8.73 535	232	8.73 600	234	11.26 400	9.99 936	53
8	8.73 767	232	8.73 832	232	11.26 168	9.99 935	52
9	8.73 997	230	8.74 063	231	11.25 937	9.99 934	51
10	8.74 226	229	8.74 292	229	11.25 708	9.99 934	50
11	8.74 454	228	8.74 521	229	11.25 479	9.99 933	49
12	8.74 680	226	8.74 748	227	11.25 252	9.99 932	48
13	8.74 906	226	8.74 974	226	11.25 026	9.99 932	47
14	8.75 130	224	8.75 199	225	11.24 801	9.99 931	46
15	8.75 353	223	8.75 423	224	11.24 577	9.99 930	45
16	8.75 575	222	8.75 645	224	11.24 355	9.99 929	44
17	8.75 795	220	8.75 867	222	11.24 133	9.99 929	43
18	8.76 015	220	8.76 087	220	11.23 913	9.99 928	42
19	8.76 234	219	8.76 306	220	11.23 694	9.99 927	41
20	8.76 451	217	8.76 525	219	11.23 475	9.99 926	40
21	8.76 667	216	8.76 742	219	11.23 258	9.99 926	39
22	8.76 883	216	8.76 958	217	11.23 042	9.99 925	38
23	8.77 097	214	8.77 173	216	11.22 827	9.99 924	37
24	8.77 310	213	8.77 387	215	11.22 613	9.99 923	36
25	8.77 522	212	8.77 600	214	11.22 400	9.99 923	35
26	8.77 733	211	8.77 811	213	11.22 189	9.99 922	34
27	8.77 943	210	8.78 022	211	11.21 978	9.99 921	33
28	8.78 152	209	8.78 232	210	11.21 768	9.99 920	32
29	8.78 360	208	8.78 441	209	11.21 559	9.99 920	31
30	8.78 568	208	8.78 649	208	11.21 351	9.99 919	30
31	8.78 774	206	8.78 855	206	11.21 145	9.99 918	29
32	8.78 979	205	8.79 061	206	11.20 939	9.99 917	28
33	8.79 183	204	8.79 266	205	11.20 734	9.99 917	27
34	8.79 386	203	8.79 470	204	11.20 530	9.99 916	26
35	8.79 588	202	8.79 673	203	11.20 327	9.99 915	25
36	8.79 789	201	8.79 875	202	11.20 125	9.99 914	24
37	8.79 990	201	8.80 076	201	11.19 924	9.99 913	23
38	8.80 189	199	8.80 277	201	11.19 723	9.99 913	22
39	8.80 388	199	8.80 476	199	11.19 524	9.99 912	21
40	8.80 585	197	8.80 674	198	11.19 326	9.99 911	20
41	8.80 782	197	8.80 872	198	11.19 128	9.99 910	19
42	8.80 978	196	8.81 068	196	11.18 932	9.99 909	18
43	8.81 173	195	8.81 264	196	11.18 736	9.99 909	17
44	8.81 367	194	8.81 459	195	11.18 541	9.99 908	16
45	8.81 560	193	8.81 653	194	11.18 347	9.99 907	15
46	8.81 752	192	8.81 846	193	11.18 154	9.99 906	14
47	8.81 944	192	8.82 038	192	11.17 962	9.99 905	13
48	8.82 134	190	8.82 230	192	11.17 770	9.99 904	12
49	8.82 324	190	8.82 420	190	11.17 580	9.99 904	11
50	8.82 513	189	8.82 610	190	11.17 390	9.99 903	10
51	8.82 701	188	8.82 799	189	11.17 201	9.99 902	9
52	8.82 888	187	8.82 987	188	11.17 013	9.99 901	8
53	8.83 075	187	8.83 175	188	11.16 825	9.99 900	7
54	8.83 261	186	8.83 301	186	11.10 039	9.99 899	6
55	8.83 446	185	8.83 547	186	11.16 453	9.99 898	5
56	8.83 630	184	8.83 732	185	11.16 268	9.99 898	4
57	8.83 813	183	8.83 916	184	11.16 084	9.99 897	3
58	8.83 996	183	8.84 100	184	11.15 900	9.99 896	2
59	8.84 177	181	8.84 282	182	11.15 718	9.99 895	1
60	8.84 358	181	8.84 464	182	11.15 536	9.99 894	0
	L Cos	d	L Cot	c d	L Tan	L Sin	′

Prop. Pts.

	239	237	235	234
2	47.8	47.4	47.0	46.8
3	71.7	71.1	70.5	70.2
4	95.6	94.8	94.0	93.6
5	119.5	118.5	117.5	117.0
6	143.4	142.2	141.0	140.4
7	167.3	165.9	164.5	163.8
8	191.2	189.6	188.0	187.2
9	215.1	213.3	211.5	210.6

	232	229	227	226
2	46.4	45.8	45.4	45.2
3	69.6	68.7	68.1	67.8
4	92.8	91.6	90.8	90.4
5	116.0	114.5	113.5	113.0
6	139.2	137.4	136.2	135.6
7	162.4	160.3	158.9	158.2
8	185.6	183.2	181.6	180.8
9	208.8	206.1	204.3	203.4

	224	222	220	219
2	44.8	44.4	44.0	43.8
3	67.2	66.6	66.0	65.7
4	89.6	88.8	88.0	87.6
5	112.0	111.0	110.0	109.5
6	134.4	133.2	132.0	131.4
7	156.8	155.4	154.0	153.3
8	179.2	177.6	176.0	175.2
9	201.6	199.8	198.0	197.1

	217	215	213	211
2	43.4	43.0	42.6	42.2
3	65.1	64.5	63.9	63.3
4	86.8	86.0	85.2	84.4
5	108.5	107.5	106.5	105.5
6	130.2	129.0	127.8	126.6
7	151.9	150.5	149.1	147.7
8	173.6	172.0	170.4	168.8
9	195.3	193.5	191.7	189.9

	208	206	203	201
2	41.6	41.2	40.6	40.2
3	62.4	61.8	60.9	60.3
4	83.2	82.4	81.2	80.4
5	104.0	103.0	101.5	100.5
6	124.8	123.6	121.8	120.6
7	145.6	144.2	142.1	140.7
8	166.4	164.8	162.4	160.8

	199	197	195	193
2	39.8	39.4	39.0	38.6
3	59.7	59.1	58.5	57.9
4	79.6	78.8	78.0	77.2
5	99.5	98.5	97.5	96.5
6	119.4	118.2	117.0	115.8
7	139.3	137.9	136.5	135.1
8	159.2	157.6	156.0	154.4
9	179.1	177.3	175.5	173.7

	192	190	188	186
2	38.4	38.0	37.6	37.2
3	57.6	57.0	56.4	55.8
4	76.8	76.0	75.2	74.4
5	96.0	95.0	94.0	93.0
6	115.2	114.0	112.8	111.6
7	134.4	133.0	131.6	130.2
8	153.6	152.0	150.4	148.8
9	172.8	171.0	169.2	167.4

	184	183	182	181
2	36.8	36.6	36.4	36.2
3	55.2	54.9	54.6	54.3
4	73.6	73.2	72.8	72.4
5	92.0	91.5	91.0	90.5
6	110.4	109.8	109.2	108.6
7	128.8	128.1	127.4	126.7
8	147.2	146.4	145.6	144.8
9	165.6	164.7	163.8	162.9

Prop. Pts.

TABLE III   4°

'	L Sin	d	L Tan	c d	L Cot	L Cos	'
0	8.84 358		8.84 464		11.15 536	9.99 894	60
		181		182			
1	8.84 539	179	8.84 646	180	11.15 354	9.99 893	59
2	8.84 718	179	8.84 826	180	11.15 174	9.99 892	58
3	8.84 897		8.85 006		11.14 994	9.99 891	57
		178		179			
4	8.85 075	177	8.85 185	178	11.14 815	9.99 891	56
5	8.85 252	177	8.85 363	177	11.14 637	9.99 890	55
6	8.85 429		8.85 540		11.14 460	9.99 889	54
		176		177			
7	8.85 605	175	8.85 717	176	11.14 283	9.99 888	53
8	8.85 780	175	8.85 893	176	11.14 107	9.99 887	52
9	8.85 955		8.86 069		11.13 931	9.99 886	51
		173		174			
10	8.86 128	173	8.86 243	174	11.13 757	9.99 885	50
11	8.86 301	173	8.86 417	174	11.13 583	9.99 884	49
12	8.86 474	171	8.86 591	172	11.13 409	9.99 883	48
13	8.86 645		8.86 763		11.13 237	9.99 882	47
		171		172			
14	8.86 816	171	8.86 935	171	11.13 065	9.99 881	46
15	8.86 987	169	8.87 106	171	11.12 894	9.99 880	45
16	8.87 156	169	8.87 277	170	11.12 723	9.99 879	44
17	8.87 325	169	8.87 447	169	11.12 553	9.99 879	43
18	8.87 494	167	8.87 616	169	11.12 384	9.99 878	42
19	8.87 661	168	8.87 785	168	11.12 215	9.99 877	41
20	8.87 829	166	8.87 953	167	11.12 047	9.99 876	40
21	8.87 995	166	8.88 120	167	11.11 880	9.99 875	39
22	8.88 161	165	8.88 287	166	11.11 713	9.99 874	38
23	8.88 326	164	8.88 453	165	11.11 547	9.99 873	37
24	8.88 490	164	8.88 618	165	11.11 382	9.99 872	36
25	8.88 654	163	8.88 783	165	11.11 217	9.99 871	35
26	8.88 817	163	8.88 948	163	11.11 052	9.99 870	34
27	8.88 980	162	8.89 111	163	11.10 889	9.99 869	33
28	8.89 142	162	8.89 274	163	11.10 726	9.99 868	32
29	8.89 304	160	8.89 437	161	11.10 563	9.99 867	31
30	8.89 464	161	8.89 598	162	11.10 402	9.99 866	30
31	8.89 625	159	8.89 760	160	11.10 240	9.99 865	29
32	8.89 784	159	8.89 920	160	11.10 080	9.99 864	28
33	8.89 943	159	8.90 080	160	11.09 920	9.99 863	27
34	8.90 102	158	8.90 240	159	11.09 760	9.99 862	26
35	8.90 260	157	8.90 399	158	11.09 601	9.99 861	25
36	8.90 417	157	8.90 557	158	11.09 443	9.99 860	24
37	8.90 574	156	8.90 715	157	11.09 285	9.99 859	23
38	8.90 730	155	8.90 872	157	11.09 128	9.99 858	22
39	8.90 885	155	8.91 029	156	11.08 971	9.99 857	21
40	8.91 040	155	8.91 185	155	11.08 815	9.99 856	20
41	8.91 195	154	8.91 340	155	11.08 660	9.99 855	19
42	8.91 349	153	8.91 495	155	11.08 505	9.99 854	18
43	8.91 502	153	8.91 650	153	11.08 350	9.99 853	17
44	8.91 655	152	8.91 803	154	11.08 197	9.99 852	16
45	8.91 807	152	8.91 957	153	11.08 043	9.99 851	15
46	8.91 959	151	8.92 110	152	11.07 890	9.99 850	14
47	8.92 110	151	8.92 262	152	11.07 738	9.99 848	13
48	8.92 261	150	8.92 414	151	11.07 586	9.99 847	12
49	8.92 411	150	8.92 565	151	11.07 435	9.99 846	11
50	8.92 561	149	8.92 716	150	11.07 284	9.99 845	10
51	8.92 710	149	8.92 866	150	11.07 134	9.99 844	9
52	8.92 859	148	8.93 016	149	11.06 984	9.99 843	8
53	8.93 007	147	8.93 165	148	11.06 835	9.99 842	7
54	8.93 154	147	8.93 313	149	11.06 687	9.99 841	6
55	8.93 301	147	8.93 462	147	11.06 538	9.99 840	5
56	8.93 448	146	8.93 609	147	11.06 391	9.99 839	4
57	8.93 594	146	8.93 756	147	11.06 244	9.99 838	3
58	8.93 740	145	8.93 903	146	11.06 097	9.99 837	2
59	8.93 885	145	8.94 049	146	11.05 951	9.99 836	1
60	8.94 030		8.94 195		11.05 805	9.99 834	0
	L Cos	d	L Cot	c d	L Tan	L Sin	'

Prop. Pts.

	182	181	180	179
2	36.4	36.2	36.0	35.8
3	54.6	54.3	54.0	53.7
4	72.8	72.4	72.0	71.6
5	91.0	90.5	90.0	89.5
6	109.2	108.6	108.0	107.4
7	127.4	126.7	126.0	125.3
8	145.6	144.8	144.0	143.2
9	163.8	162.9	162.0	161.1

	178	177	176	175
2	35.6	35.4	35.2	35.0
3	53.4	53.1	52.8	52.5
4	71.2	70.8	70.4	70.0
5	89.0	88.5	88.0	87.5
6	106.8	106.2	105.6	105.0
7	124.6	123.9	123.2	122.5
8	142.4	141.6	140.8	140.0
9	160.2	159.3	158.4	157.5

	174	173	172	171
2	34.8	34.6	34.4	34.2
3	52.2	51.9	51.6	51.3
4	69.6	69.2	68.8	68.4
5	87.0	86.5	86.0	85.5
6	104.4	103.8	103.2	102.6
7	121.8	121.1	120.4	119.7
8	139.2	138.4	137.6	136.8
9	156.6	155.7	154.8	153.9

	170	169	168	167
2	34.0	33.8	33.6	33.4
3	51.0	50.7	50.4	50.1
4	68.0	67.6	67.2	66.8
5	85.0	84.5	84.0	83.5
6	102.0	101.4	100.8	100.2
7	119.0	118.3	117.6	116.9
8	136.0	135.2	134.4	133.6
9	153.0	152.1	151.2	150.3

	166	165	164	163
2	33.2	33.0	32.8	32.6
3	49.8	49.5	49.2	48.9
4	66.4	66.0	65.6	65.2
5	83.0	82.5	82.0	81.5
6	99.6	99.0	98.4	97.8
7	116.2	115.5	114.8	114.1
8	132.8	132.0	131.2	130.4
9	149.4	148.5	147.6	146.7

	162	161	160	159
2	32.4	32.2	32.0	31.8
3	48.6	48.3	48.0	47.7
4	64.8	64.4	64.0	63.6
5	81.0	80.5	80.0	79.5
6	97.2	96.6	96.0	95.4
7	113.4	112.7	112.0	111.3
8	129.6	128.8	128.0	127.2
9	145.8	144.9	144.0	143.1

	158	157	156	155
2	31.6	31.4	31.2	31.0
3	47.4	47.1	46.8	46.5
4	63.2	62.8	62.4	62.0
5	79.0	78.5	78.0	77.5
6	94.8	94.2	93.6	93.0
7	110.6	109.9	109.2	108.5
8	126.4	125.6	124.8	124.0
9	142.2	141.3	140.4	139.5

	154	153	152
2	30.8	30.6	30.4
3	46.2	45.9	45.6
4	61.6	61.2	60.8
5	77.0	76.5	76.0
6	92.4	91.8	91.2
7	107.8	107.1	106.4
8	123.2	122.4	121.6
9	138.6	137.7	136.8

Prop. Pts.

85°

′	L Sin	d	L Tan	c d	L Cot	L Cos	
0	8.94 030		8.94 195		11.05 805	9.99 834	60
		144		145			
1	8.94 174		8.94 340		11.05 660	9.99 833	59
		143		145			
2	8.94 317		8.94 485		11.05 515	9.99 832	58
		144		145			
3	8.94 461		8.94 630		11.05 370	9.99 831	57
		142		143			
4	8.94 603		8.94 773		11.05 227	9.99 830	56
		143		144			
5	8.94 746		8.94 917		11.05 083	9.99 829	55
		141		143			
6	8.94 887		8.95 060		11.04 940	9.99 828	54
		142		142			
7	8.95 029		8.95 202		11.04 798	9.99 827	53
		141		142			
8	8.95 170		8.95 344		11.04 656	9.99 825	52
		140		142			
9	8.95 310		8.95 486		11.04 514	9.99 824	51
		140		141			
10	8.95 450		8.95 627		11.04 373	9.99 823	50
		139		140			
11	8.95 589		8.95 767		11.04 233	9.99 822	49
		139		141			
12	8.95 728		8.95 908		11.04 092	9.99 821	48
		139		139			
13	8.95 867		8.96 047		11.03 953	9.99 820	47
		138		140			
14	8.96 005		8.96 187		11.03 813	9.99 819	46
		138		138			
15	8.96 143		8.96 325		11.03 675	9.99 817	45
		137		139			
16	8.96 280		8.96 464		11.03 536	9.99 816	44
		137		138			
17	8.96 417		8.96 602		11.03 398	9.99 815	43
		136		137			
18	8.96 553		8.96 739		11.03 261	9.99 814	42
		136		138			
19	8.96 689		8.96 877		11.03 123	9.99 813	41
		136		136			
20	8.96 825		8.97 013		11.02 987	9.99 812	40
		135		137			
21	8.96 960		8.97 150		11.02 850	9.99 810	39
		135		135			
22	8.97 095		8.97 285		11.02 715	9.99 809	38
		134		136			
23	8.97 229		8.97 421		11.02 579	9.99 808	37
		134		135			
24	8.97 363		8.97 556		11.02 444	9.99 807	36
		133		135			
25	8.97 496		8.97 691		11.02 309	9.99 806	35
		133		134			
26	8.97 629		8.97 825		11.02 175	9.99 804	34
		133		134			
27	8.97 762		8.97 959		11.02 041	9.99 803	33
		132		133			
28	8.97 894		8.98 092		11.01 908	9.99 802	32
		132		133			
29	8.98 026		8.98 225		11.01 775	9.99 801	31
		131		133			
30	8.98 157		8.98 358		11.01 642	9.99 800	30
		131		132			
31	8.98 288		8.98 490		11.01 510	9.99 798	29
		131		132			
32	8.98 419		8.98 622		11.01 378	9.99 797	28
		130		131			
33	8.98 549		8.98 753		11.01 247	9.99 796	27
		130		131			
34	8.98 679		8.98 884		11.01 116	9.99 795	26
		129		131			
35	8.98 808		8.99 015		11.00 985	9.99 793	25
		129		130			
36	8.98 937		8.99 145		11.00 855	9.99 792	24
		129		130			
37	8.99 066		8.99 275		11.00 725	9.99 791	23
		128		130			
38	8.99 194		8.99 405		11.00 595	9.99 790	22
		128		129			
39	8.99 322		8.99 534		11.00 466	9.99 788	21
		128		128			
40	8.99 450		8.99 662		11.00 338	9.99 787	20
		127		129			
41	8.99 577		8.99 791		11.00 209	9.99 786	19
		127		128			
42	8.99 704		8.99 919		11.00 081	9.99 785	18
		126		127			
43	8.99 830		9.00 046		10.99 954	9.99 783	17
		126		128			
44	8.99 956		9.00 174		10.99 826	9.99 782	16
		126		127			
45	9.00 082		9.00 301		10.99 699	9.99 781	15
		125		126			
46	9.00 207		9.00 427		10.99 573	9.99 780	14
		125		126			
47	9.00 332		9.00 553		10.99 447	9.99 778	13
		124		126			
48	9.00 456		9.00 679		10.99 321	9.99 777	12
		125		126			
49	9.00 581		9.00 805		10.99 195	9.99 776	11
		123		125			
50	9.00 704		9.00 930		10.99 070	9.99 775	10
		124		125			
51	9.00 828		9.01 055		10.98 945	9.99 773	9
		123		124			
52	9.00 951		9.01 179		10.98 821	9.99 772	8
		123		124			
53	9.01 074		9.01 303		10.98 697	9.99 771	7
		122		124			
54	9.01 196		9.01 427		10.98 573	9.99 769	6
		122		123			
55	9.01 318		9.01 550		10.98 450	9.99 768	5
		122		123			
56	9.01 440		9.01 673		10.98 327	9.99 767	4
		121		123			
57	9.01 561		9.01 796		10.98 204	9.99 765	3
		121		122			
58	9.01 682		9.01 918		10.98 082	9.99 764	2
		121		122			
59	9.01 803		9.02 040		10.97 960	9.99 763	1
		120		122			
60	9.01 923		9.02 162		10.97 838	9.99 761	0
	L Cos	d	L Cot	c d	L Tan	L Sin	′

Prop. Pts.

	151	150	149	148
2	30.2	30.0	29.8	29.6
3	45.3	45.0	44.7	44.4
4	60.4	60.0	59.6	59.2
5	75.5	75.0	74.5	74.0
6	90.6	90.0	89.4	88.8
7	105.7	105.0	104.3	103.6
8	120.8	120.0	119.2	118.4
9	135.9	135.0	134.1	133.2

	147	146	145	144
2	29.4	29.2	29.0	28.8
3	44.1	43.8	43.5	43.2
4	58.8	58.4	58.0	57.6
5	73.5	73.0	72.5	72.0
6	88.2	87.6	87.0	86.4
7	102.9	102.2	101.5	100.8
8	117.6	116.8	116.0	115.2
9	132.3	131.4	130.5	129.6

	143	142	141	140
2	28.6	28.4	28.2	28.0
3	42.9	42.6	42.3	42.0
4	57.2	56.8	56.4	56.0
5	71.5	71.0	70.5	70.0
6	85.8	85.2	84.6	84.0
7	100.1	99.4	98.7	98.0
8	114.4	113.6	112.8	112.0
9	128.7	127.8	126.9	126.0

	139	138	137	136
2	27.8	27.6	27.4	27.2
3	41.7	41.4	41.1	40.8
4	55.6	55.2	54.8	54.4
5	69.5	69.0	68.5	68.0
6	83.4	82.8	82.2	81.6
7	97.3	96.6	95.9	95.2
8	111.2	110.4	109.6	108.8
9	125.1	124.2	123.3	122.4

	135	134	133	132
2	27.0	26.8	26.6	26.4
3	40.5	40.2	39.9	39.6
4	54.0	53.6	53.2	52.8
5	67.5	67.0	66.5	66.0
6	81.0	80.4	79.8	79.2
7	94.5	93.8	93.1	92.4
8	108.0	107.2	106.4	105.6
9	121.5	120.6	119.7	118.8

	131	130	129	128
2	26.2	26.0	25.8	25.6
3	39.3	39.0	38.7	38.4
4	52.4	52.0	51.6	51.2
5	65.5	65.0	64.5	64.0
6	78.6	78.0	77.4	76.8
7	91.7	91.0	90.3	89.6
8	104.8	104.0	103.2	102.4
9	117.9	117.0	116.1	115.2

	127	126	125	124
2	25.4	25.2	25.0	24.8
3	38.1	37.8	37.5	37.2
4	50.8	50.4	50.0	49.6
5	63.5	63.0	62.5	62.0
6	76.2	75.6	75.0	74.4
7	88.9	88.2	87.5	86.8
8	101.6	100.8	100.0	99.2
9	114.3	113.4	112.5	111.6

	123	122	121	120
2	24.6	24.4	24.2	24.0
3	36.9	36.6	36.3	36.0
4	49.2	48.8	48.4	48.0
5	61.5	61.0	60.5	60.0
6	73.8	73.2	72.6	72.0
7	86.1	85.4	84.7	84.0
8	98.4	97.6	96.8	96.0
9	110.7	109.8	108.9	108.0

TABLE III   6°

′	L Sin	d	L Tan	c d	L Cot	L Cos		Prop. Pts.
0	9.01 923		9.02 162		10.97 838	9.99 761	**60**	
1	9.02 043	120	9.02 283	121	10.97 717	9.99 760	59	
2	9.02 163	120	9.02 404	121	10.97 596	9.99 759	58	
3	9.02 283	120	9.02 525	121	10.97 475	9.99 757	57	
4	9.02 402	119	9.02 645	120	10.97 355	9.99 756	56	
5	9.02 520	118	9.02 766	121	10.97 234	9.99 755	55	
6	9.02 639	119	9.02 885	119	10.97 115	9.99 753	54	
7	9.02 757	118	9.03 005	120	10.96 995	9.99 752	53	
8	9.02 874	117	9.03 124	119	10.96 876	9.99 751	52	
9	9.02 992	118	9.03 242	118	10.96 758	9.99 749	51	
10	9.03 109	117	9.03 361	119	10.96 639	9.99 748	**50**	
11	9.03 226	117	9.03 479	118	10.96 521	9.99 747	49	
12	9.03 342	116	9.03 597	118	10.96 403	9.99 745	48	
13	9.03 458	116	9.03 714	117	10.96 286	9.99 744	47	
14	9.03 574	116	9.03 832	118	10.96 168	9.99 742	46	
15	9.03 690	116	9.03 948	116	10.96 052	9.99 741	45	
16	9.03 805	115	9.04 065	117	10.95 935	9.99 740	44	
17	9.03 920	115	9.04 181	116	10.95 819	9.99 738	43	
18	9.04 034	114	9.04 297	116	10.95 703	9.99 737	42	
19	9.04 149	115	9.04 413	116	10.95 587	9.99 736	41	
20	9.04 262	113	9.04 528	115	10.95 472	9.99 734	**40**	
21	9.04 376	114	9.04 643	115	10.95 357	9.99 733	39	
22	9.04 490	114	9.04 758	115	10.95 242	9.99 731	38	
23	9.04 603	113	9.04 873	115	10.95 127	9.99 730	37	
24	9.04 715	112	9.04 987	114	10.95 013	9.99 728	36	
25	9.04 828	113	9.05 101	114	10.94 899	9.99 727	35	
26	9.04 940	112	9.05 214	113	10.94 786	9.99 726	34	
27	9.05 052	112	9.05 328	114	10.94 672	9.99 724	33	
28	9.05 164	112	9.05 441	113	10.94 559	9.99 723	32	
29	9.05 275	111	9.05 553	112	10.94 447	9.99 721	31	
30	9.05 386	111	9.05 666	113	10.94 334	9.99 720	**30**	
31	9.05 497	111	9.05 778	112	10.94 222	9.99 718	29	
32	9.05 607	110	9.05 890	112	10.94 110	9.99 717	28	
33	9.05 717	110	9.06 002	112	10.93 998	9.99 716	27	
34	9.05 827	110	9.06 113	111	10.93 887	9.99 714	26	
35	9.05 937	110	9.06 224	111	10.93 776	9.99 713	25	
36	9.06 046	109	9.06 335	111	10.93 665	9.99 711	24	
37	9.06 155	109	9.06 445	110	10.93 555	9.99 710	23	
38	9.06 264	109	9.06 556	111	10.93 444	9.99 708	22	
39	9.06 372	108	9.06 666	110	10.93 334	9.99 707	21	
40	9.06 481	109	9.06 775	109	10.93 225	9.99 705	**20**	
41	9.06 589	108	9.06 885	110	10.93 115	9.99 704	19	
42	9.06 696	107	9.06 994	109	10.93 006	9.99 702	18	
43	9.06 804	108	9.07 103	109	10.92 897	9.99 701	17	
44	9.06 911	107	9.07 211	108	10.92 789	9.99 699	16	
45	9.07 018	107	9.07 320	109	10.92 680	9.99 698	15	
46	9.07 124	106	9.07 428	108	10.92 572	9.99 696	14	
47	9.07 231	107	9.07 536	108	10.92 464	9.99 695	13	
48	9.07 337	106	9.07 643	107	10.92 357	9.99 693	12	
49	9.07 442	105	9.07 751	108	10.92 249	9.99 692	11	
50	9.07 548	106	9.07 858	107	10.92 142	9.99 690	**10**	
51	9.07 653	105	9.07 964	106	10.92 036	9.99 689	9	
52	9.07 758	105	9.08 071	107	10.91 929	9.99 687	8	
53	9.07 863	105	9.08 177	106	10.91 823	9.99 686	7	
54	9.07 968	105	9.08 283	106	10.91 717	9.99 684	6	
55	9.08 072	104	9.08 389	106	10.91 611	9.99 683	5	
56	9.08 176	104	9.08 495	105	10.91 505	9.99 681	4	
57	9.08 280	104	9.08 600	105	10.91 400	9.99 680	3	
58	9.08 383	103	9.08 705	105	10.91 295	9.99 678	2	
59	9.08 486	103	9.08 810	104	10.91 190	9.99 677	1	
60	9.08 589	103	9.08 914		10.91 086	9.99 675	**0**	
	L Cos	d	L Cot	c d	L Tan	L Sin	′	Prop. Pts.

Prop. Pts.

	121	120	119
1	12.1	12.0	11.9
2	24.2	24.0	23.8
3	36.3	36.0	35.7
4	48.4	48.0	47.6
5	60.5	60.0	59.5
6	72.6	72.0	71.4
7	84.7	84.0	83.3
8	96.8	96.0	95.2
9	108.9	108.0	107.1

	118	117	116
1	11.8	11.7	11.6
2	23.6	23.4	23.2
3	35.4	35.1	34.8
4	47.2	46.8	46.4
5	59.0	58.5	58.0
6	70.8	70.2	69.6
7	82.6	81.9	81.2
8	94.4	93.6	92.8
9	106.2	105.3	104.4

	115	114	113
1	11.5	11.4	11.3
2	23.0	22.8	22.6
3	34.5	34.2	33.9
4	46.0	45.6	45.2
5	57.5	57.0	56.5
6	69.0	68.4	67.8
7	80.5	79.8	79.1
8	92.0	91.2	90.4
9	103.5	102.6	101.7

	112	111	110
1	11.2	11.1	11.0
2	22.4	22.2	22.0
3	33.6	33.3	33.0
4	44.8	44.4	44.0
5	56.0	55.5	55.0
6	67.2	66.6	66.0
7	78.4	77.7	77.0
8	89.6	88.8	88.0
9	100.8	99.9	99.0

	109	108	107	106
1	10.9	10.8	10.7	10.6
2	21.8	21.6	21.4	21.2
3	32.7	32.4	32.1	31.8
4	43.6	43.2	42.8	42.4
5	54.5	54.0	53.5	53.0
6	65.4	64.8	64.2	63.6
7	76.3	75.6	74.9	74.2
8	87.2	86.4	85.6	84.8
9	98.1	97.2	96.3	95.4

'	L Sin	d	L Tan	c d	L Cot	L Cos	
0	9.08 589	103	9.08 914	105	10.91 086	9.99 675	60
1	9.08 692	103	9.09 019	104	10.90 981	9.99 674	59
2	9.08 795	102	9.09 123	104	10.90 877	9.99 672	58
3	9.08 897	102	9.09 227	103	10.90 773	9.99 670	57
4	9.08 999	102	9.09 330	104	10.90 670	9.99 669	56
5	9.09 101	101	9.09 434	103	10.90 566	9.99 667	55
6	9.09 202	102	9.09 537	103	10.90 463	9.99 666	54
7	9.09 304	101	9.09 640	102	10.90 360	9.99 664	53
8	9.09 405	101	9.09 742	103	10.90 258	9.99 663	52
9	9.09 506	100	9.09 845	102	10.90 155	9.99 661	51
10	9.09 606	101	9.09 947	102	10.90 053	9.99 659	50
11	9.09 707	100	9.10 049	101	10.89 951	9.99 658	49
12	9.09 807	100	9.10 150	102	10.89 850	9.99 656	48
13	9.09 907	99	9.10 252	101	10.89 748	9.99 655	47
14	9.10 006	100	9.10 353	101	10.89 647	9.99 653	46
15	9.10 106	99	9.10 454	101	10.89 546	9.99 651	45
16	9.10 205	99	9.10 555	101	10.89 445	9.99 650	44
17	9.10 304	98	9.10 656	100	10.89 344	9.99 648	43
18	9.10 402	99	9.10 756	100	10.89 244	9.99 647	42
19	9.10 501	98	9.10 856	100	10.89 144	9.99 645	41
20	9.10 599	98	9.10 956	100	10.89 044	9.99 643	40
21	9.10 697	98	9.11 056	99	10.88 944	9.99 642	39
22	9.10 795	98	9.11 155	99	10.88 845	9.99 640	38
23	9.10 893	97	9.11 254	99	10.88 746	9.99 638	37
24	9.10 990	97	9.11 353	99	10.88 647	9.99 637	36
25	9.11 087	97	9.11 452	99	10.88 548	9.99 635	35
26	9.11 184	97	9.11 551	98	10.88 449	9.99 633	34
27	9.11 281	96	9.11 649	98	10.88 351	9.99 632	33
28	9.11 377	97	9.11 747	98	10.88 253	9.99 630	32
29	9.11 474	96	9.11 845	98	10.88 155	9.99 629	31
30	9.11 570	96	9.11 943	98	10.88 057	9.99 627	30
31	9.11 666	96	9.12 040	97	10.87 960	9.99 625	29
32	9.11 761	95	9.12 138	98	10.87 862	9.99 624	28
33	9.11 857	96	9.12 235	97	10.87 765	9.99 622	27
34	9.11 952	95	9.12 332	97	10.87 668	9.99 620	26
35	9.12 047	95	9.12 428	96	10.87 572	9.99 618	25
36	9.12 142	95	9.12 525	97	10.87 475	9.99 617	24
37	9.12 236	94	9.12 621	96	10.87 379	9.99 615	23
38	9.12 331	95	9.12 717	96	10.87 283	9.99 613	22
39	9.12 425	94	9.12 813	96	10.87 187	9.99 612	21
40	9.12 519	94	9.12 909	96	10.87 091	9.99 610	20
41	9.12 612	94	9.13 004	95	10.86 996	9.99 608	19
42	9.12 706	93	9.13 099	95	10.86 901	9.99 607	18
43	9.12 799	93	9.13 194	95	10.86 806	9.99 605	17
44	9.12 892	93	9.13 289	95	10.86 711	9.99 603	16
45	9.12 985	93	9.13 384	94	10.86 616	9.99 601	15
46	9.13 078	93	9.13 478	95	10.86 522	9.99 600	14
47	9 13 171	92	9.13 573	94	10.86 427	9.99 598	13
48	9.13 263	92	9.13 667	94	10.86 333	9.99 596	12
49	9.13 355	92	9.13 761	93	10.86 239	9.99 595	11
50	9.13 447	92	9.13 854	94	10.86 146	9.99 593	10
51	9.13 539	91	9.13 948	93	10.86 052	9.99 591	9
52	9.13 630	92	9.14 041	93	10.85 959	9.99 589	8
53	9.13 722	91	9.14 134	93	10.85 866	9.99 588	7
54	9.13 813	91	9.14 227	93	10.85 773	9.99 586	6
55	9.13 904	90	9.14 320	92	10.85 680	9.99 584	5
56	9.13 994	91	9.14 412	92	10.85 588	9.99 583	4
57	9.14 085	90	9.14 504	93	10.85 496	9.99 581	3
58	9.14 175	91	9.14 597	91	10.85 403	9.99 579	2
59	9.14 266	90	9.14 688	92	10.85 312	9.99 577	1
60	9.14 356		9.14 780		10.85 220	9.99 575	0
	L Cos	d	L Cot	c d	L Tan	L Sin	'

Prop. Pts.

	105	104	103
1	10.5	10.4	10.3
2	21.0	20.8	20.6
3	31.5	31.2	30.9
4	42.0	41.6	41.2
5	52.5	52.0	51.5
6	63.0	62.4	61.8
7	73.5	72.8	72.1
8	84.0	83.2	82.4
9	94.5	93.6	92.7

	102	101	99
1	10.2	10.1	9.9
2	20.4	20.2	19.8
3	30.6	30.3	29.7
4	40.8	40.4	39.6
5	51.0	50.5	49.5
6	61.2	60.6	59.4
7	71.4	70.7	69.3
8	81.6	80.8	79.2
9	91.8	90.9	89.1

	98	97	96
1	9.8	9.7	9.6
2	19.6	19.4	19.2
3	29.4	29.1	28.8
4	39.2	38.8	38.4
5	49.0	48.5	48.0
6	58.8	58.2	57.6
7	68.6	67.9	67.2
8	78.4	77.6	76.8
9	88.2	87.3	86.4

	95	94	93
1	9.5	9.4	9.3
2	19.0	18.8	18.6
3	28.5	28.2	27.9
4	38.0	37.6	37.2
5	47.5	47.0	46.5
6	57.0	56.4	55.8
7	66.5	65.8	65.1
8	76.0	75.2	74.4
9	85.5	84.6	83.7

	92	91	90
1	9.2	9.1	9.0
2	18.4	18.2	18.0
3	27.6	27.3	27.0
4	36.8	36.4	36.0
5	46.0	45.5	45.0
6	55.2	54.6	54.0
7	64.4	63.7	63.0
8	73.6	72.8	72.0
9	82.8	81.9	81.0

Prop. Pts.

TABLE III   8°

′	L Sin	d	L Tan	c d	L Cot	L Cos	
0	9.14 356	89	9.14 780	92	10.85 220	9.99 575	**60**
1	9.14 445	90	9.14 872	91	10.85 128	9.99 574	59
2	9.14 535	89	9.14 963	91	10.85 037	9.99 572	58
3	9.14 624	90	9.15 054	91	10.84 946	9.99 570	57
4	9.14 714	89	9.15 145	91	10.84 855	9.99 568	56
5	9.14 803	88	9.15 236	91	10.84 764	9.99 566	55
6	9.14 891	89	9.15 327	90	10.84 673	9.99 565	54
7	9.14 980	89	9.15 417	91	10.84 583	9.99 563	53
8	9.15 069	88	9.15 508	90	10.84 492	9.99 561	52
9	9.15 157	88	9.15 598	90	10.84 402	9.99 559	51
10	9.15 245	88	9.15 688	89	10.84 312	9.99 557	**50**
11	9.15 333	88	9.15 777	90	10.84 223	9.99 556	49
12	9.15 421	87	9.15 867	89	10.84 133	9.99 554	48
13	9.15 508	88	9.15 956	90	10.84 044	9.99 552	47
14	9.15 596	87	9.16 046	89	10.83 954	9.99 550	46
15	9.15 683	87	9.16 135	89	10.83 865	9.99 548	45
16	9.15 770	87	9.16 224	88	10.83 776	9.99 546	44
17	9.15 857	87	9.16 312	89	10.83 688	9.99 545	43
18	9.15 944	86	9.16 401	88	10.83 599	9.99 543	42
19	9.16 030	86	9.16 489	88	10.83 511	9.99 541	41
20	9.16 116	87	9.16 577	88	10.83 423	9.99 539	**40**
21	9.16 203	86	9.16 665	88	10.83 335	9.99 537	39
22	9.16 289	85	9.16 753	88	10.83 247	9.99 535	38
23	9.16 374	86	9.16 841	87	10.83 159	9.99 533	37
24	9.16 460	85	9.16 928	88	10.83 072	9.99 532	36
25	9.16 545	86	9.17 016	87	10.82 984	9.99 530	35
26	9.16 631	85	9.17 103	87	10.82 897	9.99 528	34
27	9.16 716	85	9.17 190	87	10.82 810	9.99 526	33
28	9.16 801	85	9.17 277	86	10.82 723	9.99 524	32
29	9.16 886	84	9.17 363	87	10.82 637	9.99 522	31
30	9.16 970	85	9.17 450	86	10.82 550	9.99 520	**30**
31	9.17 055	84	9.17 536	86	10.82 464	9.99 518	29
32	9.17 139	84	9.17 622	86	10.82 378	9.99 517	28
33	9.17 223	84	9.17 708	86	10.82 292	9.99 515	27
34	9.17 307	84	9.17 794	86	10.82 206	9.99 513	26
35	9.17 391	83	9.17 880	85	10.82 120	9.99 511	25
36	9.17 474	84	9.17 965	86	10.82 035	9.99 509	24
37	9.17 558	83	9.18 051	85	10.81 949	9.99 507	23
38	9.17 641	83	9.18 136	85	10.81 864	9.99 505	22
39	9.17 724	83	9.18 221	85	10.81 779	9.99 503	21
40	9.17 807	83	9.18 306	85	10.81 694	9.99 501	**20**
41	9.17 890	83	9.18 391	84	10.81 609	9.99 499	19
42	9.17 983	82	9.18 475	85	10.81 525	9.99 497	18
43	9.18 055	82	9.18 560	84	10.81 440	9.99 495	17
44	9.18 137	83	9.18 644	84	10.81 356	9.99 494	16
45	9.18 220	82	9.18 728	84	10.81 272	9.99 492	15
46	9.18 302	81	9.18 812	84	10.81 188	9.99 490	14
47	9.18 383	82	9.18 896	83	10.81 104	9.99 488	13
48	9.18 465	82	9.18 979	84	10.81 021	9.99 486	12
49	9.18 547	81	9.19 063	83	10.80 937	9.99 484	11
50	9.18 628	81	9.19 146	83	10.80 854	9.99 482	**10**
51	9.18 709	81	9.19 229	83	10.80 771	9.99 480	9
52	9.18 790	81	9.19 312	83	10.80 688	9.99 478	8
53	9.18 871	81	9.19 395	83	10.80 605	9.99 476	7
54	9.18 952	81	9.19 478	83	10.80 522	9.99 474	6
55	9.19 033	80	9.19 561	82	10.80 439	9.99 472	5
56	9.19 113	80	9.19 643	82	10.80 357	9.99 470	4
57	9.19 193	80	9.19 725	82	10.80 275	9.99 468	3
58	9.19 273	80	9.19 807	82	10.80 193	9.99 466	2
59	9.19 353	80	9.19 889	82	10.80 111	9.99 464	1
60	9.19 433		9.19 971		10.80 029	9.99 462	**0**
	L Cos	d	L Cot	c d	L Tan	L Sin	′

Prop. Pts.

	92	91	90
1	9.2	9.1	9.0
2	18.4	18.2	18.0
3	27.6	27.3	27.0
4	36.8	36.4	36.0
5	46.0	45.5	45.0
6	55.2	54.6	54.0
7	64.4	63.7	63.0
8	73.6	72.8	72.0
9	82.8	81.9	81.0

	89	88	87
1	8.9	8.8	8.7
2	17.8	17.6	17.4
3	26.7	26.4	26.1
4	35.6	35.2	34.8
5	44.5	44.0	43.5
6	53.4	52.8	52.2
7	62.3	61.6	60.9
8	71.2	70.4	69.6
9	80.1	79.2	78.3

	86	85	84
1	8.6	8.5	8.4
2	17.2	17.0	16.8
3	25.8	25.5	25.2
4	34.4	34.0	33.6
5	43.0	42.5	42.0
6	51.6	51.0	50.4
7	60.2	59.5	58.8
8	68.8	68.0	67.2
9	77.4	76.5	75.6

	83	82	81	80
1	8.3	8.2	8.1	8.0
2	16.6	16.4	16.2	16.0
3	24.9	24.6	24.3	24.0
4	33.2	32.8	32.4	32.0
5	41.5	41.0	40.5	40.0
6	49.8	49.2	48.6	48.0
7	58.1	57.4	56.7	56.0
8	66.4	65.6	64.8	64.0
9	74.7	73.8	72.9	72.0

′	L Sin	d	L Tan	c d	L Cot	L Cos	
0	9.19 433		9.19 971		10.80 029	9.99 462	60
1	9.19 513	80	9.20 053	82	10.79 947	9.99 460	59
2	9.19 592	79	9.20 134	81	10.79 866	9.99 458	58
3	9.19 672	80	9.20 216	82	10.79 784	9.99 456	57
4	9.19 751	79	9.20 297	81	10.79 703	9.99 454	56
5	9.19 830	79	9.20 378	81	10.79 622	9.99 452	55
6	9.19 909	79	9.20 459	81	10.79 541	9.99 450	54
7	9.19 988	79	9.20 540	81	10.79 460	9.99 448	53
8	9.20 067	79	9.20 621	81	10.79 379	9.99 446	52
9	9.20 145	78	9.20 701	80	10.79 299	9.99 444	51
10	9.20 223	78	9.20 782	81	10.79 218	9.99 442	50
11	9.20 302	79	9.20 862	80	10.79 138	9.99 440	49
12	9.20 380	78	9.20 942	80	10.79 058	9.99 438	48
13	9.20 458	78	9.21 022	80	10.78 978	9.99 436	47
14	9.20 535	77	9.21 102	80	10.78 898	9.99 434	46
15	9.20 613	78	9.21 182	80	10.78 818	9.99 432	45
16	9.20 691	78	9.21 261	79	10.78 739	9.99 429	44
17	9.20 768	77	9.21 341	80	10.78 659	9.99 427	43
18	9.20 845	77	9.21 420	79	10.78 580	9.99 425	42
19	9.20 922	77	9.21 499	79	10.78 501	9.99 423	41
20	9.20 999	77	9.21 578	79	10.78 422	9.99 421	40
21	9.21 076	77	9.21 657	79	10.78 343	9.99 419	39
22	9.21 153	77	9.21 736	79	10.78 264	9.99 417	38
23	9.21 229	76	9.21 814	78	10.78 186	9.99 415	37
24	9.21 306	77	9.21 893	79	10.78 107	9.99 413	36
25	9.21 382	76	9.21 971	78	10.78 029	9.99 411	35
26	9.21 458	76	9.22 049	78	10.77 951	9.99 409	34
27	9.21 534	76	9.22 127	78	10.77 873	9.99 407	33
28	9.21 610	76	9.22 205	78	10.77 795	9.99 404	32
29	9.21 685	75	9.22 283	78	10.77 717	9.99 402	31
30	9.21 761	76	9.22 361	78	10.77 639	9.99 400	30
31	9.21 836	75	9.22 438	77	10.77 562	9.99 398	29
32	9.21 912	76	9.22 516	78	10.77 484	9.99 396	28
33	9.21 987	75	9.22 593	77	10.77 407	9.99 394	27
34	9.22 062	75	9.22 670	77	10.77 330	9.99 392	26
35	9.22 137	75	9.22 747	77	10.77 253	9.99 390	25
36	9.22 211	74	9.22 824	77	10.77 176	9.99 388	24
37	9.22 286	75	9.22 901	77	10.77 099	9.99 385	23
38	9.22 361	75	9.22 977	76	10.77 023	9.99 383	22
39	9.22 435	74	9.23 054	77	10.76 946	9.99 381	21
40	9.22 509	74	9.23 130	76	10.76 870	9.99 379	20
41	9.22 583	74	9.23 206	76	10.76 794	9.99 377	19
42	9.22 657	74	9.23 283	77	10.76 717	9.99 375	18
43	9.22 731	74	9.23 359	76	10.76 641	9.99 372	17
44	9.22 805	74	9.23 435	76	10.76 565	9.99 370	16
45	9.22 878	73	9.23 510	75	10.76 490	9.99 368	15
46	9.22 952	74	9.23 586	76	10.76 414	9.99 366	14
47	9.23 025	73	9.23 661	75	10.76 339	9.99 364	13
48	9.23 098	73	9.23 737	76	10.76 263	9.99 362	12
49	9.23 171	73	9.23 812	75	10.76 188	9.99 359	11
50	9.23 244	73	9.23 887	75	10.76 113	9.99 357	10
51	9.23 317	73	9.23 962	75	10.76 038	9.99 355	9
52	9.23 390	73	9.24 037	75	10.75 963	9.99 353	8
53	9.23 462	72	9.24 112	75	10.75 888	9.99 351	7
54	9.23 535	73	9.24 186	74	10.75 814	9.99 348	6
55	9.23 607	72	9.24 261	75	10.75 739	9.99 346	5
56	9.23 679	72	9.24 335	74	10.75 665	9.99 344	4
57	9.23 752	73	9.24 410	75	10.75 590	9.99 342	3
58	9.23 823	71	9.24 484	74	10.75 516	9.99 340	2
59	9.23 895	72	9.24 558	74	10.75 442	9.99 337	1
60	9.23 967	72	9.24 632	74	10.75 368	9.99 335	0
	L Cos	d	L Cot	c d	L Tan	L Sin	′

Prop. Pts.

	82	81	80
1	8.2	8.1	8.0
2	16.4	16.2	16.0
3	24.6	24.3	24.0
4	32.8	32.4	32.0
5	41.0	40.5	40.0
6	49.2	48.6	48.0
7	57.4	56.7	56.0
8	65.6	64.8	64.0
9	73.8	72.9	72.0

	79	78	77
1	7.9	7.8	7.7
2	15.8	15.6	15.4
3	23.7	23.4	23.1
4	31.6	31.2	30.8
5	39.5	39.0	38.5
6	47.4	46.8	46.2
7	55.3	54.6	53.9
8	63.2	62.4	61.6
9	71.1	70.2	69.3

	76	75	74
1	7.6	7.5	7.4
2	15.2	15.0	14.8
3	22.8	22.5	22.2
4	30.4	30.0	29.6
5	38.0	37.5	37.0
6	45.6	45.0	44.4
7	53.2	52.5	51.8
8	60.8	60.0	59.2
9	68.4	67.5	66.6

	73	72	71
1	7.3	7.2	7.1
2	14.6	14.4	14.2
3	21.9	21.6	21.3
4	29.2	28.8	28.4
5	36.5	36.0	35.5
6	43.8	43.2	42.6
7	51.1	50.4	49.7
8	58.4	57.6	56.8
9	65.7	64.8	63.9

	3	2
1	0.3	0.2
2	0.6	0.4
3	0.9	0.6
4	1.2	0.8
5	1.5	1.0
6	1.8	1.2
7	2.1	1.4
8	2.4	1.6
9	2.7	1.8

TABLE III　　　10°

'	L Sin	d	L Tan	c d	L Cot	L Cos	d		Prop. Pts.
0	9.23 967	72	9.24 632	74	10.75 368	9.99 335	2	**60**	
1	9.24 039	71	9.24 706	73	10.75 294	9.99 333	2	59	
2	9.24 110	71	9.24 779	74	10.75 221	9.99 331	3	58	
3	9.24 181	72	9.24 853	73	10.75 147	9.99 328	2	57	
4	9.24 253	71	9.24 926	74	10.75 074	9.99 326	2	56	
5	9.24 324	71	9.25 000	73	10.75 000	9.99 324	2	55	**74 73 72**
6	9.24 395	71	9.25 073	73	10.74 927	9.99 322	3	54	1 7.4 7.3 7.2
7	9.24 466	70	9.25 146	73	10.74 854	9.99 319	2	53	2 14.8 14.6 14.4
8	9.24 536	71	9.25 219	73	10.74 781	9.99 317	2	52	3 22.2 21.9 21.6
9	9.24 607	70	9.25 292	73	10.74 708	9.99 315	2	51	4 29.6 29.2 28.8
10	9.24 677	71	9.25 365	72	10.74 635	9.99 313	3	**50**	5 37.0 36.5 36.0
11	9.24 748	70	9.25 437	73	10.74 563	9.99 310	2	49	6 44.4 43.8 43.2
12	9.24 818	70	9.25 510	72	10.74 490	9.99 308	2	48	7 51.8 51.1 50.4
13	9.24 888	70	9.25 582	73	10.74 418	9.99 306	2	47	8 59.2 58.4 57.6
14	9.24 958	70	9.25 655	72	10.74 345	9.99 304	3	46	9 66.6 65.7 64.8
15	9.25 028	70	9.25 727	72	10.74 273	9.99 301	2	45	
16	9.25 098	70	9.25 799	72	10.74 201	9.99 299	2	44	
17	9.25 168	69	9.25 871	72	10.74 129	9.99 297	3	43	
18	9.25 237	70	9.25 943	72	10.74 057	9.99 294	2	42	
19	9.25 307	69	9.26 015	71	10.73 985	9.99 292	2	41	
20	9.25 376	69	9.26 086	72	10.73 914	9.99 290	2	**40**	**71 70 69**
21	9.25 445	69	9.26 158	71	10.73 842	9.99 288	3	39	1 7.1 7.0 6.9
22	9.25 514	69	9.26 229	72	10.73 771	9.99 285	2	38	2 14.2 14.0 13.8
23	9.25 583	69	9.26 301	71	10.73 699	9.99 283	2	37	3 21.3 21.0 20.7
24	9.25 652	69	9.26 372	71	10.73 628	9.99 281	2	36	4 28.4 28.0 27.6
25	9.25 721	69	9.26 443	71	10.73 557	9.99 278	2	35	5 35.5 35.0 34.5
26	9.25 790	68	9.26 514	71	10.73 486	9.99 276	2	34	6 42.6 42.0 41.4
27	9.25 858	69	9.26 585	70	10.73 415	9.99 274	3	33	7 49.7 49.0 48.3
28	9.25 927	68	9.26 655	71	10.73 345	9.99 271	2	32	8 56.8 56.0 55.2
29	9.25 995	68	9.26 726	71	10.73 274	9.99 269	2	31	9 63.9 63.0 62.1
30	9.26 063	68	9.26 797	70	10.73 203	9.99 267	3	**30**	
31	9.26 131	68	9.26 867	70	10.73 133	9.99 264	2	29	
32	9.26 199	68	9.26 937	71	10.73 063	9.99 262	2	28	
33	9.26 267	68	9.27 008	70	10.72 992	9.99 260	3	27	**68 67 66**
34	9.26 335	68	9.27 078	70	10.72 922	9.99 257	2	26	1 6.8 6.7 6.6
35	9.26 403	67	9.27 148	70	10.72 852	9.99 255	3	25	2 13.6 13.4 13.2
36	9.26 470	68	9.27 218	70	10.72 782	9.99 252	2	24	3 20.4 20.1 19.8
37	9.26 538	67	9.27 288	69	10.72 712	9.99 250	2	23	4 27.2 26.8 26.4
38	9.26 605	67	9.27 357	70	10.72 643	9.99 248	3	22	5 34.0 33.5 33.0
39	9.26 672	67	9.27 427	69	10.72 573	9.99 245	2	21	6 40.8 40.2 39.6
40	9.26 739	67	9.27 496	70	10.72 504	9.99 243	2	**20**	7 47.6 46.9 46.2
41	9.26 806	67	9.27 566	69	10.72 434	9.99 241	3	19	8 54.4 53.6 52.8
42	9.26 873	67	9.27 635	69	10.72 365	9.99 238	2	18	9 61.2 60.3 59.4
43	9.26 940	67	9.27 704	69	10.72 296	9.99 236	3	17	
44	9.27 007	66	9.27 773	69	10.72 227	9.99 233	2	16	
45	9.27 073	67	9.27 842	69	10.72 158	9.99 231	2	15	
46	9.27 140	66	9.27 911	69	10.72 089	9.99 229	3	14	
47	9.27 206	67	9.27 980	69	10.72 020	9.99 226	2	13	**65 3 2**
48	9.27 273	66	9.28 049	68	10.71 951	9.99 224	3	12	1 6.5 0.3 0.2
49	9.27 339	66	9.28 117	69	10.71 883	9.99 221	2	11	2 13.0 0.6 0.4
50	9.27 405	66	9.28 186	68	10.71 814	9.99 219	2	**10**	3 19.5 0.9 0.6
51	9.27 471	66	9.28 254	69	10.71 746	9.99 217	3	9	4 26.0 1.2 0.8
52	9.27 537	65	9.28 323	68	10.71 677	9.99 214	2	8	5 32.5 1.5 1.0
53	9.27 602	66	9.28 391	68	10.71 609	9.99 212	3	7	6 39.0 1.8 1.2
54	9.27 668	66	9.28 459	68	10.71 541	9.99 209	2	6	7 45.5 2.1 1.4
55	9.27 734	65	9.28 527	68	10.71 473	9.99 207	3	5	8 52.0 2.4 1.6
56	9.27 799	65	9.28 595	67	10.71 405	9.99 204	2	4	9 58.5 2.7 1.8
57	9.27 864	66	9.28 662	68	10.71 338	9.99 202	2	3	
58	9.27 930	65	9.28 730	68	10.71 270	9.99 200	3	2	
59	9.27 995	65	9.28 798	67	10.71 202	9.99 197	2	1	
60	9.28 060		9.28 865		10.71 135	9.99 195		**0**	
	L Cos	d	L Cot	c d	L Tan	L Sin	d	'	Prop. Pts.

′	L Sin	d	L Tan	c d	L Cot	L Cos	d	′
0	9.28 060	65	9.28 865	68	10.71 135	9.99 195	3	60
1	9.28 125	65	9.28 933	67	10.71 067	9.99 192	2	59
2	9.28 190	64	9.29 000	67	10.71 000	9.99 190	3	58
3	9.28 254	65	9.29 067	67	10.70 933	9.99 187	2	57
4	9.28 319	65	9.29 134	67	10.70 866	9.99 185	3	56
5	9.28 384	64	9.29 201	67	10.70 799	9.99 182	2	55
6	9.28 448	64	9.29 268	67	10.70 732	9.99 180	3	54
7	9.28 512	65	9.29 335	67	10.70 665	9.99 177	2	53
8	9.28 577	64	9.29 402	66	10.70 598	9.99 175	3	52
9	9.28 641	64	9.29 468	67	10.70 532	9.99 172	2	51
10	9.28 705	64	9.29 535	66	10.70 465	9.99 170	3	50
11	9.28 769	64	9.29 601	67	10.70 399	9.99 167	2	49
12	9.28 833	63	9.29 668	66	10.70 332	9.99 165	3	48
13	9.28 896	64	9.29 734	66	10.70 266	9.99 162	2	47
14	9.28 960	64	9.29 800	66	10.70 200	9.99 160	3	46
15	9.29 024	63	9.29 866	66	10.70 134	9.99 157	2	45
16	9.29 087	63	9.29 932	66	10.70 068	9.99 155	3	44
17	9.29 150	64	9.29 998	66	10.70 002	9.99 152	2	43
18	9.29 214	63	9.30 064	66	10.69 936	9.99 150	3	42
19	9.29 277	63	9.30 130	65	10.69 870	9.99 147	2	41
20	9.29 340	63	9.30 195	66	10.69 805	9.99 145	3	40
21	9.29 403	63	9.30 261	65	10.69 739	9.99 142	2	39
22	9.29 466	63	9.30 326	65	10.69 674	9.99 140	3	38
23	9.29 529	62	9.30 391	66	10.69 609	9.99 137	2	37
24	9.29 591	63	9.30 457	65	10.69 543	9.99 135	3	36
25	9.29 654	62	9.30 522	65	10.69 478	9.99 132	2	35
26	9.29 716	63	9.30 587	65	10.69 413	9.99 130	3	34
27	9.29 779	62	0.30 652	65	10.09 348	9.99 127	3	33
28	9.29 841	62	9.30 717	65	10.69 283	9.99 124	2	32
29	9.29 903	63	9.30 782	65	10.69 218	9.99 122	3	31
30	9.29 966	62	9.30 846	64	10.69 154	9.99 119	2	30
31	9.30 028	62	9.30 911	65	10.69 089	9.99 117	3	29
32	9.30 090	61	9.30 975	64	10.69 025	9.99 114	2	28
33	9.30 151	62	9.31 040	65	10.68 960	9.99 112	3	27
34	9.30 213	62	9.31 104	64	10.68 896	9.99 109	3	26
35	9.30 275	61	9.31 168	64	10.68 832	9.99 106	2	25
36	9.30 336	62	9.31 233	65	10.68 767	9.99 104	3	24
37	9.00 098	61	9.31 297	64	10.68 703	9.99 101	2	23
38	9.30 459	62	9.31 361	64	10.68 639	9.99 099	3	22
39	9.30 521	61	9.31 425	64	10.68 575	9.99 096	3	21
40	9.30 582	61	9.31 489	64	10.68 511	9.99 093	2	20
41	9.30 643	61	9.31 552	63	10.68 448	9.99 091	3	19
42	9.30 704	61	9.31 616	64	10.68 384	9.99 088	2	18
43	9.30 765	61	9.31 679	63	10.68 321	9.99 086	3	17
44	9.30 826	61	9.31 743	64	10.68 257	9.99 083	3	16
45	9.30 887	60	9.31 806	63	10.68 194	9.99 080	2	15
46	9.30 947	61	9.31 870	64	10.68 130	9.99 078	3	14
47	9.31 008	60	9.31 933	63	10.68 067	9.99 075	3	13
48	9.31 068	61	9.31 996	63	10.68 004	9.99 072	2	12
49	9.31 129	60	9.32 059	63	10.67 941	9.99 070	3	11
50	9.31 189	61	9.32 122	63	10.67 878	9.99 067	3	10
51	9.31 250	60	9.32 185	63	10.67 815	9.99 064	2	9
52	9.31 310	60	9.32 248	63	10.67 752	9.99 062	3	8
53	9.31 370	60	9.32 311	62	10.67 689	9.99 059	3	7
54	9.31 430	60	9.32 373	63	10.67 627	9.99 056	2	6
55	9.31 490	59	9.32 436	62	10.67 564	9.99 054	3	5
56	9.31 549	60	9.32 498	63	10.67 502	9.99 051	3	4
57	9.31 609	60	9.32 561	62	10.67 439	9.99 048	2	3
58	9.31 669	59	9.32 623	62	10.67 377	9.99 046	3	2
59	9.31 728	60	9.32 685	62	10.67 315	9.99 043	3	1
60	9.31 788		9.32 747		10.67 253	9.99 040		0
	L Cos	d	L Cot	c d	L Tan	L Sin	d	′

Prop. Pts.

	68	67	66
1	6.8	6.7	6.6
2	13.6	13.4	13.2
3	20.4	20.1	19.8
4	27.2	26.8	26.4
5	34.0	33.5	33.0
6	40.8	40.2	39.6
7	47.6	46.9	46.2
8	54.4	53.6	52.8
9	61.2	60.3	59.4

	65	64	63
1	6.5	6.4	6.3
2	13.0	12.8	12.6
3	19.5	19.2	18.9
4	26.0	25.6	25.2
5	32.5	32.0	31.5
6	39.0	38.4	37.8
7	45.5	44.8	44.1
8	52.0	51.2	50.4
9	58.5	57.6	56.7

	62	61	60
1	6.2	6.1	6.0
2	12.4	12.2	12.0
3	18.6	18.3	18.0
4	24.8	24.4	24.0
5	31.0	30.5	30.0
6	37.2	36.6	36.0
7	43.4	42.7	42.0
8	49.6	48.8	48.0
9	55.8	54.9	54.0

	59	3	2
1	5.9	0.3	0.2
2	11.8	0.6	0.4
3	17.7	0.9	0.6
4	23.6	1.2	0.8
5	29.5	1.5	1.0
6	35.4	1.8	1.2
7	41.3	2.1	1.4
8	47.2	2.4	1.6
9	53.1	2.7	1.8

TABLE III   12°

′	L Sin	d	L Tan	c d	L Cot	L Cos	d		Prop. Pts.
0	9.31 788		9.32 747		10.67 253	9.99 040		**60**	
1	9.31 847	59	9.32 810	63	10.67 190	9.99 038	2	59	
2	9.31 907	60	9.32 872	62	10.67 128	9.99 035	3	58	
3	9.31 966	59	9.32 933	61	10.67 067	9.99 032	3	57	
4	9.32 025	59	9.32 995	62	10.67 005	9.99 030	2	56	
5	9.32 084	59	9.33 057	62	10.66 943	9.99 027	3	55	**63** **62** **61**
6	9.32 143	59	9.33 119	62	10.66 881	9.99 024	3	54	1 6.3 6.2 6.1
7	9.32 202	59	9.33 180	61	10.66 820	9.99 022	2	53	2 12.6 12.4 12.2
8	9.32 261	59	9.33 242	62	10.66 758	9.99 019	3	52	3 18.9 18.6 18.3
9	9.32 319	58	9.33 303	61	10.66 697	9.99 016	3	51	4 25.2 24.8 24.4
10	9.32 378	59	9.33 365	62	10.66 635	9.99 013	3	**50**	5 31.5 31.0 30.5
11	9.32 437	59	9.33 426	61	10.66 574	9.99 011	2	49	6 37.8 37.2 36.6
12	9.32 495	58	9.33 487	61	10.66 513	9.99 008	3	48	7 44.1 43.4 42.7
13	9.32 553	58	9.33 548	61	10.66 452	9.99 005	3	47	8 50.4 49.6 48.8
14	9.32 612	59	9.33 609	61	10.66 391	9.99 002	3	46	9 56.7 55.8 54.9
15	9.32 670	58	9.33 670	61	10.66 330	9.99 000	2	45	
16	9.32 728	58	9.33 731	61	10.66 269	9.98 997	3	44	
17	9.32 786	58	9.33 792	61	10.66 208	9.98 994	3	43	
18	9.32 844	58	9.33 853	61	10.66 147	9.98 991	3	42	
19	9.32 902	58	9.33 913	60	10.66 087	9.98 989	2	41	**60** **59** **58**
20	9.32 960	58	9.33 974	61	10.66 026	9.98 986	3	**40**	1 6.0 5.9 5.8
21	9.33 018	58	9.34 034	60	10.65 966	9.98 983	3	39	2 12.0 11.8 11.6
22	9.33 075	57	9.34 095	61	10.65 905	9.98 980	3	38	3 18.0 17.7 17.4
23	9.33 133	58	9.34 155	60	10.65 845	9.98 978	2	37	4 24.0 23.6 23.2
24	9.33 190	57	9.34 215	60	10.65 785	9.98 975	3	36	5 30.0 29.5 29.0
25	9.33 248	58	9.34 276	61	10.65 724	9.98 972	3	35	6 36.0 35.4 34.8
26	9.33 305	57	9.34 336	60	10.65 664	9.98 969	3	34	7 42.0 41.3 40.6
27	9.33 362	57	9.34 396	60	10.65 604	9.98 967	2	33	8 48.0 47.2 46.4
28	9.33 420	58	9.34 456	60	10.65 544	9.98 964	3	32	9 54.0 53.1 52.2
29	9.33 477	57	9.34 516	60	10.65 484	9.98 961	3	31	
30	9.33 534	57	9.34 576	60	10.65 424	9.98 958	3	**30**	
31	9.33 591	57	9.34 635	59	10.65 365	9.98 955	3	29	
32	9.33 647	56	9.34 695	60	10.65 305	9.98 953	2	28	
33	9.33 704	57	9.34 755	60	10.65 245	9.98 950	3	27	**57** **56** **55**
34	9.33 761	57	9.34 814	59	10.65 186	9.98 947	3	26	1 5.7 5.6 5.5
35	9.33 818	57	9.34 874	60	10.65 126	9.98 944	3	25	2 11.4 11.2 11.0
36	9.33 874	56	9.34 933	59	10.65 067	9.98 941	3	24	3 17.1 16.8 16.5
37	9.33 931	57	9.34 992	59	10.65 008	9.98 938	2	23	4 22.8 22.4 22.0
38	9.33 987	56	9.35 051	59	10.64 949	9.98 936	3	22	5 28.5 28.0 27.5
39	9.34 043	57	9.35 111	60	10.64 889	9.98 933	3	21	6 34.2 33.6 33.0
40	9.34 100	56	9.35 170	59	10.64 830	9.98 930	3	**20**	7 39.9 39.2 38.5
41	9.34 156	56	9.35 229	59	10.64 771	9.98 927	3	19	8 45.6 44.8 44.0
42	9.34 212	56	9.35 288	59	10.64 712	9.98 924	3	18	9 51.3 50.4 49.5
43	9.34 268	56	9.35 347	58	10.64 653	9.98 921	2	17	
44	9.34 324	56	9.35 405	59	10.64 595	9.98 919	3	16	
45	9.34 380	56	9.35 464	59	10.64 536	9.98 916	3	15	
46	9.34 436	55	9.35 523	58	10.64 477	9.98 913	3	14	
47	9.34 491	56	9.35 581	59	10.64 419	9.98 910	3	13	
48	9.34 547	55	9.35 640	58	10.64 360	9.98 907	3	12	**3** **2**
49	9.34 602	56	9.35 698	59	10.64 302	9.98 904	3	11	1 0.3 0.2
50	9.34 658	55	9.35 757	58	10.64 243	9.98 901	3	**10**	2 0.6 0.4
51	9.34 713	56	9.35 815	58	10.64 185	9.98 898	2	9	3 0.9 0.6
52	9.34 769	55	9.35 873	58	10.64 127	9.98 896	3	8	4 1.2 0.8
53	9.34 824	55	9.35 931	58	10.64 069	9.98 893	3	7	5 1.5 1.0
54	9.34 879	55	9.35 989	58	10.64 011	9.98 890	3	6	6 1.8 1.2
55	9.34 934	55	9.36 047	58	10.63 953	9.98 887	3	5	7 2.1 1.4
56	9.34 989	55	9.36 105	58	10.63 895	9.98 884	3	4	8 2.4 1.6
57	9.35 044	55	9.36 163	58	10.63 837	9.98 881	3	3	9 2.7 1.8
58	9.35 099	55	9.36 221	58	10.63 779	9.98 878	3	2	
59	9.35 154	55	9.36 279	57	10.63 721	9.98 875	3	1	
60	9.35 209		9.36 336		10.63 664	9.98 872		**0**	
	L Cos	d	L Cot	c d	L Tan	L Sin	d	′	Prop. Pts.

'	L Sin	d	L Tan	c d	L Cot	L Cos	d	'	Prop. Pts.
0	9.35 209		9.36 336		10.63 664	9.98 872		60	
1	9.35 263	54	9.36 394	58	10.63 606	9.98 869	3	59	
2	9.35 318	55	9.36 452	58	10.63 548	9.98 867	2	58	
3	9.35 373	55	9.36 509	57	10.63 491	9.98 864	3	57	
4	9.35 427	54	9.36 566	57	10.63 434	9.98 861	3	56	
5	9.35 481	54	9.36 624	58	10.63 376	9.98 858	3	55	
6	9.35 536	55	9.36 681	57	10.63 319	9.98 855	3	54	
7	9.35 590	54	9.36 738	57	10.63 262	9.98 852	3	53	
8	9.35 644	54	9.36 795	57	10.63 205	9.98 849	3	52	
9	9.35 698	54	9.36 852	57	10.63 148	9.98 846	3	51	
10	9.35 752	54	9.36 909	57	10.63 091	9.98 843	3	50	
11	9.35 806	54	9.36 966	57	10.63 034	9.98 840	3	49	
12	9.35 860	54	9.37 023	57	10.62 977	9.98 837	3	48	
13	9.35 914	54	9.37 080	57	10.62 920	9.98 834	3	47	
14	9.35 968	54	9.37 137	56	10.62 863	9.98 831	3	46	
15	9.36 022	53	9.37 193	57	10.62 807	9.98 828	3	45	
16	9.36 075	54	9.37 250	56	10.62 750	9.98 825	3	44	
17	9.36 129	53	9.37 306	57	10.62 694	9.98 822	3	43	
18	9.36 182	54	9.37 363	56	10.62 637	9.98 819	3	42	
19	9.36 236	53	9.37 419	57	10.62 581	9.98 816	3	41	
20	9.36 289	53	9.37 476	56	10.62 524	9.98 813	3	40	
21	9.36 342	53	9.37 532	56	10.62 468	9.98 810	3	39	
22	9.36 395	53	9.37 588	56	10.62 412	9.98 807	3	38	
23	9.36 449	54	9.37 644	56	10.62 356	9.98 804	3	37	
24	9.36 502	53	9.37 700	56	10.62 300	9.98 801	3	36	
25	9.36 555	53	9.37 756	56	10.62 244	9.98 798	3	35	
26	9.36 608	53	9.37 812	56	10.62 188	9.98 795	3	34	
27	9.36 660	52	9.37 868	56	10.62 132	9.98 792	3	33	
28	9.36 713	53	9.37 924	56	10.62 076	9.98 789	3	32	
29	9.36 766	53	9.37 980	55	10.62 020	9.98 786	3	31	
30	9.36 819	53	9.38 035	56	10.61 965	9.98 783	3	30	
31	9.36 871	52	9.38 091	56	10.61 909	9.98 780	3	29	
32	9.36 924	53	9.38 147	55	10.61 853	9.98 777	3	28	
33	9.36 976	52	9.38 202	55	10.61 798	9.98 774	3	27	
34	9.37 028	52	9.38 257	56	10.61 743	9.98 771	3	26	
35	9.37 081	53	9.38 313	55	10.61 687	9.98 768	3	25	
36	9.37 133	52	9.38 368	55	10.61 632	9.98 765	3	24	
37	9.37 185	52	9.38 423	56	10.61 577	9.98 762	3	23	
38	9.37 237	52	9.38 479	55	10.61 521	9.98 759	3	22	
39	9.37 289	52	9.38 534	55	10.61 466	9.98 756	3	21	
40	9.37 341	52	9.38 589	55	10.61 411	9.98 753	3	20	
41	9.37 393	52	9.38 644	55	10.61 356	9.98 750	4	19	
42	9.37 445	52	9.38 699	55	10.61 301	9.98 746	3	18	
43	9.37 497	52	9.38 754	54	10.61 246	9.98 743	3	17	
44	9.37 549	51	9.38 808	55	10.61 192	9.98 740	3	16	
45	9.37 600	52	9.38 863	55	10.61 137	9.98 737	3	15	
46	9.37 652	51	9.38 918	54	10.61 082	9.98 734	3	14	
47	9.37 703	52	9.38 972	55	10.61 028	9.98 731	3	13	
48	9.37 755	51	9.39 027	55	10.60 973	9.98 728	3	12	
49	9.37 806	52	9.39 082	54	10.60 918	9.98 725	3	11	
50	9.37 858	51	9.39 136	54	10.60 864	9.98 722	3	10	
51	9.37 909	51	9.39 190	55	10.60 810	9.98 719	4	9	
52	9.37 960	51	9.39 245	54	10.60 755	9.98 715	3	8	
53	9.38 011	51	9.39 299	54	10.60 701	9.98 712	3	7	
54	9.38 062	51	9.39 353	54	10.60 647	9.98 709	3	6	
55	9.38 113	51	9.39 407	54	10.60 593	9.98 706	3	5	
56	9.38 164	51	9.39 461	54	10.60 539	9.98 703	3	4	
57	9.38 215	51	9.39 515	54	10.60 485	9.98 700	3	3	
58	9.38 266	51	9.39 569	54	10.60 431	9.98 697	3	2	
59	9.38 317	51	9.39 623	54	10.60 377	9.98 694	4	1	
60	9.38 368		9.39 677		10.60 323	9.98 690		0	
	L Cos	d	L Cot	c d	L Tan	L Sin	d	'	Prop. Pts.

Prop. Pts.

	58	57	56
1	5.8	5.7	5.6
2	11.6	11.4	11.2
3	17.4	17.1	16.8
4	23.2	22.8	22.4
5	29.0	28.5	28.0
6	34.8	34.2	33.6
7	40.6	39.9	39.2
8	46.4	45.6	44.8
9	52.2	51.3	50.4

	55	54	53
1	5.5	5.4	5.3
2	11.0	10.8	10.6
3	16.5	16.2	15.9
4	22.0	21.6	21.2
5	27.5	27.0	26.5
6	33.0	32.4	31.8
7	38.5	37.8	37.1
8	44.0	43.2	42.4
9	49.5	48.6	47.7

	52	51
1	5.2	5.1
2	10.4	10.2
3	15.6	15.3
4	20.8	20.4
5	26.0	25.5
6	31.2	30.6
7	36.4	35.7
8	41.6	40.8
9	46.8	45.9

	4	3	2
1	0.4	0.3	0.2
2	0.8	0.6	0.4
3	1.2	0.9	0.6
4	1.6	1.2	0.8
5	2.0	1.5	1.0
6	2.4	1.8	1.2
7	2.8	2.1	1.4
8	3.2	2.4	1.6
9	3.6	2.7	1.8

TABLE III   **14°**

′	L Sin	d	L Tan	c d	L Cot	L Cos	d	′	Prop. Pts.
0	9.38 368	50	9.39 677	54	10.60 323	9.98 690	3	**60**	
1	9.38 418	51	9.39 731	54	10.60 269	9.98 687	3	59	
2	9.38 469	50	9.39 785	53	10.60 215	9.98 684	3	58	
3	9.38 519	51	9.39 838	54	10.60 162	9.98 681	3	57	
4	9.38 570	50	9.39 892	53	10.60 108	9.98 678	3	56	
5	9.38 620	50	9.39 945	54	10.60 055	9.98 675	3	55	**54** **53** **52**
6	9.38 670	51	9.39 999	53	10.60 001	9.98 671	4	54	1 5.4 5.3 5.2
7	9.38 721	50	9.40 052	54	10.59 948	9.98 668	3	53	2 10.8 10.6 10.4
8	9.38 771	50	9.40 106	53	10.59 894	9.98 665	3	52	3 16.2 15.9 15.6
9	9.38 821	50	9.40 159	53	10.59 841	9.98 662	3	51	4 21.6 21.2 20.8
10	9.38 871	50	9.40 212	54	10.59 788	9.98 659	3	**50**	5 27.0 26.5 26.0
11	9.38 921	50	9.40 266	53	10.59 734	9.98 656	4	49	6 32.4 31.8 31.2
12	9.38 971	50	9.40 319	53	10.59 681	9.98 652	3	48	7 37.8 37.1 36.4
13	9.39 021	50	9.40 372	53	10.59 628	9.98 649	3	47	8 43.2 42.4 41.6
14	9.39 071	50	9.40 425	53	10.59 575	9.98 646	3	46	9 48.6 47.7 46.8
15	9.39 121	49	9.40 478	53	10.59 522	9.98 643	3	45	
16	9.39 170	50	9.40 531	53	10.59 469	9.98 640	4	44	
17	9.39 220	50	9.40 584	52	10.59 416	9.98 636	3	43	
18	9.39 270	49	9.40 636	53	10.59 364	9.98 633	3	42	
19	9.39 319	50	9.40 689	53	10.59 311	9.98 630	3	41	**51** **50** **49**
20	9.39 369	49	9.40 742	53	10.59 258	9.98 627	4	**40**	1 5.1 5.0 4.9
21	9.39 418	49	9.40 795	52	10.59 205	9.98 623	3	39	2 10.2 10.0 9.8
22	9.39 467	50	9.40 847	53	10.59 153	9.98 620	3	38	3 15.3 15.0 14.7
23	9.39 517	49	9.40 900	52	10.59 100	9.98 617	3	37	4 20.4 20.0 19.6
24	9.39 566	49	9.40 952	53	10.59 048	9.98 614	4	36	5 25.5 25.0 24.5
25	9.39 615	49	9.41 005	52	10.58 995	9.98 610	3	35	6 30.6 30.0 29.4
26	9.39 664	49	9.41 057	52	10.58 943	9.98 607	3	34	7 35.7 35.0 34.3
27	9.39 713	49	9.41 109	52	10.58 891	9.98 604	3	33	8 40.8 40.0 39.2
28	9.39 762	49	9.41 161	53	10.58 839	9.98 601	4	32	9 45.9 45.0 44.1
29	9.39 811	49	9.41 214	52	10.58 786	9.98 597	3	31	
30	9.39 860	49	9.41 266	52	10.58 734	9.98 594	3	**30**	
31	9.39 909	49	9.41 318	52	10.58 682	9.98 591	3	29	
32	9.93 958	48	9.41 370	52	10.58 630	9.98 588	4	28	
33	9.40 006	49	9.41 422	52	10.58 578	9.98 584	3	27	**48** **47**
34	9.40 055	48	9.41 474	52	10.58 526	9.98 581	3	26	1 4.8 4.7
35	9.40 103	49	9.41 526	52	10.58 474	9.98 578	4	25	2 9.6 9.4
36	9.40 152	48	9.41 578	51	10.58 422	9.98 574	3	24	3 14.4 14.1
37	9.40 200	49	9.41 629	52	10.58 371	9.98 571	3	23	4 19.2 18.8
38	9.40 249	48	9.41 681	52	10.58 319	9.98 568	3	22	5 24.0 23.5
39	9.40 297	49	9.41 733	51	10.58 267	9.98 565	4	21	6 28.8 28.2
40	9.40 346	48	9.41 784	52	10.58 216	9.98 561	3	**20**	7 33.6 32.9
41	9.40 394	48	9.41 836	51	10.58 164	9.98 558	3	19	8 38.4 37.6
42	9.40 442	48	9.41 887	52	10.58 113	9.98 555	4	18	9 43.2 42.3
43	9.40 490	48	9.41 939	51	10.58 061	9.98 551	3	17	
44	9.40 538	48	9.41 990	51	10.58 010	9.98 548	3	16	
45	9.40 586	48	9.42 041	52	10.57 959	9.98 545	4	15	
46	9.40 634	48	9.42 093	51	10.57 907	9.98 541	3	14	
47	9.40 682	48	9.42 144	51	10.57 856	9.98 538	3	13	**4** **3**
48	9.40 730	48	9.42 195	51	10.57 805	9.98 535	4	12	1 0.4 0.3
49	9.40 778	47	9.42 246	51	10.57 754	9.98 531	3	11	2 0.8 0.6
50	9.40 825	48	9.42 297	51	10.57 703	9.98 528	3	**10**	3 1.2 0.9
51	9.40 873	48	9.42 348	51	10.57 652	9.98 525	4	9	4 1.6 1.2
52	9.40 921	47	9.42 399	51	10.57 601	9.98 521	3	8	5 2.0 1.5
53	9.40 968	48	9.42 450	51	10.57 550	9.98 518	3	7	6 2.4 1.8
54	9.41 016	47	9.42 501	51	10.57 499	9.98 515	4	6	7 2.8 2.1
55	9.41 063	48	9.42 552	51	10.57 448	9.98 511	3	5	8 3.2 2.4
56	9.41 111	47	9.42 603	50	10.57 397	9.98 508	3	4	9 3.6 2.7
57	9.41 158	47	9.42 653	51	10.57 347	9.98 505	4	3	
58	9.41 205	47	9.42 704	51	10.57 296	9.98 501	3	2	
59	9.41 252	48	9.42 755	50	10.57 245	9.98 498	4	1	
60	9.41 300		9.42 805		10.57 195	9.98 494		**0**	
	L Cos	d	L Cot	c d	L Tan	L Sin	d	′	Prop. Pts.

′	L Sin	d	L Tan	c d	L Cot	L Cos	d		Prop. Pts.
0	9.41 300		9.42 805		10.57 195	9.98 494		60	
1	9.41 347	47	9.42 856	51	10.57 144	9.98 491	3	59	
2	9.41 394	47	9.42 906	50	10.57 094	9.98 488	3	58	
3	9.41 441	47	9.42 957	51	10.57 043	9.98 484	4	57	
4	9.41 488	47	9.43 007	50	10.56 993	9.98 481	3	56	
5	9.41 535	47	9.43 057	50	10.56 943	9.98 477	4	55	**51** **50** **49**
6	9.41 582	47	9.43 108	51	10.56 892	9.98 474	3	54	1 5.1 5.0 4.9
7	9.41 628	46	9.43 158	50	10.56 842	9.98 471	3	53	2 10.2 10.0 9.8
8	9.41 675	47	9.43 208	50	10.56 792	9.98 467	4	52	3 15.3 15.0 14.7
9	9.41 722	47	9.43 258	50	10.56 742	9.98 464	3	51	4 20.4 20.0 19.6
10	9.41 768	46	9.43 308	50	10.56 692	9.98 460	4	50	5 25.5 25.0 24.5
11	9.41 815	47	9.43 358	50	10.56 642	9.98 457	3	49	6 30.6 30.0 29.4
12	9.41 861	46	9.43 408	50	10.56 592	9.98 453	4	48	7 35.7 35.0 34.3
13	9.41 908	47	9.43 458	50	10.56 542	9.98 450	3	47	8 40.8 40.0 39.2
14	9.41 954	46	9.43 508	50	10.56 492	9.98 447	4	46	9 45.9 45.0 44.1
15	9.42 001	47	9.43 558	50	10.56 442	9.98 443	3	45	
16	9.42 047	46	9.43 607	49	10.56 393	9.98 440	4	44	
17	9.42 093	46	9.43 657	50	10.56 343	9.98 436	3	43	
18	9.42 140	47	9.43 707	50	10.56 293	9.98 433	4	42	
19	9.42 186	46	9.43 756	49	10.56 244	9.98 429	4	41	
20	9.42 232	46	9.43 806	50	10.56 194	9.98 426	3	40	**48** **47** **46**
21	9.42 278	46	9.43 855	49	10.56 145	9.98 422	4	39	1 4.8 4.7 4.6
22	9.42 324	46	9.43 905	50	10.56 095	9.98 419	3	38	2 9.6 9.4 9.2
23	9.42 370	46	9.43 954	49	10.56 046	9.98 415	4	37	3 14.4 14.1 13.8
24	9.42 416	46	9.44 004	50	10.55 996	9.98 412	3	36	4 19.2 18.8 18.4
25	9.42 461	45	9.44 053	49	10.55 947	9.98 409	3	35	5 24.0 23.5 23.0
26	9.42 507	46	9.44 102	49	10.55 898	9.98 405	4	34	6 28.8 28.2 27.6
27	9.42 553	46	9.44 151	49	10.55 849	9.98 402	3	33	7 33.6 32.9 32.2
28	9.42 599	45	9.44 201	50	10.55 799	9.98 398	4	32	8 38.4 37.6 36.8
29	9.42 644	46	9.44 250	49	10.55 750	9.98 395	3	31	9 43.2 42.3 41.4
30	9.42 690	45	9.44 299	49	10.55 701	9.98 391	4	30	
31	9.42 735	46	9.44 348	49	10.55 652	9.98 388	3	29	
32	9.42 781	45	9.44 397	49	10.55 603	9.98 384	4	28	
33	9.42 826	46	9.44 446	49	10.55 554	9.98 381	3	27	
34	9.42 872	45	9.44 495	49	10.55 505	9.98 377	4	26	**45** **44**
35	9.42 917	45	9.44 544	48	10.55 456	9.98 373	3	25	1 4.5 4.4
36	9.42 962	46	9.44 592	49	10.55 408	9.98 370	4	24	2 9.0 8.8
37	9.43 008	45	9.44 641	49	10.55 359	9.98 366	3	23	3 13.5 13.2
38	9.43 053	45	9.44 690	48	10.55 310	9.98 363	4	22	4 18.0 17.6
39	9.43 098	45	9.44 738	49	10.55 262	9.98 359	3	21	5 22.5 22.0
40	9.43 143	45	9.44 787	49	10.55 213	9.98 356	4	20	6 27.0 26.4
41	9.43 188	45	9.44 836	48	10.55 164	9.98 352	3	19	7 31.5 30.8
42	9.43 233	45	9.44 884	49	10.55 116	9.98 349	4	18	8 36.0 35.2
43	9.43 278	45	9.44 933	48	10.55 067	9.98 345	3	17	9 40.5 39.6
44	9.43 323	44	9.44 981	48	10.55 019	9.98 342	4	16	
45	9.43 367	45	9.45 029	49	10.54 971	9.98 338	4	15	
46	9.43 412	45	9.45 078	48	10.54 922	9.98 334	3	14	
47	9.43 457	45	9.45 126	48	10.54 874	9.98 331	4	13	**4** **3**
48	9.43 502	44	9.45 174	48	10.54 826	9.98 327	3	12	1 0.4 0.3
49	9.43 546	45	9.45 222	49	10.54 778	9.98 324	4	11	2 0.8 0.6
50	9.43 591	44	9.45 271	48	10.54 729	9.98 320	3	10	3 1.2 0.9
51	9.43 635	45	9.45 319	48	10.54 681	9.98 317	4	9	4 1.6 1.2
52	9.43 680	44	9.45 367	48	10.54 633	9.98 313	4	8	5 2.0 1.5
53	9.43 724	45	9.45 415	48	10.54 585	9.98 309	3	7	6 2.4 1.8
54	9.43 769	44	9.45 463	48	10.54 537	9.98 306	4	6	7 2.8 2.1
55	9.43 813	44	9.45 511	48	10.54 489	9.98 302	3	5	8 3.2 2.4
56	9.43 857	44	9.45 559	47	10.54 441	9.98 299	4	4	9 3.6 2.7
57	9.43 901	45	9.45 606	48	10.54 394	9.98 295	4	3	
58	9.43 946	44	9.45 654	48	10.54 346	9.98 291	3	2	
59	9.43 990	44	9.45 702	48	10.54 298	9.98 288	4	1	
60	9.44 034		9.45 750		10.54 250	9.98 284		0	
	L Cos	d	L Cot	c d	L Tan	L Sin	d	′	Prop. Pts.

TABLE III   16°

'	L Sin	d	L Tan	c d	L Cot	L Cos	d	'
0	9.44 034	44	9.45 750	47	10.54 250	9.98 284	3	60
1	9.44 078	44	9.45 797	48	10.54 203	9.98 281	4	59
2	9.44 122	44	9.45 845	47	10.54 155	9.98 277	4	58
3	9.44 166	44	9.45 892	48	10.54 108	9.98 273	3	57
4	9.44 210	43	9.45 940	47	10.54 060	9.98 270	4	56
5	9.44 253	44	9.45 987	48	10.54 013	9.98 266	4	55
6	9.44 297	44	9.46 035	47	10.53 965	9.98 262	3	54
7	9.44 341	44	9.46 082	48	10.53 918	9.98 259	4	53
8	9.44 385	43	9.46 130	47	10.53 870	9.98 255	4	52
9	9.44 428	44	9.46 177	47	10.53 823	9.98 251	3	51
10	9.44 472	44	9.46 224	47	10.53 776	9.98 248	4	50
11	9.44 516	43	9.46 271	48	10.53 729	9.98 244	4	49
12	9.44 559	43	9.46 319	47	10.53 681	9.98 240	3	48
13	9.44 602	44	9.46 366	47	10.53 634	9.98 237	4	47
14	9.44 646	43	9.46 413	47	10.53 587	9.98 233	4	46
15	9.44 689	44	9.46 460	47	10.53 540	9.98 229	3	45
16	9.44 733	43	9.46 507	47	10.53 493	9.98 226	4	44
17	9.44 776	43	9.46 554	47	10.53 446	9.98 222	4	43
18	9.44 819	43	9.46 601	47	10.53 399	9.98 218	3	42
19	9.44 862	43	9.46 648	46	10.53 352	9.98 215	4	41
20	9.44 905	43	9.46 694	47	10.53 306	9.98 211	4	40
21	9.44 948	44	9.46 741	47	10.53 259	9.98 207	3	39
22	9.44 992	43	9.46 788	47	10.53 212	9.98 204	4	38
23	9.45 035	42	9.46 835	46	10.53 165	9.98 200	4	37
24	9.45 077	43	9.46 881	47	10.53 119	9.98 196	4	36
25	9.45 120	43	9.46 928	47	10.53 072	9.98 192	3	35
26	9.45 163	43	9.46 975	46	10.53 025	9.98 189	4	34
27	9.45 206	43	9.47 021	47	10.52 979	9.98 185	4	33
28	9.45 249	43	9.47 068	46	10.52 932	9.98 181	4	32
29	9.45 292	42	9.47 114	46	10.52 886	9.98 177	3	31
30	9.45 334	43	9.47 160	47	10.52 840	9.98 174	4	30
31	9.45 377	42	9.47 207	46	10.52 793	9.98 170	4	29
32	9.45 419	43	9.47 253	46	10.52 747	9.98 166	4	28
33	9.45 462	42	9.47 299	47	10.52 701	9.98 162	3	27
34	9.45 504	43	9.47 346	46	10.52 654	9.98 159	4	26
35	9.45 547	42	9.47 392	46	10.52 608	9.98 155	4	25
36	9.45 589	43	9.47 438	46	10.52 562	9.98 151	4	24
37	9.45 632	42	9.47 484	46	10.52 516	9.98 147	3	23
38	9.45 674	42	9.47 530	46	10.52 470	9.98 144	4	22
39	9.45 716	42	9.47 576	46	10.52 424	9.98 140	4	21
40	9.45 758	43	9.47 622	46	10.52 378	9.98 136	4	20
41	9.45 801	42	9.47 668	46	10.52 332	9.98 132	3	19
42	9.45 843	42	9.47 714	46	10.52 286	9.98 129	4	18
43	9.45 885	42	9.47 760	46	10.52 240	9.98 125	4	17
44	9.45 927	42	9.47 806	46	10.52 194	9.98 121	4	16
45	9.45 969	42	9.47 852	45	10.52 148	9.98 117	4	15
46	9.46 011	42	9.47 897	46	10.52 103	9.98 113	3	14
47	9.46 053	42	9.47 943	46	10.52 057	9.98 110	4	13
48	9.46 095	41	9.47 989	46	10.52 011	9.98 106	4	12
49	9.46 136	42	9.48 035	46	10.51 965	9.98 102	4	11
50	9.46 178	42	9.48 080	45	10.51 920	9.98 098	4	10
51	9.46 220	42	9.48 126	46	10.51 874	9.98 094	4	9
52	9.46 262	41	9.48 171	45	10.51 829	9.98 090	3	8
53	9.46 303	42	9.48 217	46	10.51 783	9.98 087	4	7
54	9.46 345	41	9.48 262	45	10.51 738	9.98 083	4	6
55	9.46 386	42	9.48 307	45	10.51 693	9.98 079	4	5
56	9.46 428	41	9.48 353	46	10.51 647	9.98 075	4	4
57	9.46 469	42	9.48 398	45	10.51 602	9.98 071	4	3
58	9.46 511	41	9.48 443	45	10.51 557	9.98 067	4	2
59	9.46 552	42	9.48 489	46	10.51 511	9.98 063	3	1
60	9.46 594		9.48 534		10.51 466	9.98 060		0
	L Cos	d	L Cot	c d	L Tan	L Sin	d	'

Prop. Pts.

	48	47	46
1	4.8	4.7	4.6
2	9.6	9.4	9.2
3	14.4	14.1	13.8
4	19.2	18.8	18.4
5	24.0	23.5	23.0
6	28.8	28.2	27.6
7	33.6	32.9	32.2
8	38.4	37.6	36.8
9	43.2	42.3	41.4

	45	44	43
1	4.5	4.4	4.3
2	9.0	8.8	8.6
3	13.5	13.2	12.9
4	18.0	17.6	17.2
5	22.5	22.0	21.5
6	27.0	26.4	25.8
7	31.5	30.8	30.1
8	36.0	35.2	34.4
9	40.5	39.6	38.7

	42	41
1	4.2	4.1
2	8.4	8.2
3	12.6	12.3
4	16.8	16.4
5	21.0	20.5
6	25.2	24.6
7	29.4	28.7
8	33.6	32.8
9	37.8	36.9

	4	3
1	0.4	0.3
2	0.8	0.6
3	1.2	0.9
4	1.6	1.2
5	2.0	1.5
6	2.4	1.8
7	2.8	2.1
8	3.2	2.4
9	3.6	2.7

'	L Sin	d	L Tan	c d	L Cot	L Cos	d		Prop. Pts.
0	9.46 594		9.48 534		10.51 466	9.98 060		**60**	
1	9.46 635	41	9.48 579	45	10.51 421	9.98 056	4	59	
2	9.46 676	41	9.48 624	45	10.51 376	9.98 052	4	58	
3	9.46 717	41	9.48 669	45	10.51 331	9.98 048	4	57	
4	9.46 758	41	9.48 714	45	10.51 286	9.98 044	4	56	
5	9.46 800	42	9.48 759	45	10.51 241	9.98 040	4	55	
6	9.46 841	41	9.48 804	45	10.51 196	9.98 036	4	54	
7	9.46 882	41	9.48 849	45	10.51 151	9.98 032	4	53	
8	9.46 923	41	9.48 894	45	10.51 106	9.98 029	3	52	
9	9.46 964	41	9.48 939	45	10.51 061	9.98 025	4	51	
10	9.47 005	41	9.48 984	45	10.51 016	9.98 021	4	**50**	
11	9.47 045	40	9.49 029	45	10.50 971	9.98 017	4	49	
12	9.47 086	41	9.49 073	44	10.50 927	9.98 013	4	48	
13	9.47 127	41	9.49 118	45	10.50 882	9.98 009	4	47	
14	9.47 168	41	9.49 163	45	10.50 837	9.98 005	4	46	
15	9.47 209	41	9.49 207	44	10.50 793	9.98 001	4	45	
16	9.47 249	40	9.49 252	45	10.50 748	9.97 997	4	44	
17	9.47 290	41	9.49 296	44	10.50 704	9.97 993	4	43	
18	9.47 330	40	9.49 341	45	10.50 659	9.97 989	4	42	
19	9.47 371	41	9.49 385	44	10.50 615	9.97 986	3	41	
20	9.47 411	40	9.49 430	45	10.50 570	9.97 982	4	**40**	
21	9.47 452	40	9.49 474	44	10.50 526	9.97 978	4	39	
22	9.47 492	41	9.49 519	45	10.50 481	9.97 974	4	38	
23	9.47 533	40	9.49 563	44	10.50 437	9.97 970	4	37	
24	9.47 573	40	9.49 607	45	10.50 393	9.97 966	4	36	
25	9.47 613	41	9.49 652	44	10.50 348	9.97 962	4	35	
26	9.47 654	40	9.49 696	44	10.50 304	9.97 958	4	34	
27	9.47 694	40	9.49 740	44	10.50 260	9.97 954	4	33	
28	9.47 734	40	9.49 784	44	10.50 216	9.97 950	4	32	
29	9.47 774	40	9.49 828	44	10.50 172	9.97 946	4	31	
30	9.47 814	40	9.49 872	44	10.50 128	9.97 942	4	**30**	
31	9.47 854	40	9.49 916	44	10.50 084	9.97 938	4	29	
32	9.47 894	40	9.49 960	44	10.50 040	9.97 934	4	28	
33	9.47 934	40	9.50 004	44	10.49 996	9.97 930	4	27	
34	9.47 974	40	9.50 048	44	10.49 952	9.97 926	4	26	
35	9.48 014	40	9.50 092	44	10.49 908	9.97 922	4	25	
36	9.48 054	40	9.50 136	44	10.49 864	9.97 918	4	24	
37	9.48 094	39	9.50 180	43	10.49 820	9.97 914	4	23	
38	9.48 133	40	9.50 223	44	10.49 777	9.97 910	4	22	
39	9.48 173	40	9.50 267	44	10.49 733	9.97 906	4	21	
40	9.48 213	39	9.50 311	44	10.49 689	9.97 902	4	**20**	
41	9.48 252	40	9.50 355	43	10.49 645	9.97 898	4	19	
42	9.48 292	40	9.50 398	44	10.49 602	9.97 894	4	18	
43	9.48 332	39	9.50 442	43	10.49 558	9.97 890	4	17	
44	9.48 371	40	9.50 485	44	10.49 515	9.97 886	4	16	
45	9.48 411	39	9.50 529	43	10.49 471	9.97 882	4	15	
46	9.48 450	40	9.50 572	44	10.49 428	9.97 878	4	14	
47	9.48 490	39	9.50 616	43	10.49 384	9.97 874	4	13	
48	9.48 529	39	9.50 659	44	10.49 341	9.97 870	4	12	
49	9.48 568	39	9.50 703	43	10.49 297	9.97 866	5	11	
50	9.48 607	40	9.50 746	43	10.49 254	9.97 861	4	**10**	
51	9.48 647	39	9.50 789	44	10.49 211	9.97 857	4	9	
52	9.48 686	39	9.50 833	43	10.49 167	9.97 853	4	8	
53	9.48 725	39	9.50 876	43	10.49 124	9.97 849	4	7	
54	9.48 764	39	9.50 919	43	10.49 081	9.97 845	4	6	
55	9.48 803	39	9.50 962	43	10.49 038	9.97 841	4	5	
56	9.48 842	39	9.51 005	43	10.48 995	9.97 837	4	4	
57	9.48 881	39	9.51 048	44	10.48 952	9.97 833	4	3	
58	9.48 920	39	9.51 092	43	10.48 908	9.97 829	4	2	
59	9.48 959	39	9.51 135	43	10.48 865	9.97 825	4	1	
60	9.48 998		9.51 178		10.48 822	9.97 821		**0**	
	L Cos	d	L Cot	c d	L Tan	L Sin	d	'	Prop. Pts.

Prop. Pts.

	45	44	43
1	4.5	4.4	4.3
2	9.0	8.8	8.6
3	13.5	13.2	12.9
4	18.0	17.6	17.2
5	22.5	22.0	21.5
6	27.0	26.4	25.8
7	31.5	30.8	30.1
8	36.0	35.2	34.4
9	40.5	39.6	38.7

	42	41
1	4.2	4.1
2	8.4	8.2
3	12.6	12.3
4	16.8	16.4
5	21.0	20.5
6	25.2	24.6
7	29.4	28.7
8	33.6	32.8
9	37.8	36.9

	40	39
1	4.0	3.9
2	8.0	7.8
3	12.0	11.7
4	16.0	15.6
5	20.0	19.5
6	24.0	23.4
7	28.0	27.3
8	32.0	31.2
9	36.0	35.1

	5	4	3
1	0.5	0.4	0.3
2	1.0	0.8	0.6
3	1.5	1.2	0.9
4	2.0	1.6	1.2
5	2.5	2.0	1.5
6	3.0	2.4	1.8
7	3.5	2.8	2.1
8	4.0	3.2	2.4
9	4.5	3.6	2.7

TABLE III   18°

'	L Sin	d	L Tan	c d	L Cot	L Cos	d		Prop. Pts.
0	9.48 998		9.51 178		10.48 822	9.97 821		60	
1	9.49 037	39	9.51 221	43	10.48 779	9.97 817	4	59	
2	9.49 076	39	9.51 264	43	10.48 736	9.97 812	5	58	
3	9.49 115	39	9.51 306	42	10.48 694	9.97 808	4	57	
4	9.49 153	38	9.51 349	43	10.48 651	9.97 804	4	56	
5	9.49 192	39	9.51 392	43	10.48 608	9.97 800	4	55	
6	9.49 231	39	9.51 435	43	10.48 565	9.97 796	4	54	
7	9.49 269	38	9.51 478	43	10.48 522	9.97 792	4	53	
8	9.49 308	39	9.51 520	42	10.48 480	9.97 788	4	52	**43 42 41**
9	9.49 347	39	9.51 563	43	10.48 437	9.97 784	4	51	1 4.3 4.2 4.1
10	9.49 385	38	9.51 606	43	10.48 394	9.97 779	5	50	2 8.6 8.4 8.2
11	9.49 424	39	9.51 648	42	10.48 352	9.97 775	4	49	3 12.9 12.6 12.3
12	9.49 462	38	9.51 691	43	10.48 309	9.97 771	4	48	4 17.2 16.8 16.4
13	9.49 500	38	9.51 734	43	10.48 266	9.97 767	4	47	5 21.5 21.0 20.5
14	9.49 539	39	9.51 776	42	10.48 224	9.97 763	4	46	6 25.8 25.2 24.6
15	9.49 577	38	9.51 819	43	10.48 181	9.97 759	4	45	7 30.1 29.4 28.7
16	9.49 615	38	9.51 861	42	10.48 139	9.97 754	5	44	8 34.4 33.6 32.8
17	9.49 654	39	9.51 903	42	10.48 097	9.97 750	4	43	9 38.7 37.8 36.9
18	9.49 692	38	9.51 946	43	10.48 054	9.97 746	4	42	
19	9.49 730	38	9.51 988	42	10.48 012	9.97 742	4	41	
20	9.49 768	38	9.52 031	43	10.47 969	9.97 738	4	40	
21	9.49 806	38	9.52 073	42	10.47 927	9.97 734	5	39	
22	9.49 844	38	9.52 115	42	10.47 885	9.97 729	4	38	
23	9.49 882	38	9.52 157	42	10.47 843	9.97 725	4	37	
24	9.49 920	38	9.52 200	43	10.47 800	9.97 721	4	36	
25	9.49 958	38	9.52 242	42	10.47 758	9.97 717	4	35	
26	9.49 996	38	9.52 284	42	10.47 716	9.97 713	5	34	**39 38 37**
27	9.50 034	38	9.52 326	42	10.47 674	9.97 708	4	33	1 3.9 3.8 3.7
28	9.50 072	38	9.52 368	42	10.47 632	9.97 704	4	32	2 7.8 7.6 7.4
29	9.50 110	38	9.52 410	42	10.47 590	9.97 700	4	31	3 11.7 11.4 11.1
30	9.50 148	37	9.52 452	42	10.47 548	9.97 696	5	30	4 15.6 15.2 14.8
31	9.50 185	38	9.52 494	42	10.47 506	9.97 691	4	29	5 19.5 19.0 18.5
32	9.50 223	38	9.52 536	42	10.47 464	9.97 687	4	28	6 23.4 22.8 22.2
33	9.50 261	37	9.52 578	42	10.47 422	9.97 683	4	27	7 27.3 26.6 25.9
34	9.50 298	38	9.52 620	41	10.47 380	9.97 679	5	26	8 31.2 30.4 29.6
35	9.50 336	38	9.52 661	42	10.47 339	9.97 674	4	25	9 35.1 34.2 33.3
36	9.50 374	37	9.52 703	42	10.47 297	9.97 670	4	24	
37	9.50 411	38	9.52 745	42	10.47 255	9.97 666	4	23	
38	9.50 449	37	9.52 787	42	10.47 213	9.97 662	5	22	
39	9.50 486	37	9.52 829	41	10.47 171	9.97 657	4	21	
40	9.50 523	38	9.52 870	42	10.47 130	9.97 653	4	20	
41	9.50 561	37	9.52 912	41	10.47 088	9.97 649	4	19	
42	9.50 598	37	9.52 953	42	10.47 047	9.97 645	5	18	
43	9.50 635	38	9.52 995	42	10.47 005	9.97 640	4	17	
44	9.50 673	37	9.53 037	41	10.46 963	9.97 636	4	16	**36 5 4**
45	9.50 710	37	9.53 078	42	10.46 922	9.97 632	4	15	1 3.6 0.5 0.4
46	9.50 747	37	9.53 120	41	10.46 880	9.97 628	5	14	2 7.2 1.0 0.8
47	9.50 784	37	9.53 161	41	10.46 839	9.97 623	4	13	3 10.8 1.5 1.2
48	9.50 821	37	9.53 202	42	10.46 798	9.97 619	4	12	4 14.4 2.0 1.6
49	9.50 858	38	9.53 244	41	10.46 756	9.97 615	5	11	5 18.0 2.5 2.0
50	9.50 896	37	9.53 285	42	10.46 715	9.97 610	4	10	6 21.6 3.0 2.4
51	9.50 933	37	9.53 327	41	10.46 673	9.97 606	4	9	7 25.2 3.5 2.8
52	9.50 970	37	9.53 368	41	10.46 632	9.97 602	5	8	8 28.8 4.0 3.2
53	9.51 007	36	9.53 409	41	10.46 591	9.97 597	4	7	9 32.4 4.5 3.6
54	9.51 043	37	9.53 450	42	10.46 550	9.97 593	4	6	
55	9.51 080	37	9.53 492	41	10.46 508	9.97 589	5	5	
56	9.51 117	37	9.53 533	41	10.46 467	9.97 584	4	4	
57	9.51 154	37	9.53 574	41	10.46 426	9.97 580	4	3	
58	9.51 191	36	9.53 615	41	10.46 385	9.97 576	5	2	
59	9.51 227	37	9.53 656	41	10.46 344	9.97 571	4	1	
60	9.51 264		9.53 697		10.46 303	9.97 567		0	
	L Cos	d	L Cot	c d	L Tan	L Sin	d	'	Prop. Pts.

′	L Sin	d	L Tan	c d	L Cot	L Cos	d	′
0	9.51 264	37	9.53 697	41	10.46 303	9.97 567	4	60
1	9.51 301	37	9.53 738	41	10.46 262	9.97 563	5	59
2	9.51 338	36	9.53 779	41	10.46 221	9.97 558	4	58
3	9.51 374	37	9.53 820	41	10.46 180	9.97 554	4	57
4	9.51 411	36	9.53 861	41	10.46 139	9.97 550	5	56
5	9.51 447	37	9.53 902	41	10.46 098	9.97 545	4	55
6	9.51 484	36	9.53 943	41	10.46 057	9.97 541	5	54
7	9.51 520	37	9.53 984	41	10.46 016	9.97 536	4	53
8	9.51 557	36	9.54 025	40	10.45 975	9.97 532	4	52
9	9.51 593	36	9.54 065	41	10.45 935	9.97 528	5	51
10	9.51 629	37	9.54 106	41	10.45 894	9.97 523	4	50
11	9.51 666	36	9.54 147	40	10.45 853	9.97 519	4	49
12	9.51 702	36	9.54 187	41	10.45 813	9.97 515	5	48
13	9.51 738	36	9.54 228	41	10.45 772	9.97 510	4	47
14	9.51 774	37	9.54 269	40	10.45 731	9.97 506	5	46
15	9.51 811	36	9.54 309	41	10.45 691	9.97 501	4	45
16	9.51 847	36	9.54 350	40	10.45 650	9.97 497	5	44
17	9.51 883	36	9.54 390	41	10.45 610	9.97 492	4	43
18	9.51 919	36	9.54 431	40	10.45 569	9.97 488	4	42
19	9.51 955	36	9.54 471	41	10.45 529	9.97 484	5	41
20	9.51 991	36	9.54 512	40	10.45 488	9.97 479	4	40
21	9.52 027	36	9.54 552	41	10.45 448	9.97 475	5	39
22	9.52 063	36	9.54 593	40	10.45 407	9.97 470	4	38
23	9.52 099	36	9.54 633	40	10.45 367	9.97 466	5	37
24	9.52 135	36	9.54 673	41	10.45 327	9.97 461	4	36
25	9.52 171	36	9.54 714	40	10.45 286	9.97 457	4	35
26	9.52 207	35	9.54 754	40	10.45 246	9.97 453	5	34
27	9.52 242	36	9.54 794	41	10.45 206	9.97 448	4	33
28	9.52 278	36	9.54 835	40	10.45 165	9.97 444	5	32
29	9.52 314	36	9.54 875	40	10.45 125	9.97 439	4	31
30	9.52 350	35	9.54 915	40	10.45 085	9.97 435	5	30
31	9.52 385	36	9.54 955	40	10.45 045	9.97 430	4	29
32	9.52 421	35	9.54 995	40	10.45 005	9.97 426	5	28
33	9.52 456	36	9.55 035	40	10.44 965	9.97 421	4	27
34	9.52 492	35	9.55 075	40	10.44 925	9.97 417	5	26
35	9.52 527	36	9.55 115	40	10.44 885	9.97 412	4	25
36	9.52 563	35	9.55 155	40	10.44 845	9.97 408	5	24
37	9.52 598	36	9.55 195	40	10.44 805	9.97 403	4	23
38	9.52 634	35	9.55 235	40	10.44 765	9.97 399	5	22
39	9.52 669	36	9.55 275	40	10.44 725	9.97 394	4	21
40	9.52 705	35	9.55 315	40	10.44 685	9.97 390	5	20
41	9.52 740	35	9.55 355	40	10.44 645	9.97 385	4	19
42	9.52 775	36	9.55 395	39	10.44 605	9.97 381	5	18
43	9.52 811	35	9.55 434	40	10.44 566	9.97 376	4	17
44	9.52 846	35	9.55 474	40	10.44 526	9.97 372	5	16
45	9.52 881	35	9.55 514	40	10.44 486	9.97 367	4	15
46	9.52 916	35	9.55 554	39	10.44 446	9.97 363	5	14
47	9.52 951	35	9.55 593	40	10.44 407	9.97 358	5	13
48	9.52 986	35	9.55 633	40	10.44 367	9.97 353	4	12
49	9.53 021	35	9.55 673	39	10.44 327	9.97 349	5	11
50	9.53 056	36	9.55 712	40	10.44 288	9.97 344	4	10
51	9.53 092	34	9.55 752	39	10.44 248	9.97 340	5	9
52	9.53 126	35	9.55 791	40	10.44 209	9.97 335	4	8
53	9.53 161	35	9.55 831	39	10.44 169	9.97 331	5	7
54	9.53 196	35	9.55 870	40	10.44 130	9.97 326	4	6
55	9.53 231	35	9.55 910	39	10.44 090	9.97 322	5	5
56	9.53 266	35	9.55 949	40	10.44 051	9.97 317	5	4
57	9.53 301	34	9.55 989	39	10.44 011	9.97 312	4	3
58	9.53 336	35	9.56 028	39	10.43 972	9.97 308	5	2
59	9.53 370	35	9.56 067	40	10.43 933	9.97 303	4	1
60	9.53 405		9.56 107		10.43 893	9.97 299		0
	L Cos	d	L Cot	c d	L Tan	L Sin	d	′

Prop. Pts.

	41	40	39
1	4.1	4.0	3.9
2	8.2	8.0	7.8
3	12.3	12.0	11.7
4	16.4	16.0	15.6
5	20.5	20.0	19.5
6	24.6	24.0	23.4
7	28.7	28.0	27.3
8	32.8	32.0	31.2
9	36.9	36.0	35.1

	37	36	35
1	3.7	3.6	3.5
2	7.4	7.2	7.0
3	11.1	10.8	10.5
4	14.8	14.4	14.0
5	18.5	18.0	17.5
6	22.2	21.6	21.0
7	25.9	25.2	24.5
8	29.6	28.8	28.0
9	33.3	32.4	31.5

	34	5	4
1	3.4	0.5	0.4
2	6.8	1.0	0.8
3	10.2	1.5	1.2
4	13.6	2.0	1.6
5	17.0	2.5	2.0
6	20.4	3.0	2.4
7	23.8	3.5	2.8
8	27.2	4.0	3.2
9	30.6	4.5	3.6

TABLE III   20°

′	L Sin	d	L Tan	c d	L Cot	L Cos	d		Prop. Pts.
0	9.53 405		9.56 107		10.43 893	9.97 299		**60**	
1	9.53 440	35	9.56 146	39	10.43 854	9.97 294	5	59	
2	9.53 475	35	9.56 185	39	10.43 815	9.97 289	5	58	
3	9.53 509	34	9.56 224	39	10.43 776	9.97 285	4	57	
4	9.53 544	35	9.56 264	40	10.43 736	9.97 280	5	56	
5	9.53 578	34	9.56 303	39	10.43 697	9.97 276	4	55	
6	9.53 613	35	9.56 342	39	10.43 658	9.97 271	5	54	
7	9.53 647	34	9.56 381	39	10.43 619	9.97 266	5	53	
8	9.53 682	35	9.56 420	39	10.43 580	9.97 262	4	52	
9	9.53 716	34	9.56 459	39	10.43 541	9.97 257	5	51	
10	9.53 751	35	9.56 498	39	10.43 502	9.97 252	5	**50**	
11	9.53 785	34	9.56 537	39	10.43 463	9.97 248	4	49	
12	9.53 819	35	9.56 576	39	10.43 424	9.97 243	5	48	
13	9.53 854	34	9.56 615	39	10.43 385	9.97 238	5	47	
14	9.53 888	34	9.56 654	39	10.43 346	9.97 234	4	46	
15	9.53 922	35	9.56 693	39	10.43 307	9.97 229	5	45	
16	9.53 957	34	9.56 732	39	10.43 268	9.97 224	5	44	
17	9.53 991	34	9.56 771	39	10.43 229	9.97 220	4	43	
18	9.54 025	34	9.56 810	39	10.43 190	9.97 215	5	42	
19	9.54 059	34	9.56 849	38	10.43 151	9.97 210	5	41	
20	9.54 093	34	9.56 887	39	10.43 113	9.97 206	4	**40**	
21	9.54 127	34	9.56 926	39	10.43 074	9.97 201	5	39	
22	9.54 161	34	9.56 965	39	10.43 035	9.97 196	5	38	
23	9.54 195	34	9.57 004	38	10.42 996	9.97 192	4	37	
24	9.54 229	34	9.57 042	39	10.42 958	9.97 187	5	36	
25	9.54 263	34	9.57 081	39	10.42 919	9.97 182	5	35	
26	9.54 297	34	9.57 120	38	10.42 880	9.97 178	4	34	
27	9.54 331	34	9.57 158	39	10.42 842	9.97 173	5	33	
28	9.54 365	34	9.57 197	38	10.42 803	9.97 168	5	32	
29	9.54 399	34	9.57 235	39	10.42 765	9.97 163	4	31	
30	9.54 433	33	9.57 274	38	10.42 726	9.97 159	5	**30**	
31	9.54 466	34	9.57 312	39	10.42 688	9.97 154	5	29	
32	9.54 500	34	9.57 351	38	10.42 649	9.97 149	4	28	
33	9.54 534	33	9.57 389	39	10.42 611	9.97 145	5	27	
34	9.54 567	34	9.57 428	38	10.42 572	9.97 140	5	26	
35	9.54 601	34	9.57 466	38	10.42 534	9.97 135	5	25	
36	9.54 635	33	9.57 504	39	10.42 496	9.97 130	4	24	
37	9.54 668	34	9.57 543	38	10.42 457	9.97 126	5	23	
38	9.54 702	33	9.57 581	38	10.42 419	9.97 121	5	22	
39	9.54 735	34	9.57 619	39	10.42 381	9.97 116	5	21	
40	9.54 769	33	9.57 658	38	10.42 342	9.97 111	4	**20**	
41	9.54 802	34	9.57 696	38	10.42 304	9.97 107	5	19	
42	9.54 836	33	9.57 734	38	10.42 266	9.97 102	5	18	
43	9.54 869	34	9.57 772	38	10.42 228	9.97 097	5	17	
44	9.54 903	33	9.57 810	39	10.42 190	9.97 092	5	16	
45	9.54 936	33	9.57 849	38	10.42 151	9.97 087	4	15	
46	9.54 969	34	9.57 887	38	10.42 113	9.97 083	5	14	
47	9.55 003	33	9.57 925	38	10.42 075	9.97 078	5	13	
48	9.55 036	33	9.57 963	38	10.42 037	9.97 073	5	12	
49	9.55 069	33	9.58 001	38	10.41 999	9.97 068	5	11	
50	9.55 102	34	9.58 039	38	10.41 961	9.97 063	4	**10**	
51	9.55 136	33	9.58 077	38	10.41 923	9.97 059	5	9	
52	9.55 169	33	9.58 115	38	10.41 885	9.97 054	5	8	
53	9.55 202	33	9.58 153	38	10.41 847	9.97 049	5	7	
54	9.55 235	33	9.58 191	38	10.41 809	9.97 044	5	6	
55	9.55 268	33	9.58 229	38	10.41 771	9.97 039	4	5	
56	9.55 301	33	9.58 267	37	10.41 733	9.97 035	5	4	
57	9.55 334	33	9.58 304	38	10.41 696	9.97 030	5	3	
58	9.55 367	33	9.58 342	38	10.41 658	9.97 025	5	2	
59	9.55 400	33	9.58 380	38	10.41 620	9.97 020	5	1	
60	9.55 433		9.58 418		10.41 582	9.97 015		**0**	
	L Cos	d	L Cot	c d	L Tan	L Sin	d	′	Prop. Pts.

Prop. Pts.

	40	39	38
1	4.0	3.9	3.8
2	8.0	7.8	7.6
3	12.0	11.7	11.4
4	16.0	15.6	15.2
5	20.0	19.5	19.0
6	24.0	23.4	22.8
7	28.0	27.3	26.6
8	32.0	31.2	30.4
9	36.0	35.1	34.2

	37	35	34
1	3.7	3.5	3.4
2	7.4	7.0	6.8
3	11.1	10.5	10.2
4	14.8	14.0	13.6
5	18.5	17.5	17.0
6	22.2	21.0	20.4
7	25.9	24.5	23.8
8	29.6	28.0	27.2
9	33.3	31.5	30.6

	33	5	4
1	3.3	0.5	0.4
2	6.6	1.0	0.8
3	9.9	1.5	1.2
4	13.2	2.0	1.6
5	16.5	2.5	2.0
6	19.8	3.0	2.4
7	23.1	3.5	2.8
8	26.4	4.0	3.2
9	29.7	4.5	3.6

'	L Sin	d	L Tan	c d	L Cot	L Cos	d	'
0	9.55 433		9.58 418		10.41 582	9.97 015		60
1	9.55 466	33	9.58 455	37	10.41 545	9.97 010	5	59
2	9.55 499	33	9.58 493	38	10.41 507	9.97 005	5	58
3	9.55 532	33	9.58 531	38	10.41 469	9.97 001	4	57
4	9.55 564	32	9.58 569	38	10.41 431	9.96 996	5	56
5	9.55 597	33	9.58 606	37	10.41 394	9.96 991	5	55
6	9.55 630	33	9.58 644	38	10.41 356	9.96 986	5	54
7	9.55 663	33	9.58 681	37	10.41 319	9.96 981	5	53
8	9.55 695	32	9.58 719	38	10.41 281	9.96 976	5	52
9	9.55 728	33	9.58 757	38	10.41 243	9.96 971	5	51
10	9.55 761	33	9.58 794	37	10.41 206	9.96 966	5	50
11	9.55 793	32	9.58 832	38	10.41 168	9.96 962	4	49
12	9.55 826	33	9.58 869	37	10.41 131	9.96 957	5	48
13	9.55 858	32	9.58 907	38	10.41 093	9.96 952	5	47
14	9.55 891	33	9.58 944	37	10.41 056	9.96 947	5	46
15	9.55 923	32	9.58 981	37	10.41 019	9.96 942	5	45
16	9.55 956	33	9.59 019	38	10.40 981	9.96 937	5	44
17	9.55 988	32	9.59 056	37	10.40 944	9.96 932	5	43
18	9.56 021	33	9.59 094	38	10.40 906	9.96 927	5	42
19	9.56 053	32	9.59 131	37	10.40 869	9.96 922	5	41
20	9.56 085	32	9.59 168	37	10.40 832	9.96 917	5	40
21	9.56 118	33	9.59 205	38	10.40 795	9.96 912	5	39
22	9.56 150	32	9.59 243	37	10.40 757	9.96 907	5	38
23	9.56 182	32	9.59 280	37	10.40 720	9.96 903	4	37
24	9.56 215	33	9.59 317	37	10.40 683	9.96 898	5	36
25	9.56 247	32	9.59 354	37	10.40 646	9.96 893	5	35
26	9.56 279	32	9.59 391	38	10.40 609	9.96 888	5	34
27	9.56 311	32	9.59 429	37	10.40 571	9.96 883	5	33
28	9.56 343	32	9.59 466	37	10.40 534	9.96 878	5	32
29	9.56 375	33	9.59 503	37	10.40 497	9.96 873	5	31
30	9.56 408	32	9.59 540	37	10.40 460	9.96 868	5	30
31	9.56 440	32	9.59 577	37	10.40 423	9.96 863	5	29
32	9.56 472	32	9.59 614	37	10.40 386	9.96 858	5	28
33	9.56 504	32	9.59 651	37	10.40 349	9.96 853	5	27
34	9.56 536	32	9.59 688	37	10.40 312	9.96 848	5	26
35	9.56 568	31	9.59 725	37	10.40 275	9.96 843	5	25
36	9.56 599	32	9.59 762	37	10.40 238	9.96 838	5	24
37	9.56 631	32	9.59 799	36	10.40 201	9.96 833	5	23
38	9.56 663	32	9.59 835	37	10.40 165	9.96 828	5	22
39	9.56 695	32	9.59 872	37	10.40 128	9.96 823	5	21
40	9.56 727	32	9.59 909	37	10.40 091	9.96 818	5	20
41	9.56 759	31	9.59 946	37	10.40 054	9.96 813	5	19
42	9.56 790	32	9.59 983	36	10.40 017	9.96 808	5	18
43	9.56 822	32	9.60 019	37	10.39 981	9.96 803	5	17
44	9.56 854	32	9.60 056	37	10.39 944	9.96 798	5	16
45	9.56 886	31	9.60 093	37	10.39 907	9.96 793	5	15
46	9.56 917	32	9.60 130	36	10.39 870	9.96 788	5	14
47	9.56 949	31	9.60 166	37	10.39 834	9.96 783	5	13
48	9.56 980	32	9.60 203	37	10.39 797	9.96 778	6	12
49	9.57 012	32	9.60 240	36	10.39 760	9.96 772	5	11
50	9.57 044	31	9.60 276	37	10.39 724	9.96 767	5	10
51	9.57 075	32	9.60 313	36	10.39 687	9.96 762	5	9
52	9.57 107	31	9.60 349	37	10.39 651	9.96 757	5	8
53	9.57 138	31	9.60 386	36	10.39 614	9.96 752	5	7
54	9.57 169	32	9.60 422	37	10.39 578	9.96 747	5	6
55	9.57 201	31	9.60 459	36	10.39 541	9.96 742	5	5
56	9.57 232	32	9.60 495	37	10.39 505	9.96 737	5	4
57	9.57 264	31	9.60 532	36	10.39 468	9.96 732	5	3
58	9.57 295	31	9.60 568	37	10.39 432	9.96 727	5	2
59	9.57 326	32	9.60 605	36	10.39 395	9.96 722	5	1
60	9.57 358		9.60 641		10.39 359	9.96 717		0
	L Cos	d	L Cot	c d	L Tan	L Sin	d	'

Prop. Pts.

	38	37	36
1	3.8	3.7	3.6
2	7.6	7.4	7.2
3	11.4	11.1	10.8
4	15.2	14.8	14.4
5	19.0	18.5	18.0
6	22.8	22.2	21.6
7	26.6	25.9	25.2
8	30.4	29.6	28.8
9	34.2	33.3	32.4

	33	32	31
1	3.3	3.2	3.1
2	6.6	6.4	6.2
3	9.9	9.6	9.3
4	13.2	12.8	12.4
5	16.5	16.0	15.5
6	19.8	19.2	18.6
7	23.1	22.4	21.7
8	26.4	25.6	24.8
9	29.7	28.8	27.9

	6	5	4
1	0.6	0.5	0.4
2	1.2	1.0	0.8
3	1.8	1.5	1.2
4	2.4	2.0	1.6
5	3.0	2.5	2.0
6	3.6	3.0	2.4
7	4.2	3.5	2.8
8	4.8	4.0	3.2
9	5.4	4.5	3.6

TABLE III   22°

′	L Sin	d	L Tan	c d	L Cot	L Cos	d		Prop. Pts.
0	9.57 358		9.60 641		10.39 359	9.96 717		**60**	
1	9.57 389	31	9.60 677	36	10.39 323	9.96 711	6	59	
2	9.57 420	31	9.60 714	37	10.39 286	9.96 706	5	58	
3	9.57 451	31	9.60 750	36	10.39 250	9.96 701	5	57	
4	9.57 482	31	9.60 786	36	10.39 214	9.96 696	5	56	
5	9.57 514	32	9.60 823	37	10.39 177	9.96 691	5	55	
6	9.57 545	31	9.60 859	36	10.39 141	9.96 686	5	54	
7	9.57 576	31	9.60 895	36	10.39 105	9.96 681	5	53	
8	9.57 607	31	9.60 931	36	10.39 069	9.96 676	5	52	
9	9.57 638	31	9.60 967	36	10.39 033	9.96 670	6	51	
10	9.57 669	31	9.61 004	37	10.38 996	9.96 665	5	**50**	
11	9.57 700	31	9.61 040	36	10.38 960	9.96 660	5	49	
12	9.57 731	31	9.61 076	36	10.38 924	9.96 655	5	48	
13	9.57 762	31	9.61 112	36	10.38 888	9.96 650	5	47	
14	9.57 793	31	9.61 148	36	10.38 852	9.96 645	5	46	
15	9.57 824	31	9.61 184	36	10.38 816	9.96 640	5	45	
16	9.57 855	31	9.61 220	36	10.38 780	9.96 634	6	44	
17	9.57 885	30	9.61 256	36	10.38 744	9.96 629	5	43	
18	9.57 916	31	9.61 292	36	10.38 708	9.96 624	5	42	
19	9.57 947	31	9.61 328	36	10.38 672	9.96 619	5	41	
20	9.57 978	31	9.61 364	36	10.38 636	9.96 614	6	**40**	
21	9.58 008	30	9.61 400	36	10.38 600	9.96 608	5	39	
22	9.58 039	31	9.61 436	36	10.38 564	9.96 603	5	38	
23	9.58 070	31	9.61 472	36	10.38 528	9.96 598	5	37	
24	9.58 101	31	9.61 508	36	10.38 492	9.96 593	5	36	
25	9.58 131	30	9.61 544	35	10.38 456	9.96 588	6	35	
26	9.58 162	31	9.61 579	36	10.38 421	9.96 582	5	34	
27	9.58 192	30	9.61 615	36	10.38 385	9.96 577	5	33	
28	9.58 223	31	9.61 651	36	10.38 349	9.96 572	5	32	
29	9.58 253	30	9.61 687	35	10.38 313	9.96 567	5	31	
30	9.58 284	31	9.61 722	36	10.38 278	9.96 562	6	**30**	
31	9.58 314	30	9.61 758	36	10.38 242	9.96 556	5	29	
32	9.58 345	31	9.61 794	36	10.38 206	9.96 551	5	28	
33	9.58 375	30	9.61 830	35	10.38 170	9.96 546	5	27	
34	9.58 406	31	9.61 865	36	10.38 135	9.96 541	6	26	
35	9.58 436	30	9.61 901	35	10.38 099	9.96 535	5	25	
36	9.58 467	31	9.61 936	36	10.38 064	9.96 530	5	24	
37	9.58 497	30	9.61 972	36	10.38 028	9.96 525	5	23	
38	9.58 527	30	9.62 008	35	10.37 992	9.96 520	6	22	
39	9.58 557	30	9.62 043	36	10.37 957	9.96 514	5	21	
40	9.58 588	31	9.62 079	35	10.37 921	9.96 509	5	**20**	
41	9.58 618	30	9.62 114	36	10.37 886	9.96 504	6	19	
42	9.58 648	30	9.62 150	35	10.37 850	9.96 498	5	18	
43	9.58 678	30	9.62 185	36	10.37 815	9.96 493	5	17	
44	9.58 709	31	9.62 221	35	10.37 779	9.96 488	5	16	
45	9.58 739	30	9.62 256	36	10.37 744	9.96 483	6	15	
46	9.58 769	30	9.62 292	35	10.37 708	9.96 477	5	14	
47	9.58 799	30	9.62 327	35	10.37 673	9.96 472	5	13	
48	9.58 829	30	9.62 362	36	10.37 638	9.96 467	6	12	
49	9.58 859	30	9.62 398	35	10.37 602	9.96 461	5	11	
50	9.58 889	30	9.62 433	35	10.37 567	9.96 456	5	**10**	
51	9.58 919	30	9.62 468	36	10.37 532	9.96 451	6	9	
52	9.58 949	30	9.62 504	35	10.37 496	9.96 445	5	8	
53	9.58 979	30	9.62 539	35	10.37 461	9.96 440	5	7	
54	9.59 009	30	9.62 574	35	10.37 426	9.96 435	6	6	
55	9.59 039	30	9.62 609	36	10.37 391	9.96 429	5	5	
56	9.59 069	29	9.62 645	35	10.37 355	9.96 424	5	4	
57	9.59 098	30	9.62 680	35	10.37 320	9.96 419	6	3	
58	9.59 128	30	9.62 715	35	10.37 285	9.96 413	5	2	
59	9.59 158	30	9.62 750	35	10.37 250	9.96 408	5	1	
60	9.59 188		9.62 785		10.37 215	9.96 403		**0**	
	L Cos	d	L Cot	c d	L Tan	L Sin	d	′	Prop. Pts.

Prop. Pts.

	37	36	35
1	3.7	3.6	3.5
2	7.4	7.2	7.0
3	11.1	10.8	10.5
4	14.8	14.4	14.0
5	18.5	18.0	17.5
6	22.2	21.6	21.0
7	25.9	25.2	24.5
8	29.6	28.8	28.0
9	33.3	32.4	31.5

	32	31	30
1	3.2	3.1	3.0
2	6.4	6.2	6.0
3	9.6	9.3	9.0
4	12.8	12.4	12.0
5	16.0	15.5	15.0
6	19.2	18.6	18.0
7	22.4	21.7	21.0
8	25.6	24.8	24.0
9	28.8	27.9	27.0

	29	6	5
1	2.9	0.6	0.5
2	5.8	1.2	1.0
3	8.7	1.8	1.5
4	11.6	2.4	2.0
5	14.5	3.0	2.5
6	17.4	3.6	3.0
7	20.3	4.2	3.5
8	23.2	4.8	4.0
9	26.1	5.4	4.5

′	L Sin	d	L Tan	c d	L Cot	L Cos	d		Prop. Pts.
0	9.59 188	30	9.62 785	35	10.37 215	9.96 403		60	
1	9.59 218	29	9.62 820	35	10.37 180	9.96 397	6	59	
2	9.59 247	30	9.62 855	35	10.37 145	9.96 392	5	58	
3	9.59 277	30	9.62 890	36	10.37 110	9.96 387	5	57	
4	9.59 307	29	9.62 926	35	10.37 074	9.96 381	6	56	
5	9.59 336	30	9.62 961	35	10.37 039	9.96 376	5	55	
6	9.59 366	30	9.62 996	35	10.37 004	9.96 370	6	54	
7	9.59 396	29	9.63 031	35	10.36 969	9.96 365	5	53	
8	9.59 425	30	9.63 066	35	10.36 934	9.96 360	5	52		36 35 34
9	9.59 455	29	9.63 101	34	10.36 899	9.96 354	6	51	1 3.6 3.5 3.4
10	9.59 484	30	9.63 135	35	10.36 865	9.96 349	5	50	2 7.2 7.0 6.8
11	9.59 514	29	9.63 170	35	10.36 830	9.96 343	6	49	3 10.8 10.5 10.2
12	9.59 543	30	9.63 205	35	10.36 795	9.96 338	5	48	4 14.4 14.0 13.6
13	9.59 573	29	9.63 240	35	10.36 760	9.96 333	5	47	5 18.0 17.5 17.0
14	9.59 602	30	9.63 275	35	10.36 725	9.96 327	6	46	6 21.6 21.0 20.4
15	9.59 632	29	9.63 310	35	10.36 690	9.96 322	5	45	7 25.2 24.5 23.8
16	9.59 661	29	9.63 345	34	10.36 655	9.96 316	6	44	8 28.8 28.0 27.2
17	9.59 690	30	9.63 379	35	10.36 621	9.96 311	5	43	9 32.4 31.5 30.6
18	9.59 720	29	9.63 414	35	10.36 586	9.96 305	6	42	
19	9.59 749	29	9.63 449	35	10.36 551	9.96 300	5	41	
20	9.59 778	30	9.63 484	35	10.36 516	9.96 294	6	40	
21	9.59 808	29	9.63 519	34	10.36 481	9.96 289	5	39	
22	9.59 839	29	9.63 553	35	10.36 447	9.96 284	5	38	
23	9.59 866	29	9.63 588	35	10.36 412	9.96 278	6	37	
24	9.59 895	29	9.63 623	34	10.36 377	9.96 273	5	36	
25	9.59 924	30	9.63 657	35	10.36 343	9.96 267	5	35	
26	9.59 954	29	9.63 692	34	10.36 308	9.96 262	6	34		30 29 28
27	9.59 983	29	9.63 726	35	10.36 274	9.96 256	5	33	1 3.0 2.9 2.8
28	9.60 012	29	9.63 761	35	10.36 239	9.96 251	6	32	2 6.0 5.8 5.6
29	9.60 041	29	9.63 796	34	10.36 204	9.96 245	5	31	3 9.0 8.7 8.4
30	9.60 070	29	9.63 830	35	10.36 170	9.96 240	6	30	4 12.0 11.6 11.2
31	9.60 099	29	9.63 865	34	10.36 135	9.96 234	5	29	5 15.0 14.5 14.0
32	9.60 128	29	9.63 899	35	10.36 101	9.96 229	6	28	6 18.0 17.4 16.8
33	9.60 157	29	9.63 934	34	10.36 066	9.96 223	5	27	7 21.0 20.3 19.6
34	9.60 186	29	9.63 968	35	10.36 032	9.96 218	6	26	8 24.0 23.2 22.4
35	9.60 215	29	9.64 003	34	10.35 997	9.96 212	5	25	9 27.0 26.1 25.2
36	9.60 244	29	9.64 037	35	10.35 963	9.96 207	6	24	
37	9.60 273	29	9.64 072	34	10.35 928	9.96 201	5	23	
38	9.60 302	29	9.64 106	34	10.35 894	9.96 196	6	22	
39	9.60 331	28	9.64 140	35	10.35 860	9.96 190	5	21	
40	9.60 359	29	9.64 175	34	10.35 825	9.96 185	6	20	
41	9.60 388	29	9.64 209	34	10.35 791	9.96 179	5	19	
42	9.60 417	29	9.64 243	35	10.35 757	9.96 174	6	18	
43	9.60 446	28	9.64 278	34	10.35 722	9.96 168	6	17	
44	9.60 474	29	9.64 312	34	10.35 688	9.96 162	5	16		6 5
45	9.60 503	29	9.64 346	35	10.35 654	9.96 157	6	15	1 0.6 0.5
46	9.60 532	29	9.64 381	34	10.35 619	9.96 151	5	14	2 1.2 1.0
47	9.60 561	28	9.64 415	34	10.35 585	9.96 146	6	13	3 1.8 1.5
48	9.60 589	29	9.64 449	34	10.35 551	9.96 140	5	12	4 2.4 2.0
49	9.60 618	28	9.64 483	34	10.35 517	9.96 135	6	11	5 3.0 2.5
50	9.60 646	29	9.64 517	35	10.35 483	9.96 129	6	10	6 3.6 3.0
51	9.60 675	29	9.64 552	34	10.35 448	9.96 123	5	9	7 4.2 3.5
52	9.60 704	28	9.64 586	34	10.35 414	9.96 118	6	8	8 4.8 4.0
53	9.60 732	29	9.64 620	34	10.35 380	9.96 112	5	7	9 5.4 4.5
54	9.60 761	28	9.04 054	34	10.35 340	9.90 107	6	6	
55	9.60 789	29	9.64 688	34	10.35 312	9.96 101	5	5	
56	9.60 818	28	9.64 722	34	10.35 278	9.96 095	5	4	
57	9.60 846	29	9.64 756	34	10.35 244	9.96 090	6	3	
58	9.60 875	28	9.64 790	34	10.35 210	9.96 084	5	2	
59	9.60 903	28	9.64 824	34	10.35 176	9.96 079	6	1	
60	9.60 931		9.64 858		10.35 142	9.96 073		0	
	L Cos	d	L Cot	c d	L Tan	L Sin	d	′	Prop. Pts.

TABLE III   24°

'	L Sin	d	L Tan	c d	L Cot	L Cos	d	'	Prop. Pts.
0	9.60 931		9.64 858		10.35 142	9.96 073		60	
1	9.60 960	29	9.64 892	34	10.35 108	9.96 067	6	59	
2	9.60 988	28	9.64 926	34	10.35 074	9.96 062	5	58	
3	9.61 016	28	9.64 960	34	10.35 040	9.96 056	6	57	
4	9.61 045	29	9.64 994	34	10.35 006	9.96 050	6	56	
5	9.61 073	28	9.65 028	34	10.34 972	9.96 045	5	55	
6	9.61 101	28	9.65 062	34	10.34 938	9.96 039	6	54	
7	9.61 129	28	9.65 096	34	10.34 904	9.96 034	5	53	
8	9.61 158	29	9.65 130	34	10.34 870	9.96 028	6	52	
9	9.61 186	28	9.65 164	34	10.34 836	9.96 022	6	51	
10	9.61 214	28	9.65 197	33	10.34 803	9.96 017	5	50	
11	9.61 242	28	9.65 231	34	10.34 769	9.96 011	6	49	
12	9.61 270	28	9.65 265	34	10.34 735	9.96 005	6	48	
13	9.61 298	28	9.65 299	34	10.34 701	9.96 000	5	47	
14	9.61 326	28	9.65 333	34	10.34 667	9.95 994	6	46	
15	9.61 354	28	9.65 366	33	10.34 634	9.95 988	6	45	
16	9.61 382	28	9.65 400	34	10.34 600	9.95 982	6	44	
17	9.61 411	29	9.65 434	34	10.34 566	9.95 977	5	43	
18	9.61 438	27	9.65 467	33	10.34 533	9.95 971	6	42	
19	9.61 466	28	9.65 501	34	10.34 499	9.95 965	6	41	
20	9.61 494	28	9.65 535	34	10.34 465	9.95 960	5	40	
21	9.61 522	28	9.65 568	33	10.34 432	9.95 954	6	39	
22	9.61 550	28	9.65 602	34	10.34 398	9.95 948	6	38	
23	9.61 578	28	9.65 636	34	10.34 364	9.95 942	5	37	
24	9.61 606	28	9.65 669	33	10.34 331	9.95 937	6	36	
25	9.61 634	28	9.65 703	34	10.34 297	9.95 931	6	35	
26	9.61 662	27	9.65 736	33	10.34 264	9.95 925	5	34	
27	9.61 689	28	9.65 770	34	10.34 230	9.95 920	6	33	
28	9.61 717	28	9.65 803	33	10.34 197	9.95 914	6	32	
29	9.61 745	28	9.65 837	34	10.34 163	9.95 908	6	31	
30	9.61 773	27	9.65 870	33	10.34 130	9.95 902	5	30	
31	9.61 800	28	9.65 904	34	10.34 096	9.95 897	6	29	
32	9.61 828	28	9.65 937	33	10.34 063	9.95 891	6	28	
33	9.61 856	27	9.65 971	34	10.34 029	9.95 885	6	27	
34	9.61 883	28	9.66 004	33	10.33 996	9.95 879	6	26	
35	9.61 911	28	9.66 038	34	10.33 962	9.95 873	5	25	
36	9.61 939	27	9.66 071	33	10.33 929	9.95 868	6	24	
37	9.61 966	28	9.66 104	34	10.33 896	9.95 862	6	23	
38	9.61 994	27	9.66 138	33	10.33 862	9.95 856	6	22	
39	9.62 021	28	9.66 171	33	10.33 829	9.95 850	6	21	
40	9.62 049	27	9.66 204	34	10.33 796	9.95 844	5	20	
41	9.62 076	28	9.66 238	33	10.33 762	9.95 839	6	19	
42	9.62 104	27	9.66 271	33	10.33 729	9.95 833	6	18	
43	9.62 131	28	9.66 304	33	10.33 696	9.95 827	6	17	
44	9.62 159	27	9.66 337	34	10.33 663	9.95 821	6	16	
45	9.62 186	28	9.66 371	33	10.33 629	9.95 815	6	15	
46	9.62 214	27	9.66 404	33	10.33 596	9.95 810	6	14	
47	9.62 241	27	9.66 437	33	10.33 563	9.95 804	6	13	
48	9.62 268	28	9.66 470	33	10.33 530	9.95 798	6	12	
49	9.62 296	27	9.66 503	34	10.33 497	9.95 792	6	11	
50	9.62 323	27	9.66 537	33	10.33 463	9.95 786	6	10	
51	9.62 350	27	9.66 570	33	10.33 430	9.95 780	5	9	
52	9.62 377	28	9.66 603	33	10.33 397	9.95 775	6	8	
53	9.62 405	27	9.66 636	33	10.33 364	9.95 769	6	7	
54	9.62 432	27	9.66 669	33	10.33 331	9.95 763	6	6	
55	9.62 459	27	9.66 702	33	10.33 298	9.95 757	6	5	
56	9.62 486	27	9.66 735	33	10.33 265	9.95 751	6	4	
57	9.62 513	28	9.66 768	33	10.33 232	9.95 745	6	3	
58	9.62 541	27	9.66 801	33	10.33 199	9.95 739	6	2	
59	9.62 568	27	9.66 834	33	10.33 166	9.95 733	5	1	
60	9.62 595		9.66 867		10.33 133	9.95 728		0	
	L Cos	d	L Cot	c d	L Tan	L Sin	d	'	Prop. Pts.

Prop. Pts.

	34	33
1	3.4	3.3
2	6.8	6.6
3	10.2	9.9
4	13.6	13.2
5	17.0	16.5
6	20.4	19.8
7	23.8	23.1
8	27.2	26.4
9	30.6	29.7

	29	28	27
1	2.9	2.8	2.7
2	5.8	5.6	5.4
3	8.7	8.4	8.1
4	11.6	11.2	10.8
5	14.5	14.0	13.5
6	17.4	16.8	16.2
7	20.3	19.6	18.9
8	23.2	22.4	21.6
9	26.1	25.2	24.3

	6	5
1	0.6	0.5
2	1.2	1.0
3	1.8	1.5
4	2.4	2.0
5	3.0	2.5
6	3.6	3.0
7	4.2	3.5
8	4.8	4.0
9	5.4	4.5

′	L Sin	d	L Tan	c d	L Cot	L Cos	d		Prop. Pts.
0	9.62 595		9.66 867		10.33 133	9.95 728		**60**	
1	9.62 622	27	9.66 900	33	10.33 100	9.95 722	6	59	
2	9.62 649	27	9.66 933	33	10.33 067	9.95 716	6	58	
3	9.62 676	27	9.66 966	33	10.33 034	9.95 710	6	57	
4	9.62 703	27	9.66 999	33	10.33 001	9.95 704	6	56	
5	9.62 730	27	9.67 032	33	10.32 968	9.95 698	6	55	
6	9.62 757	27	9.67 065	33	10.32 935	9.95 692	6	54	
7	9.62 784	27	9.67 098	33	10.32 902	9.95 686	6	53	
8	9.62 811	27	9.67 131	33	10.32 869	9.95 680	6	52	
9	9.62 838	27	9.67 163	32	10.32 837	9.95 674	6	51	**33** **32**
10	9.62 865	27	9.67 196	33	10.32 804	9.95 668	5	**50**	1 3.3 3.2
11	9.62 892	27	9.67 229	33	10.32 771	9.95 663	6	49	2 6.6 6.4
12	9.62 918	26	9.67 262	33	10.32 738	9.95 657	6	48	3 9.9 9.6
13	9.62 945	27	9.67 295	33	10.32 705	9.95 651	6	47	4 13.2 12.8
14	9.62 972	27	9.67 327	32	10.32 673	9.95 645	6	46	5 16.5 16.0
15	9.62 999	27	9.67 360	33	10.32 640	9.95 639	6	45	6 19.8 19.2
16	9.63 026	27	9.67 393	33	10.32 607	9.95 633	6	44	7 23.1 22.4
17	9.63 052	26	9.67 426	33	10.32 574	9.95 627	6	43	8 26.4 25.6
18	9.63 079	27	9.67 458	32	10.32 542	9.95 621	6	42	9 29.7 28.8
19	9.63 106	27	9.67 491	33	10.32 509	9.95 615	6	41	
20	9.63 133	27	9.67 524	33	10.32 476	9.95 609	6	**40**	
21	9.63 159	26	9.67 556	32	10.32 444	9.95 603	6	39	
22	9.63 186	27	9.67 589	33	10.32 411	9.95 597	6	38	
23	9.63 213	27	9.67 622	33	10.32 378	9.95 591	6	37	
24	9.63 239	26	9.67 654	32	10.32 346	9.95 585	6	36	
25	9.63 266	27	9.67 687	33	10.32 313	9.95 579	6	35	
26	9.63 292	26	9.67 719	32	10.32 281	9.95 573	6	34	**27** **26**
27	9.63 319	27	9.67 752	33	10.32 248	9.95 567	6	33	1 2.7 2.6
28	9.63 345	26	9.67 785	33	10.32 215	9.95 561	6	32	2 5.4 5.2
29	9.63 372	27	9.67 817	32	10.32 183	9.95 555	6	31	3 8.1 7.8
30	9.63 398	26	9.67 850	33	10.32 150	9.95 549	6	**30**	4 10.8 10.4
31	9.63 425	27	9.67 882	32	10.32 118	9.95 543	6	29	5 13.5 13.0
32	9.63 451	26	9.67 915	33	10.32 085	9.95 537	6	28	6 16.2 15.6
33	9.63 478	27	9.67 947	32	10.32 053	9.95 531	6	27	7 18.9 18.2
34	9.63 504	26	9.67 980	33	10.32 020	9.95 525	6	26	8 21.6 20.8
35	9.63 531	27	9.68 012	32	10.31 988	9.95 519	6	25	9 24.3 23.4
36	9.63 557	26	9.68 044	32	10.31 956	9.95 513	6	24	
37	9.63 583	26	9.68 077	33	10.31 923	9.95 507	7	23	
38	9.63 610	27	9.68 109	33	10.31 891	9.95 500	6	22	
39	9.63 636	26	9.68 142	32	10.31 858	9.95 494	6	21	
40	9.63 662	26	9.68 174	32	10.31 826	9.95 488	6	**20**	
41	9.63 689	27	9.68 206	33	10.31 794	9.95 482	6	19	
42	9.63 715	26	9.68 239	32	10.31 761	9.95 476	6	18	
43	9.63 741	26	9.68 271	32	10.31 729	9.95 470	6	17	**7** **6** **5**
44	9.63 767	26	9.68 303	33	10.31 697	9.95 464	6	16	1 0.7 0.6 0.5
45	9.63 794	27	9.68 336	32	10.31 664	9.95 458	6	15	2 1.4 1.2 1.0
46	9.63 820	26	9.68 368	32	10.31 632	9.95 452	6	14	3 2.1 1.8 1.5
47	9.63 846	26	9.68 400	32	10.31 600	9.95 446	6	13	4 2.8 2.4 2.0
48	9.63 872	26	9.68 432	33	10.31 568	9.95 440	6	12	5 3.5 3.0 2.5
49	9.63 898	26	9.68 465	32	10.31 535	9.95 434	7	11	6 4.2 3.6 3.0
50	9.63 924	26	9.68 497	32	10.31 503	9.95 427	6	**10**	7 4.9 4.2 3.5
51	9.63 950	26	9.68 529	32	10.31 471	9.95 421	6	9	8 5.6 4.8 4.0
52	9.63 976	26	9.68 561	32	10.31 439	9.95 415	6	8	9 6.3 5.4 4.5
53	9.64 002	26	9.68 593	33	10.31 407	9.95 409	6	7	
54	9.64 028	26	9.68 626	32	10.31 374	9.95 403	6	6	
55	9.64 054	26	9.68 658	32	10.31 342	9.95 397	6	5	
56	9.64 080	26	9.68 690	32	10.31 310	9.95 391	7	4	
57	9.64 106	26	9.68 722	32	10.31 278	9.95 384	6	3	
58	9.64 132	26	9.68 754	32	10.31 246	9.95 378	6	2	
59	9.64 158	26	9.68 786	32	10.31 214	9.95 372	6	1	
60	9.64 184		9.68 818		10.31 182	9.95 366		**0**	
	L Cos	d	L Cot	c d	L Tan	L Sin	d	′	Prop. Pts.

TABLE III   **26°**

′	L Sin	d	L Tan	c d	L Cot	L Cos	d		Prop. Pts.
0	9.64 184		9.68 818		10.31 182	9.95 366		**60**	
1	9.64 210	26	9.68 850	32	10.31 150	9.95 360	6	59	
2	9.64 236	26	9.68 882	32	10.31 118	9.95 354	6	58	
3	9.64 262	26	9.68 914	32	10.31 086	9.95 348	6	57	
4	9.64 288	26	9.68 946	32	10.31 054	9.95 341	7	56	
5	9.64 313	25	9.68 978	32	10.31 022	9.95 335	6	55	
6	9.64 339	26	9.69 010	32	10.30 990	9.95 329	6	54	
7	9.64 365	26	9.69 042	32	10.30 958	9.95 323	6	53	
8	9.64 391	26	9.69 074	32	10.30 926	9.95 317	6	52	
9	9.64 417	26	9.69 106	32	10.30 894	9.95 310	7	51	
10	9.64 442	25	9.69 138	32	10.30 862	9.95 304	6	**50**	
11	9.64 468	26	9.69 170	32	10.30 830	9.95 298	6	49	
12	9.64 494	26	9.69 202	32	10.30 798	9.95 292	6	48	
13	9.64 519	25	9.69 234	32	10.30 766	9.95 286	6	47	
14	9.64 545	26	9.69 266	32	10.30 734	9.95 279	7	46	
15	9.64 571	26	9.69 298	32	10.30 702	9.95 273	6	45	
16	9.64 596	25	9.69 329	31	10.30 671	9.95 267	6	44	
17	9.64 622	26	9.69 361	32	10.30 639	9.95 261	6	43	
18	9.64 647	25	9.69 393	32	10.30 607	9.95 254	7	42	
19	9.64 673	26	9.69 425	32	10.30 575	9.95 248	6	41	
20	9.64 698	25	9.69 457	32	10.30 543	9.95 242	6	**40**	
21	9.64 724	26	9.69 488	31	10.30 512	9.95 236	6	39	
22	9.64 749	25	9.69 520	32	10.30 480	9.95 229	7	38	
23	9.64 775	26	9.69 552	32	10.30 448	9.95 223	6	37	
24	9.64 800	25	9.69 584	32	10.30 416	9.95 217	6	36	
25	9.64 826	26	9.69 615	31	10.30 385	9.95 211	6	35	
26	9.64 851	25	9.69 647	32	10.30 353	9.95 204	7	34	
27	9.64 877	26	9.69 679	32	10.30 321	9.95 198	6	33	
28	9.64 902	25	9.69 710	31	10.30 290	9.95 192	6	32	
29	9.64 927	25	9.69 742	32	10.30 258	9.95 185	7	31	
30	9.64 953	26	9.69 774	32	10.30 226	9.95 179	6	**30**	
31	9.64 978	25	9.69 805	31	10.30 195	9.95 173	6	29	
32	9.65 003	25	9.69 837	32	10.30 163	9.95 167	6	28	
33	9.65 029	26	9.69 868	31	10.30 132	9.95 160	7	27	
34	9.65 054	25	9.69 900	32	10.30 100	9.95 154	6	26	
35	9.65 079	25	9.69 932	32	10.30 068	9.95 148	6	25	
36	9.65 104	25	9.69 963	31	10.30 037	9.95 141	7	24	
37	9.65 130	26	9.69 995	32	10.30 005	9.95 135	6	23	
38	9.65 155	25	9.70 026	31	10.29 974	9.95 129	6	22	
39	9.65 180	25	9.70 058	32	10.29 942	9.95 122	7	21	
40	9.65 205	25	9.70 089	31	10.29 911	9.95 116	6	**20**	
41	9.65 230	25	9.70 121	32	10.29 879	9.95 103	6	19	
42	9.65 255	25	9.70 152	31	10.29 848	9.95 103	7	18	
43	9.65 281	26	9.70 184	32	10.29 816	9.95 097	6	17	
44	9.65 306	25	9.70 215	31	10.29 785	9.95 090	7	16	
45	9.65 331	25	9.70 247	32	10.29 753	9.95 084	6	15	
46	9.65 356	25	9.70 278	31	10.29 722	9.95 078	6	14	
47	9.65 381	25	9.70 309	31	10.29 691	9.95 071	7	13	
48	9.65 406	25	9.70 341	32	10.29 659	9.95 065	6	12	
49	9.65 431	25	9.70 372	31	10.29 628	9.95 059	6	11	
50	9.65 456	25	9.70 404	32	10.29 596	9.95 052	7	**10**	
51	9.65 481	25	9.70 435	31	10.29 565	9.95 046	6	9	
52	9.65 506	25	9.70 466	31	10.29 534	9.95 039	7	8	
53	9.65 531	25	9.70 498	32	10.29 502	9.95 033	6	7	
54	9.65 556	24	9.70 529	31	10.29 471	9.95 027	6	6	
55	9.65 580	25	9.70 560	31	10.29 440	9.95 020	7	5	
56	9.65 605	25	9.70 592	32	10.29 408	9.95 014	6	4	
57	9.65 630	25	9.70 623	31	10.29 377	9.95 007	7	3	
58	9.65 655	25	9.70 654	31	10.29 346	9.95 001	6	2	
59	9.65 680	25	9.70 685	31	10.29 315	9.94 995	6	1	
60	9.65 705		9.70 717	32	10.29 283	9.94 988	7	**0**	
	L Cos	d	L Cot	c d	L Tan	L Sin	d	′	Prop. Pts.

Prop. Pts.

	32	31
1	3.2	3.1
2	6.4	6.2
3	9.6	9.3
4	12.8	12.4
5	16.0	15.5
6	19.2	18.6
7	22.4	21.7
8	25.6	24.8
9	28.8	27.9

	26	25	24
1	2.6	2.5	2.4
2	5.2	5.0	4.8
3	7.8	7.5	7.2
4	10.4	10.0	9.6
5	13.0	12.5	12.0
6	15.6	15.0	14.4
7	18.2	17.5	16.8
8	20.8	20.0	19.2
9	23.4	22.5	21.6

	7	6
1	0.7	0.6
2	1.4	1.2
3	2.1	1.8
4	2.8	2.4
5	3.5	3.0
6	4.2	3.6
7	4.9	4.2
8	5.6	4.8
9	6.3	5.4

′	L Sin	d	L Tan	c d	L Cot	L Cos	d	′	Prop. Pts.
0	9.65 705	24	9.70 717	31	10.29 283	9.94 988	6	60	
1	9.65 729	25	9.70 748	31	10.29 252	9.94 982	7	59	
2	9.65 754	25	9.70 779	31	10.29 221	9.94 975	6	58	
3	9.65 779	25	9.70 810	31	10.29 190	9.94 969	7	57	
4	9.65 804	24	9.70 841	32	10.29 159	9.94 962	6	56	
5	9.65 828	25	9.70 873	31	10.29 127	9.94 956	7	55	
6	9.65 853	25	9.70 904	31	10.29 096	9.94 949	6	54	
7	9.65 878	24	9.70 935	31	10.29 065	9.94 943	7	53	
8	9.65 902	25	9.70 966	31	10.29 034	9.94 936	6	52	**32** / **31** / **30**
9	9.65 927	25	9.70 997	31	10.29 003	9.94 930	7	51	1 3.2 / 3.1 / 3.0
10	9.65 952	24	9.71 028	31	10.28 972	9.94 923	6	50	2 6.4 / 6.2 / 6.0
11	9.65 976	25	9.71 059	31	10.28 941	9.94 917	6	49	3 9.6 / 9.3 / 9.0
12	9.66 001	24	9.71 090	31	10.28 910	9.94 911	7	48	4 12.8 / 12.4 / 12.0
13	9.66 025	25	9.71 121	32	10.28 879	9.94 904	6	47	5 16.0 / 15.5 / 15.0
14	9.66 050	25	9.71 153	31	10.28 847	9.94 898	7	46	6 19.2 / 18.6 / 18.0
15	9.66 075	24	9.71 184	31	10.28 816	9.94 891	6	45	7 22.4 / 21.7 / 21.0
16	9.66 099	25	9.71 215	31	10.28 785	9.94 885	7	44	8 25.6 / 24.8 / 24.0
17	9.66 124	24	9.71 246	31	10.28 754	9.94 878	7	43	9 28.8 / 27.9 / 27.0
18	9.66 148	25	9.71 277	31	10.28 723	9.94 871	6	42	
19	9.66 173	24	9.71 308	31	10.28 692	9.94 865	7	41	
20	9.66 197	24	9.71 339	31	10.28 661	9.94 858	6	40	
21	9.66 221	25	9.71 370	31	10.28 630	9.94 852	7	39	
22	9.66 246	24	9.71 401	30	10.28 599	9.94 845	6	38	
23	9.66 270	25	9.71 431	31	10.28 569	9.94 839	7	37	
24	9.66 295	24	9.71 462	31	10.28 538	9.94 832	6	36	
25	9.66 319	24	9.71 493	31	10.28 507	9.94 826	7	35	
26	9.66 343	25	9.71 524	31	10.28 476	9.94 819	6	34	**25** / **24** / **23**
27	9.66 368	24	9.71 555	31	10.28 445	9.94 813	7	33	1 2.5 / 2.4 / 2.3
28	9.66 392	24	9.71 586	31	10.28 414	9.94 806	7	32	2 5.0 / 4.8 / 4.6
29	9.66 416	25	9.71 617	31	10.28 383	9.94 799	6	31	3 7.5 / 7.2 / 6.9
30	9.66 441	24	9.71 648	31	10.28 352	9.94 793	7	30	4 10.0 / 9.6 / 9.2
31	9.66 465	24	9.71 679	30	10.28 321	9.94 786	6	29	5 12.5 / 12.0 / 11.5
32	9.66 489	24	9.71 709	31	10.28 291	9.94 780	7	28	6 15.0 / 14.4 / 13.8
33	9.66 513	24	9.71 740	31	10.28 260	9.94 773	6	27	7 17.5 / 16.8 / 16.1
34	9.66 537	25	9.71 771	31	10.28 229	9.94 767	7	26	8 20.0 / 19.2 / 18.4
35	9.66 562	24	9.71 802	31	10.28 198	9.94 760	7	25	9 22.5 / 21.6 / 20.7
36	9.66 586	24	9.71 833	30	10.28 167	9.94 753	6	24	
37	9.66 610	24	9.71 863	31	10.28 137	9.94 747	7	23	
38	9.66 634	24	9.71 894	31	10.28 106	9.94 740	6	22	
39	9.66 658	24	9.71 925	30	10.28 075	9.94 734	7	21	
40	9.66 682	24	9.71 955	31	10.28 045	9.94 727	7	20	
41	9.66 706	25	9.71 986	31	10.28 014	9.94 720	6	19	
42	9.66 731	24	9.72 017	31	10.27 983	9.94 714	7	18	
43	9.66 755	24	9.72 048	30	10.27 952	9.94 707	7	17	
44	9.66 779	24	9.72 078	31	10.27 922	9.94 700	6	16	**7** / **6**
45	9.66 803	24	9.72 109	31	10.27 891	9.94 694	7	15	1 0.7 / 0.6
46	9.66 827	24	9.72 140	30	10.27 860	9.94 687	7	14	2 1.4 / 1.2
47	9.66 851	24	9.72 170	31	10.27 830	9.94 680	6	13	3 2.1 / 1.8
48	9.66 875	24	9.72 201	30	10.27 799	9.94 674	7	12	4 2.8 / 2.4
49	9.66 899	23	9.72 231	31	10.27 769	9.94 667	7	11	5 3.5 / 3.0
50	9.66 922	24	9.72 262	31	10.27 738	9.94 660	6	10	6 4.2 / 3.6
51	9.66 946	24	9.72 293	30	10.27 707	9.94 654	7	9	7 4.9 / 4.2
52	9.66 970	24	9.72 323	31	10.27 677	9.94 647	7	8	8 5.6 / 4.8
53	9.66 994	24	9.72 354	30	10.27 646	9.94 640	6	7	9 6.3 / 5.4
54	9.67 018	24	9.72 384	31	10.27 616	9.94 634	7	6	
55	9.67 042	24	9.72 415	30	10.27 585	9.94 627	7	5	
56	9.67 066	24	9.72 445	31	10.27 555	9.94 620	6	4	
57	9.67 090	23	9.72 476	30	10.27 524	9.94 614	7	3	
58	9.67 113	24	9.72 506	31	10.27 494	9.94 607	7	2	
59	9.67 137	24	9.72 537	30	10.27 463	9.94 600	7	1	
60	9.67 161		9.72 567		10.27 433	9.94 593		0	
	L Cos	d	L Cot	c d	L Tan	L Sin	d	′	Prop. Pts.

′	L Sin	d	L Tan	c d	L Cot	L Cos	d	′
0	9.67 161	24	9.72 567	31	10.27 433	9.94 593	6	60
1	9.67 185	23	9.72 598	30	10.27 402	9.94 587	7	59
2	9.67 208	24	9.72 628	31	10.27 372	9.94 580	7	58
3	9.67 232	24	9.72 659	30	10.27 341	9.94 573	6	57
4	9.67 256	24	9.72 689	31	10.27 311	9.94 567	7	56
5	9.67 280	23	9.72 720	30	10.27 280	9.94 560	7	55
6	9.67 303	24	9.72 750	30	10.27 250	9.94 553	7	54
7	9.67 327	23	9.72 780	31	10.27 220	9.94 546	6	53
8	9.67 350	24	9.72 811	30	10.27 189	9.94 540	7	52
9	9.67 374	24	9.72 841	31	10.27 159	9.94 533	7	51
10	9.67 398	23	9.72 872	30	10.27 128	9.94 526	7	50
11	9.67 421	24	9.72 902	30	10.27 098	9.94 519	6	49
12	9.67 445	23	9.72 932	31	10.27 068	9.94 513	7	48
13	9.67 468	24	9.72 963	30	10.27 037	9.94 506	7	47
14	9.67 492	23	9.72 993	30	10.27 007	9.94 499	7	46
15	9.67 515	24	9.73 023	31	10.26 977	9.94 492	7	45
16	9.67 539	23	9.73 054	30	10.26 946	9.94 485	6	44
17	9.67 562	24	9.73 084	30	10.26 916	9.94 479	7	43
18	9.67 586	23	9.73 114	30	10.26 886	9.94 472	7	42
19	9.67 609	24	9.73 144	31	10.26 856	9.94 465	7	41
20	9.67 633	23	9.73 175	30	10.26 825	9.94 458	7	40
21	9.67 656	24	9.73 205	30	10.26 795	9.94 451	6	39
22	9.67 680	23	9.73 235	30	10.26 765	9.94 445	7	38
23	9.67 703	23	9.73 265	30	10.26 735	9.94 438	7	37
24	9.67 726	24	9.73 295	31	10.26 705	9.94 431	7	36
25	9.67 750	23	9.73 326	30	10.26 674	9.94 424	7	35
26	9.67 773	23	9.73 356	30	10.26 644	9.94 417	7	34
27	9.67 796	24	9.73 386	30	10.26 614	9.94 410	6	33
28	9.67 820	23	9.73 416	30	10.26 584	9.94 404	7	32
29	9.67 843	23	9.73 446	30	10.26 554	9.94 397	7	31
30	9.67 866	24	9.73 476	31	10.26 524	9.94 390	7	30
31	9.67 890	23	9.73 507	30	10.26 493	9.94 383	7	29
32	9.67 913	23	9.73 537	30	10.26 463	9.94 376	7	28
33	9.67 936	23	9.73 567	30	10.26 433	9.94 369	7	27
34	9.67 959	23	9.73 597	30	10.26 403	9.94 362	7	26
35	9.67 982	24	9.73 627	30	10.26 373	9.94 355	6	25
36	9.68 006	23	9.73 657	30	10.26 343	9.94 349	7	24
37	9.68 029	23	9.73 687	30	10.26 313	9.94 342	7	23
38	9.68 052	23	9.73 717	30	10.26 283	9.94 335	7	22
39	9.68 075	23	9.73 747	30	10.26 253	9.94 328	7	21
40	9.68 098	23	9.73 777	30	10.26 223	9.94 321	7	20
41	9.68 121	23	9.73 807	30	10.26 193	9.94 314	7	19
42	9.68 144	23	9.73 837	30	10.26 163	9.94 307	7	18
43	9.68 167	23	9.73 867	30	10.26 133	9.94 300	7	17
44	9.68 190	23	9.73 897	30	10.26 103	9.94 293	7	16
45	9.68 213	24	9.73 927	30	10.26 073	9.94 286	7	15
46	9.68 237	23	9.73 957	30	10.26 043	9.94 279	6	14
47	9.68 260	23	9.73 987	30	10.26 013	9.94 273	7	13
48	9.68 283	22	9.74 017	30	10.25 983	9.94 266	7	12
49	9.68 305	23	9.74 047	30	10.25 953	9.94 259	7	11
50	9.68 328	23	9.74 077	30	10.25 923	9.94 252	7	10
51	9.68 351	23	9.74 107	30	10.25 893	9.94 245	7	9
52	9.68 374	23	9.74 137	29	10.25 863	9.94 238	7	8
53	9.68 397	23	9.74 166	30	10.25 834	9.94 231	7	7
54	9.68 420	23	9.74 196	30	10.25 804	9.94 224	7	6
55	9.68 443	23	9.74 226	30	10.25 774	9.94 217	7	5
56	9.68 466	23	9.74 256	30	10.25 744	9.94 210	7	4
57	9.68 489	23	9.74 286	30	10.25 714	9.94 203	7	3
58	9.68 512	22	9.74 316	29	10.25 684	9.94 196	7	2
59	9.68 534	23	9.74 345	30	10.25 655	9.94 189	7	1
60	9.68 557		9.74 375		10.25 625	9.94 182		0
′	L Cos	d	L Cot	c d	L Tan	L Sin	d	′

Prop. Pts.

	31	30	29
1	3.1	3.0	2.9
2	6.2	6.0	5.8
3	9.3	9.0	8.7
4	12.4	12.0	11.6
5	15.5	15.0	14.5
6	18.6	18.0	17.4
7	21.7	21.0	20.3
8	24.8	24.0	23.2
9	27.9	27.0	26.1

	24	23	22
1	2.4	2.3	2.2
2	4.8	4.6	4.4
3	7.2	6.9	6.6
4	9.6	9.2	8.8
5	12.0	11.5	11.0
6	14.4	13.8	13.2
7	16.8	16.1	15.4
8	19.2	18.4	17.6
9	21.6	20.7	19.8

	7	6
1	0.7	0.6
2	1.4	1.2
3	2.1	1.8
4	2.8	2.4
5	3.5	3.0
6	4.2	3.6
7	4.9	4.2
8	5.6	4.8
9	6.3	5.4

′	L Sin	d	L Tan	c d	L Cot	L Cos	d		Prop. Pts.
0	9.68 557		9.74 375		10.25 625	9.94 182		**60**	
1	9.68 580	23	9.74 405	30	10.25 595	9.94 175	7	59	
2	9.68 603	23	9.74 435	30	10.25 565	9.94 168	7	58	
3	9.68 625	22	9.74 465	30	10.25 535	9.94 161	7	57	
4	9.68 648	23	9.74 494	29	10.25 506	9.94 154	7	56	
5	9.68 671	23	9.74 524	30	10.25 476	9.94 147	7	55	
6	9.68 694	23	9.74 554	30	10.25 446	9.94 140	7	54	
7	9.68 716	22	9.74 583	29	10.25 417	9.94 133	7	53	
8	9.68 739	23	9.74 613	30	10.25 387	9.94 126	7	52	
9	9.68 762	23	9.74 643	30	10.25 357	9.94 119	7	51	
10	9.68 784	22	9.74 673	30	10.25 327	9.94 112	7	**50**	
11	9.68 807	23	9.74 702	29	10.25 298	9.94 105	7	49	
12	9.68 829	22	9.74 732	30	10.25 268	9.94 098	7	48	
13	9.68 852	23	9.74 762	30	10.25 238	9.94 090	8	47	
14	9.68 875	23	0.71 791	29	10.25 200	0.04 083	7	46	
15	9.68 897	22	9.74 821	30	10.25 179	9.94 076	7	45	
16	9.68 920	23	9.74 851	30	10.25 149	9.94 069	7	44	
17	9.68 942	22	9.74 880	29	10.25 120	9.94 062	7	43	
18	9.68 965	23	9.74 910	30	10.25 090	9.94 055	7	42	
19	9.68 987	22	9.74 939	29	10.25 061	9.94 048	7	41	
20	9.69 010	23	9.74 969	30	10.25 031	9.94 041	7	**40**	
21	9.69 032	22	9.74 998	29	10.25 002	9.94 034	7	39	
22	9.69 055	23	9.75 028	30	10.24 972	9.94 027	7	38	
23	9.69 077	22	9.75 058	30	10.24 942	9.94 020	7	37	
24	9.69 100	23	9.75 087	29	10.24 913	9.94 012	8	36	
25	9.69 122	22	9.75 117	30	10.24 883	9.94 005	7	35	
26	9.69 144	22	9.75 146	29	1C.24 854	9.93 998	7	34	
27	9.69 167	23	9.75 176	30	10.24 824	9.93 991	7	33	
28	9.69 189	22	9.75 205	29	10.24 795	9.93 984	7	32	
29	9.69 212	23	9.75 235	30	10.24 765	9.93 977	7	31	
30	9.69 234	22	9.75 264	29	10.24 736	9.93 970	7	**30**	
31	9.69 256	22	9.75 294	30	10.24 706	9.93 963	7	29	
32	9.69 279	23	9.75 323	29	10.24 677	9.93 955	8	28	
33	9.69 301	22	9.75 353	30	10.24 647	9.93 948	7	27	
34	9.69 323	22	9.75 382	29	10.24 618	9.93 941	7	26	
35	9.69 345	22	9.75 411	29	10.24 589	9.93 934	7	25	
36	9.69 368	23	9.75 441	30	10.24 559	9.93 927	7	24	
37	9.60 390	22	0.75 470	29	10.24 530	9.93 920	7	23	
38	9.69 412	22	9.75 500	30	10.24 500	9.93 912	8	22	
39	9.69 434	22	9.75 529	29	10.24 471	9.93 905	7	21	
40	9.69 456	22	9.75 558	29	10.24 442	9.93 898	7	**20**	
41	9.69 479	23	9.75 588	30	10.24 412	9.93 891	7	19	
42	9.69 501	22	9.75 617	29	10.24 383	9.93 884	7	18	
43	9.69 523	22	9.75 647	30	10.24 353	9.93 876	8	17	
44	9.69 545	22	9.75 676	29	10.24 324	9.93 869	7	16	
45	9.69 567	22	9.75 705	29	10.24 295	9.93 862	7	15	
46	9.69 589	22	9.75 735	30	10.24 265	9.93 855	7	14	
47	9.69 611	22	9.75 764	29	10.24 236	9.93 847	8	13	
48	9.69 633	22	9.75 793	29	10.24 207	9.93 840	7	12	
49	9.69 655	22	9.75 822	30	10.24 178	9.93 833	7	11	
50	9.69 677	22	9.75 852	29	10.24 148	9.93 826	7	**10**	
51	9.69 699	22	9.75 881	29	10.24 119	9.93 819	7	9	
52	9.69 721	22	9.75 910	29	10.24 090	9.93 811	8	8	
53	9.69 743	22	9.75 939	30	10.24 061	9.93 804	7	7	
54	9.69 765	22	9.75 969	29	10.24 031	9.93 797	7	6	
55	9.69 787	22	9.75 998	29	10.24 002	9.93 789	8	5	
56	9.69 809	22	9.76 027	29	10.23 973	9.93 782	7	4	
57	9.69 831	22	9.76 056	30	10.23 944	9.93 775	7	3	
58	9.69 853	22	9.76 086	29	10.23 914	9.93 768	8	2	
59	9.69 875	22	9.76 115	29	10.23 885	9.93 760	7	1	
60	9.69 897		9.76 144		10.23 856	9.93 753		0	
	L Cos	d	L Cot	c d	L Tan	L Sin	d	′	Prop. Pts.

Prop. Pts.

	30	29
1	3.0	2.9
2	6.0	5.8
3	9.0	8.7
4	12.0	11.6
5	15.0	14.5
6	18.0	17.4
7	21.0	20.3
8	24.0	23.2
9	27.0	26.1

	23	22
1	2.3	2.2
2	4.6	4.4
3	6.9	6.6
4	9.2	8.8
5	11.5	11.0
6	13.8	13.2
7	16.1	15.4
8	18.4	17.6
9	20.7	19.8

	8	7
1	0.8	0.7
2	1.6	1.4
3	2.4	2.1
4	3.2	2.8
5	4.0	3.5
6	4.8	4.2
7	5.6	4.9
8	6.4	5.6
9	7.2	6.3

60°

57

TABLE III **30°**

′	L Sin	d	L Tan	c d	L Cot	L Cos	d		Prop. Pts.
0	9.69 897		9.76 144		10.23 856	9.93 753		60	
1	9.69 919	22	9.76 173	29	10.23 827	9.93 746	7	59	
2	9.69 941	22	9.76 202	29	10.23 798	9.93 738	8	58	
3	9.69 963	22	9.76 231	29	10.23 769	9.93 731	7	57	
4	9.69 984	21	9.76 261	30	10.23 739	9.93 724	7	56	
5	9.70 006	22	9.76 290	29	10.23 710	9.93 717	7	55	
6	9.70 028	22	9.76 319	29	10.23 681	9.93 709	8	54	
7	9.70 050	22	9.76 348	29	10.23 652	9.93 702	7	53	
8	9.70 072	22	9.76 377	29	10.23 623	9.93 695	7	52	
9	9.70 093	21	9.76 406	29	10.23 594	9.93 687	8	51	
		22		29			7		
10	9.70 115		9.76 435		10.23 565	9.93 680		**50**	
11	9.70 137	22	9.76 464	29	10.23 536	9.93 673	7	49	
12	9.70 159	22	9.76 493	29	10.23 507	9.93 665	8	48	
13	9.70 180	21	9.76 522	29	10.23 478	9.93 658	7	47	
14	9.70 202	22	9.76 551	29	10.23 449	9.93 650	8	46	
15	9.70 224	22	9.76 580	29	10.23 420	9.93 643	7	45	
16	9.70 245	21	9.76 609	29	10.23 391	9.93 636	7	44	
17	9.70 267	22	9.76 639	30	10.23 361	9.93 628	8	43	
18	9.70 288	21	9.76 668	29	10.23 332	9.93 621	7	42	
19	9.70 310	22	9.76 697	29	10.23 303	9.93 614	7	41	
		22		28			8		
20	9.70 332		9.76 725		10.23 275	9.93 606		**40**	
21	9.70 353	21	9.76 754	29	10.23 246	9.93 599	7	39	
22	9.70 375	22	9.76 783	29	10.23 217	9.93 591	8	38	
23	9.70 396	21	9.76 812	29	10.23 188	9.93 584	7	37	
24	9.70 418	22	9.76 841	29	10.23 159	9.93 577	7	36	
25	9.70 439	21	9.76 870	29	10.23 130	9.93 569	8	35	
26	9.70 461	22	9.76 899	29	10.23 101	9.93 562	7	34	
27	9.70 482	21	9.76 928	29	10.23 072	9.93 554	8	33	
28	9.70 504	22	9.76 957	29	10.23 043	9.93 547	7	32	
29	9.70 525	21	9.76 986	29	10.23 014	9.93 539	8	31	
		22		29			7		
30	9.70 547		9.77 015		10.22 985	9.93 532		**30**	
31	9.70 568	21	9.77 044	29	10.22 956	9.93 525	7	29	
32	9.70 590	22	9.77 073	29	10.22 927	9.93 517	8	28	
33	9.70 611	21	9.77 101	28	10.22 899	9.93 510	7	27	
34	9.70 633	22	9.77 130	29	10.22 870	9.93 502	8	26	
35	9.70 654	21	9.77 159	29	10.22 841	9.93 495	7	25	
36	9.70 675	21	9.77 188	29	10.22 812	9.93 487	8	24	
37	9.70 796	22	9.77 217	29	10.22 783	9.93 480	7	23	
38	9.70 718	21	9.77 246	28	10.22 754	9.93 472	7	22	
39	9.70 739	21	9.77 274	29	10.22 726	9.93 465	8	21	
		22		29			7		
40	9.70 761		9.77 303		10.22 697	9.93 457		**20**	
41	9.70 782	21	9.77 332	29	10.22 668	9.93 450	8	19	
42	9.70 803	21	9.77 361	29	10.22 639	9.93 442	7	18	
43	9.70 824	21	9.77 390	28	10.22 610	9.93 435	8	17	
44	9.70 846	22	9.77 418	29	10.22 582	9.93 427	7	16	
45	9.70 867	21	9.77 447	29	10.22 553	9.93 420	8	15	
46	9.70 888	21	9.77 476	29	10.22 524	9.93 412	7	14	
47	9.70 909	21	9.77 505	28	10.22 495	9.93 405	8	13	
48	9.70 931	22	9.77 533	29	10.22 467	9.93 397	7	12	
49	9.70 952	21	9.77 562	29	10.22 438	9.93 390	8	11	
		21		29			7		
50	9.70 973		9.77 591		10.22 409	9.93 382		**10**	
51	9.70 994	21	9.77 619	28	10.22 381	9.93 375	8	9	
52	9.71 015	21	9.77 648	29	10.22 352	9.93 367	7	8	
53	9.71 036	22	9.77 677	29	10.22 323	9.93 360	8	7	
54	9.71 058	21	9.77 706	28	10.22 294	9.93 352	8	6	
55	9.71 079	21	9.77 734	29	10.22 266	9.93 344	7	5	
56	9.71 100	21	9.77 763	28	10.22 237	9.93 337	8	4	
57	9.71 121	21	9.77 791	29	10.22 209	9.93 329	7	3	
58	9.71 142	21	9.77 820	29	10.22 180	9.93 322	8	2	
59	9.71 163	21	9.77 849	28	10.22 151	9.93 314	7	1	
60	9.71 184		9.77 877		10.22 123	9.93 307		**0**	
	L Cos	d	L Cot	c d	L Tan	L Sin	d	′	Prop. Pts.

Prop. Pts.

	30	29	28
1	3.0	2.9	2.8
2	6.0	5.8	5.6
3	9.0	8.7	8.4
4	12.0	11.6	11.2
5	15.0	14.5	14.0
6	18.0	17.4	16.8
7	21.0	20.3	19.6
8	24.0	23.2	22.4
9	27.0	26.1	25.2

	22	21
1	2.2	2.1
2	4.4	4.2
3	6.6	6.3
4	8.8	8.4
5	11.0	10.5
6	13.2	12.6
7	15.4	14.7
8	17.6	16.8
9	19.8	18.9

	8	7
1	0.8	0.7
2	1.6	1.4
3	2.4	2.1
4	3.2	2.8
5	4.0	3.5
6	4.8	4.2
7	5.6	4.9
8	6.4	5.6
9	7.2	6.3

59°

'	L Sin	d	L Tan	c d	L Cot	L Cos	d	'
0	9.71 184		9.77 877		10.22 123	9.93 307		60
1	9.71 205	21	9.77 906	29	10.22 094	9.93 299	8	59
2	9.71 226	21	9.77 935	29	10.22 065	9.93 291	8	58
3	9.71 247	21	9.77 963	28	10.22 037	9.93 284	7	57
4	9.71 268	21	9.77 992	29	10.22 008	9.93 276	8	56
5	9.71 289	21	9.78 020	28	10.21 980	9.93 269	7	55
6	9.71 310	21	9.78 049	29	10.21 951	9.93 261	8	54
7	9.71 331	21	9.78 077	28	10.21 923	9.93 253	8	53
8	9.71 352	21	9.78 106	29	10.21 894	9.93 246	7	52
9	9.71 373	21	9.78 135	29	10.21 865	9.93 238	8	51
10	9.71 393	20	9.78 163	28	10.21 837	9.93 230	8	50
11	9.71 414	21	9.78 192	29	10.21 808	9.93 223	7	49
12	9.71 435	21	9.78 220	28	10.21 780	9.93 215	8	48
13	9.71 456	21	9.78 249	29	10.21 751	9.93 207	8	47
14	9.71 477	21	9.78 277	28	10.21 723	9.93 200	7	46
15	9.71 498	21	9.78 306	29	10.21 694	9.93 192	8	45
16	9.71 519	21	9.78 334	28	10.21 666	9.93 184	8	44
17	9.71 539	20	9.78 363	29	10.21 637	9.93 177	7	43
18	9.71 560	21	9.78 391	28	10.21 609	9.93 169	8	42
19	9.71 581	21	9.78 419	28	10.21 581	9.93 161	8	41
20	9.71 602	21	9.78 448	29	10.21 552	9.93 154	7	40
21	9.71 622	20	9.78 476	28	10.21 524	9.93 146	8	39
22	9.71 643	21	9.78 505	29	10.21 495	9.93 138	8	38
23	9.71 664	21	9.78 533	28	10.21 467	9.93 131	7	37
24	9.71 685	21	9.78 562	29	10.21 438	9.93 123	8	36
25	9.71 705	20	9.78 590	28	10.21 410	9.93 115	8	35
26	9.71 726	21	9.78 618	28	10.21 382	9.93 108	7	34
27	9.71 747	21	9.78 647	29	10.21 353	9.93 100	8	33
28	9.71 767	20	9.78 675	28	10.21 325	9.93 092	8	32
29	9.71 788	21	9.78 704	29	10.21 296	9.93 084	8	31
30	9.71 809	21	9.78 732	28	10.21 268	9.93 077	7	30
31	9.71 829	20	9.78 760	28	10.21 240	9.93 069	8	29
32	9.71 850	21	9.78 789	29	10.21 211	9.93 061	8	28
33	9.71 870	20	9.78 817	28	10.21 183	9.93 053	7	27
34	9.71 891	21	9.78 845	28	10.21 155	9.93 046	8	26
35	9.71 911	20	9.78 874	29	10.21 126	9.93 038	8	25
36	9.71 932	21	9.78 902	28	10.21 098	9.93 030	8	24
37	9.71 952	20	9.78 930	29	10.21 070	9.93 022	8	23
38	9.71 973	21	9.78 959	28	10.21 041	9.93 014	7	22
39	9.71 994	20	9.78 987	28	10.21 013	9.93 007	8	21
40	9.72 014	20	9.79 015	28	10.20 985	9.92 999	8	20
41	9.72 034	20	9.79 043	29	10.20 957	9.92 991	8	19
42	9.72 055	21	9.79 072	28	10.20 928	9.92 983	7	18
43	9.72 075	20	9.79 100	28	10.20 900	9.92 976	8	17
44	9.72 096	21	9.79 128	28	10.20 872	9.92 968	8	16
45	9.72 116	20	9.79 156	29	10.20 844	9.92 960	8	15
46	9.72 137	21	9.79 185	28	10.20 815	9.92 952	8	14
47	9.72 157	20	9.79 213	28	10.20 787	9.92 944	8	13
48	9.72 177	20	9.79 241	28	10.20 759	9.92 936	7	12
49	9.72 198	21	9.79 269	28	10.20 731	9.92 929	8	11
50	9.72 218	20	9.79 297	29	10.20 703	9.92 921	8	10
51	9.72 238	20	9.79 326	28	10.20 674	9.92 913	8	9
52	9.72 259	21	9.79 354	28	10.20 646	9.92 905	8	8
53	9.72 279	20	9 79 382	28	10.20 618	9.92 897	8	7
54	9.72 299	20	9.79 410	28	10.20 590	9.92 889	8	6
55	9.72 320	20	9.79 438	28	10.20 562	9.92 881	7	5
56	9.72 340	20	9.79 466	29	10.20 534	9.92 874	8	4
57	9.72 360	20	9.79 495	28	10.20 505	9.92 866	8	3
58	9.72 381	21	9.79 523	28	10.20 477	9.92 858	8	2
59	9.72 401	20	9.79 551	28	10.20 449	9.92 850	8	1
60	9.72 421		9.79 579		10.20 421	9.92 842		0
	L Cos	d	L Cot	c d	L Tan	L Sin	d	'

Prop. Pts.

	29	28
1	2.9	2.8
2	5.8	5.6
3	8.7	8.4
4	11.6	11.2
5	14.5	14.0
6	17.4	16.8
7	20.3	19.6
8	23.2	22.4
9	26.1	25.2

	21	20
1	2.1	2.0
2	4.2	4.0
3	6.3	6.0
4	8.4	8.0
5	10.5	10.0
6	12.6	12.0
7	14.7	14.0
8	16.8	16.0
9	18.9	18.0

	8	7
1	0.8	0.7
2	1.6	1.4
3	2.4	2.1
4	3.2	2.8
5	4.0	3.5
6	4.8	4.2
7	5.6	4.9
8	6.4	5.6
9	7.2	6.3

TABLE III   32°

	L Sin	d	L Tan	c d	L Cot	L Cos	d		Prop. Pts.
0	9.72 421		9.79 579		10.20 421	9.92 842		**60**	
1	9.72 441	20	9.79 607	28	10.20 393	9.92 834	8	59	
2	9.72 461	20	9.79 635	28	10.20 365	9.92 826	8	58	
3	9.72 482	21	9.79 663	28	10.20 337	9.92 818	8	57	
4	9.72 502	20	9.79 691	28	10.20 309	9.92 810	8	56	
5	9.72 522	20	9.79 719	28	10.20 281	9.92 803	7	55	
6	9.72 542	20	9.79 747	28	10.20 253	9.92 795	8	54	
7	9.72 562	20	9.79 776	29	10.20 224	9.92 787	8	53	
8	9.72 582	20	9.79 804	28	10.20 196	9.92 779	8	52	
9	9.72 602	20	9.79 832	28	10.20 168	9.92 771	8	51	
10	9.72 622	20	9.79 860	28	10.20 140	9.92 763	8	**50**	
11	9.72 643	21	9.79 888	28	10.20 112	9.92 755	8	49	
12	9.72 663	20	9.79 916	28	10.20 084	9.92 747	8	48	
13	9.72 683	20	9.79 944	28	10.20 056	9.92 739	8	47	
14	9.72 703	20	9.79 972	28	10.20 028	9.92 731	8	46	
15	9.72 723	20	9.80 000	28	10.20 000	9.92 723	8	45	
16	9.72 743	20	9.80 028	28	10.19 972	9.92 715	8	44	
17	9.72 763	20	9.80 056	28	10.19 944	9.92 707	8	43	
18	9.72 783	20	9.80 084	28	10.19 916	9.92 699	8	42	
19	9.72 803	20	9.80 112	28	10.19 888	9.92 691	8	41	
20	9.72 823	20	9.80 140	28	10.19 860	9.92 683	8	**40**	
21	9.72 843	20	9.80 168	27	10.19 832	9.92 675	8	39	
22	9.72 863	20	9.80 195	28	10.19 805	9.92 667	8	38	
23	9.72 883	19	9.80 223	28	10.19 777	9.92 659	8	37	
24	9.72 902	20	9.80 251	28	10.19 749	9.92 651	8	36	
25	9.72 922	20	9.80 279	28	10.19 721	9.92 643	8	35	
26	9.72 942	20	9.80 307	28	10.19 693	9.92 635	8	34	
27	9.72 962	20	9.80 335	28	10.19 665	9.92 627	8	33	
28	9.72 982	20	9.80 363	28	10.19 637	9.92 619	8	32	
29	9.73 002	20	9.80 391	28	10.19 609	9.92 611	8	31	
30	9.73 022	19	9.80 419	28	10.19 581	9.92 603	8	**30**	
31	9.73 041	20	9.80 447	27	10.19 553	9.92 595	8	29	
32	9.73 061	20	9.80 474	28	10.19 526	9.92 587	8	28	
33	9.73 081	20	9.80 502	28	10.19 498	9.92 579	8	27	
34	9.73 101	20	9.80 530	28	10.19 470	9.92 571	8	26	
35	9.73 121	19	9.80 558	28	10.19 442	9.92 563	8	25	
36	9.73 140	20	9.80 586	28	10.19 414	9.92 555	9	24	
37	9.73 160	20	9.80 614	28	10.19 386	9.92 546	8	23	
38	9.73 180	20	9.80 642	27	10.19 358	9.92 538	8	22	
39	9.73 200	19	9.80 669	28	10.19 331	9.92 530	8	21	
40	9.73 219	20	9.80 697	28	10.19 303	9.92 522	8	**20**	
41	9.73 239	20	9.80 725	28	10.19 275	9.92 514	8	19	
42	9.73 259	19	9.80 753	28	10.19 247	9.92 506	8	18	
43	9.73 278	20	9.80 781	27	10.19 219	9.92 498	8	17	
44	9.73 298	20	9.80 808	28	10.19 192	9.92 490	8	16	
45	9.73 318	19	9.80 836	28	10.19 164	9.92 482	9	15	
46	9.73 337	20	9.80 864	28	10.19 136	9.92 473	8	14	
47	9.73 357	20	9.80 892	27	10.19 108	9.92 465	8	13	
48	9.73 377	19	9.80 919	28	10.19 081	9.92 457	8	12	
49	9.73 396	20	9.80 947	28	10.19 053	9.92 449	8	11	
50	9.73 416	19	9.80 975	28	10.19 025	9.92 441	8	**10**	
51	9.73 435	20	9.81 003	27	10.18 997	9.92 433	8	9	
52	9.73 455	19	9.81 030	28	10.18 970	9.92 425	9	8	
53	9.73 474	20	9.81 058	28	10.18 942	9.92 416	8	7	
54	9.73 494	19	9.81 086	27	10.18 914	9.92 408	8	6	
55	9.73 513	20	9.81 113	28	10.18 887	9.92 400	8	5	
56	9.73 533	19	9.81 141	28	10.18 859	9.92 392	8	4	
57	9.73 552	20	9.81 169	27	10.18 831	9.92 384	8	3	
58	9.73 572	19	9.81 196	28	10.18 804	9.92 376	9	2	
59	9.73 591	20	9.81 224	28	10.18 776	9.92 367	8	1	
60	9.73 611		9.81 252		10.18 748	9.92 359		**0**	
	L Cos	d	L Cot	c d	L Tan	L Sin	d	'	Prop. Pts.

Prop. Pts.

	29	28	27
1	2.9	2.8	2.7
2	5.8	5.6	5.4
3	8.7	8.4	8.1
4	11.6	11.2	10.8
5	14.5	14.0	13.5
6	17.4	16.8	16.2
7	20.3	19.6	18.9
8	23.2	22.4	21.6
9	26.1	25.2	24.3

	21	20	19
1	2.1	2.0	1.9
2	4.2	4.0	3.8
3	6.3	6.0	5.7
4	8.4	8.0	7.6
5	10.5	10.0	9.5
6	12.6	12.0	11.4
7	14.7	14.0	13.3
8	16.8	16.0	15.2
9	18.9	18.0	17.1

	9	8	7
1	0.9	0.8	0.7
2	1.8	1.6	1.4
3	2.7	2.4	2.1
4	3.6	3.2	2.8
5	4.5	4.0	3.5
6	5.4	4.8	4.2
7	6.3	5.6	4.9
8	7.2	6.4	5.6
9	8.1	7.2	6.3

′	L Sin	d	L Tan	c d	L Cot	L Cos	d		Prop. Pts.
0	9.73 611		9.81 252		10.18 748	9.92 359		**60**	
1	9.73 630	19	9.81 279	27	10.18 721	9.92 351	8	59	
2	9.73 650	20	9.81 307	28	10.18 693	9.92 343	8	58	
3	9.73 669	19	9.81 335	28	10.18 665	9.92 335	8	57	
4	9.73 689	20	9.81 362	27	10.18 638	9.92 326	9	56	
5	9.73 708	19	9.81 390	28	10.18 610	9.92 318	8	55	
6	9.73 727	19	9.81 418	28	10.18 582	9.92 310	8	54	
7	9.73 747	20	9.81 445	27	10.18 555	9.92 302	8	53	
8	9.73 766	19	9.81 473	28	10.18 527	9.92 293	9	52	
9	9.73 785	19	9.81 500	27	10.18 500	9.92 285	8	51	
10	9.73 805	20	9.81 528	28	10.18 472	9.92 277	8	**50**	
11	9.73 824	19	9.81 556	28	10.18 444	9.92 269	8	49	
12	9.73 843	19	9.81 583	27	10.18 417	9.92 260	9	48	
13	9.73 863	20	9.81 611	28	10.18 389	9.92 252	8	47	
14	9.73 882	19	9.81 638	27	10.18 362	9.92 244	8	46	
15	9.73 901	19	9.81 666	28	10.18 334	9.92 235	9	45	
16	9.73 921	20	9.81 693	27	10.18 307	9.92 227	8	44	
17	9.73 940	19	9.81 721	28	10.18 279	9.92 219	8	43	
18	9.73 959	19	9.81 748	27	10.18 252	9.92 211	8	42	
19	9.73 978	19	9.81 776	28	10.18 224	9.92 202	9	41	
20	9.73 997	19	9.81 803	27	10.18 197	9.92 194	8	**40**	
21	9.74 017	20	9.81 831	28	10.18 169	9.92 186	8	39	
22	9.74 036	19	9.81 858	27	10.18 142	9.92 177	8	38	
23	9.74 055	19	9.81 886	28	10.18 114	9.92 169	8	37	
24	9.74 074	19	9.81 913	27	10.18 087	9.92 161	9	36	
25	9.74 093	19	9.81 941	28	10.18 059	9.92 152	8	35	
26	9.74 113	20	9.81 968	27	10.18 032	9.92 144	8	34	
27	9.74 132	19	9.81 996	28	10.18 004	9.92 136	8	33	
28	9.74 151	19	9.82 023	27	10.17 977	9.92 127	9	32	
29	9.74 170	19	9.82 051	28	10.17 949	9.92 119	8	31	
30	9.74 189	19	9.82 078	27	10.17 922	9.92 111	8	**30**	
31	9.74 208	19	9.82 106	28	10.17 894	9.92 102	9	29	
32	9.74 227	19	9.82 133	27	10.17 867	9.92 094	8	28	
33	9.74 246	19	9.82 161	28	10.17 839	9.92 086	8	27	
34	9.74 265	19	9.82 188	27	10.17 812	9.92 077	9	26	
35	9.74 284	19	9.82 215	27	10.17 785	9.92 069	8	25	
36	9.74 303	19	9.82 243	28	10.17 757	9.92 060	8	24	
37	9.74 322	19	9.82 270	27	10.17 730	9.92 052	8	23	
38	9.74 341	19	9.82 298	28	10.17 702	9.92 044	9	22	
39	9.74 360	19	9.82 325	27	10.17 675	9.92 035	8	21	
40	9.74 379	19	9.82 352	28	10.17 648	9.92 027	9	**20**	
41	9.74 398	19	9.82 380	27	10.17 620	9.92 018	8	19	
42	9.74 417	19	9.82 407	28	10.17 593	9.92 010	8	18	
43	9.74 436	19	9.82 435	27	10.17 565	9.92 002	9	17	
44	9.74 455	19	9.82 462	27	10.17 538	9.91 993	8	16	
45	9.74 474	19	9.82 489	28	10.17 511	9.91 985	9	15	
46	9.74 493	19	9.82 517	27	10.17 483	9.91 976	8	14	
47	9.74 512	19	9.82 544	27	10.17 456	9.91 968	9	13	
48	9.74 531	18	9.82 571	28	10.17 429	9.91 959	8	12	
49	9.74 549	19	9.82 599	27	10.17 401	9.91 951	9	11	
50	9.74 568	19	9.82 626	27	10.17 374	9.91 942	8	**10**	
51	9.74 587	19	9.82 653	28	10.17 347	9.91 934	9	9	
52	9.74 606	19	9.82 681	27	10.17 319	9.91 925	8	8	
53	9.74 625	19	9.82 708	27	10.17 292	9.91 917	9	7	
54	9.74 644	18	9.82 735	27	10.17 265	9.91 908	8	6	
55	9.74 662	19	9.82 762	28	10.17 238	9.91 900	9	5	
56	9.74 681	19	9.82 790	27	10.17 210	9.91 891	8	4	
57	9.74 700	19	9.82 817	27	10.17 183	9.91 883	9	3	
58	9.74 719	18	9.82 844	27	10.17 156	9.91 874	8	2	
59	9.74 737	19	9.82 871	28	10.17 129	9.91 866	9	1	
60	9.74 756		9.82 899		10.17 101	9.91 857		**0**	
	L Cos	d	L Cot	c d	L Tan	L Sin	d	′	Prop. Pts.

Prop. Pts. columns:

	28	27
1	2.8	2.7
2	5.6	5.4
3	8.4	8.1
4	11.2	10.8
5	14.0	13.5
6	16.8	16.2
7	19.6	18.9
8	22.4	21.6
9	25.2	24.3

	20	19	18
1	2.0	1.9	1.8
2	4.0	3.8	3.6
3	6.0	5.7	5.4
4	8.0	7.6	7.2
5	10.0	9.5	9.0
6	12.0	11.4	10.8
7	14.0	13.3	12.6
8	16.0	15.2	14.4
9	18.0	17.1	16.2

	9	8
1	0.9	0.8
2	1.8	1.6
3	2.7	2.4
4	3.6	3.2
5	4.5	4.0
6	5.4	4.8
7	6.3	5.6
8	7.2	6.4
9	8.1	7.2

TABLE III   34°

'	L Sin	d	L Tan	c d	L Cot	L Cos	d		Prop. Pts.
0	9.74 756		9.82 899		10.17 101	9.91 857		60	
1	9.74 775	19	9.82 926	27	10.17 074	9.91 849	8	59	
2	9.74 794	19	9.82 953	27	10.17 047	9.91 840	9	58	
3	9.74 812	18	9.82 980	27	10.17 020	9.91 832	8	57	
4	9.74 831	19	9.83 008	28	10.16 992	9.91 823	9	56	
5	9.74 850	19	9.83 035	27	10.16 965	9.91 815	8	55	
6	9.74 868	18	9.83 062	27	10.16 938	9.91 806	9	54	
7	9.74 887	19	9.83 089	27	10.16 911	9.91 798	8	53	
8	9.74 906	19	9.83 117	28	10.16 883	9.91 789	9	52	
9	9.74 924	18	9.83 144	27	10.16 856	9.91 781	8	51	
10	9.74 943	19	9.83 171	27	10.16 829	9.91 772	9	50	
11	9.74 961	18	9.83 198	27	10.16 802	9.91 763	9	49	
12	9.74 980	19	9.83 225	27	10.16 775	9.91 755	8	48	
13	9.74 999	19	9.83 252	27	10.16 748	9.91 746	9	47	
14	9.75 017	18	9.83 280	28	10.16 720	9.91 738	8	46	
15	9.75 036	19	9.83 307	27	10.16 693	9.91 729	9	45	
16	9.75 054	18	9.83 334	27	10.16 666	9.91 720	9	44	
17	9.75 073	19	9.83 361	27	10.16 639	9.91 712	8	43	
18	9.75 091	18	9.83 388	27	10.16 612	9.91 703	9	42	
19	9.75 110	19	9.83 415	27	10.16 585	9.91 695	8	41	
20	9.75 128	18	9.83 442	28	10.16 558	9.91 686	9	40	
21	9.75 147	19	9.83 470	27	10.16 530	9.91 677	9	39	
22	9.75 165	18	9.83 497	27	10.16 503	9.91 669	8	38	
23	9.75 184	19	9.83 524	27	10.16 476	9.91 660	9	37	
24	9.75 202	18	9.83 551	27	10.16 449	9.91 651	9	36	
25	9.75 221	19	9.83 578	27	10.16 422	9.91 643	8	35	
26	9.75 239	18	9.83 605	27	10.16 395	9.91 634	9	34	
27	9.75 258	19	9.83 632	27	10.16 368	9.91 625	8	33	
28	9.75 276	18	9.83 659	27	10.16 341	9.91 617	9	32	
29	9.75 294	18	9.83 686	27	10.16 314	9.91 608	9	31	
30	9.75 313	19	9.83 713	27	10.16 287	9.91 599	8	30	
31	9.75 331	18	9.83 740	28	10.16 260	9.91 591	9	29	
32	9.75 350	19	9.83 768	27	10.16 232	9.91 582	9	28	
33	9.75 368	18	9.83 795	27	10.16 205	9.91 573	8	27	
34	9.75 386	18	9.83 822	27	10.16 178	9.91 565	9	26	
35	9.75 405	19	9.83 849	27	10.16 151	9.91 556	9	25	
36	9.75 423	18	9.83 876	27	10.16 124	9.91 547	9	24	
37	9.75 441	18	9.83 903	27	10.16 097	9.91 538	8	23	
38	9.75 459	18	9.83 930	27	10.16 070	9.91 530	9	22	
39	9.75 478	19	9.83 957	27	10.16 043	9.91 521	9	21	
40	9.75 496	18	9.83 984	27	10.16 016	9.91 512	8	20	
41	9.75 514	18	9.84 011	27	10.15 989	9.91 504	9	19	
42	9.75 533	19	9.84 038	27	10.15 962	9.91 495	9	18	
43	9.75 551	18	9.84 065	27	10.15 935	9.91 486	9	17	
44	9.75 569	18	9.84 092	27	10.15 908	9.91 477	8	16	
45	9.75 587	18	9.84 119	27	10.15 881	9.91 469	9	15	
46	9.75 605	19	9.84 146	27	10.15 854	9.91 460	9	14	
47	9.75 624	18	9.84 173	27	10.15 827	9.91 451	9	13	
48	9.75 642	18	9.84 200	27	10.15 800	9.91 442	9	12	
49	9.75 660	18	9.84 227	27	10.15 773	9.91 433	8	11	
50	9.75 678	18	9.84 254	26	10.15 746	9.91 425	9	10	
51	9.75 696	18	9.84 280	27	10.15 720	9.91 416	9	9	
52	9.75 714	19	9.84 307	27	10.15 693	9.91 407	9	8	
53	9.75 733	18	9.84 334	27	10.15 666	9.91 398	9	7	
54	9.75 751	18	9.84 361	27	10.15 639	9.91 389	8	6	
55	9.75 769	18	9.84 388	27	10.15 612	9.91 381	9	5	
56	9.75 787	18	9.84 415	27	10.15 585	9.91 372	9	4	
57	9.75 805	18	9.84 442	27	10.15 558	9.91 363	9	3	
58	9.75 823	18	9.84 469	27	10.15 531	9.91 354	9	2	
59	9.75 841	18	9.84 496	27	10.15 504	9.91 345	9	1	
60	9.75 859		9.84 523		10.15 477	9.91 336		0	
	L Cos	d	L Cot	c d	L Tan	L Sin	d	'	Prop. Pts.

Prop. Pts.

	28	27	26
1	2.8	2.7	2.6
2	5.6	5.4	5.2
3	8.4	8.1	7.8
4	11.2	10.8	10.4
5	14.0	13.5	13.0
6	16.8	16.2	15.6
7	19.6	18.9	18.2
8	22.4	21.6	20.8
9	25.2	24.3	23.4

	19	18
1	1.9	1.8
2	3.8	3.6
3	5.7	5.4
4	7.6	7.2
5	9.5	9.0
6	11.4	10.8
7	13.3	12.6
8	15.2	14.4
9	17.1	16.2

	9	8
1	0.9	0.8
2	1.8	1.6
3	2.7	2.4
4	3.6	3.2
5	4.5	4.0
6	5.4	4.8
7	6.3	5.6
8	7.2	6.4
9	8.1	7.2

′	L Sin	d	L Tan	c d	L Cot	L Cos	d		Prop. Pts.
0	9.75 859	18	9.84 523	27	10.15 477	9.91 336	8	**60**	
1	9.75 877	18	9.84 550	26	10.15 450	9.91 328	9	59	
2	9.75 895	18	9.84 576	27	10.15 424	9.91 319	9	58	
3	9.75 913	18	9.84 603	27	10.15 397	9.91 310	9	57	
4	9.75 931	18	9.84 630	27	10.15 370	9.91 301	9	56	
5	9.75 949	18	9.84 657	27	10.15 343	9.91 292	9	55	
6	9.75 967	18	9.84 684	27	10.15 316	9.91 283	9	54	
7	9.75 985	18	9.84 711	27	10.15 289	9.91 274	8	53	
8	9.76 003	18	9.84 738	26	10.15 262	9.91 266	9	52	
9	9.76 021	18	9.84 764	27	10.15 236	9.91 257	9	51		27	26
10	9.76 039	18	9.84 791	27	10.15 209	9.91 248	9	**50**	1 2.7 2.6
11	9.76 057	18	9.84 818	27	10.15 182	9.91 239	9	49	2 5.4 5.2
12	9.76 075	18	9.84 845	27	10.15 155	9.91 230	9	48	3 8.1 7.8
13	9.76 093	18	9.84 872	27	10.15 128	9.91 221	9	47	4 10.8 10.4
14	9.76 111	18	9.84 899	26	10.15 101	9.91 212	9	46	5 13.5 13.0
15	9.76 129	17	9.84 925	27	10.15 075	9.91 203	9	45	6 16.2 15.6
16	9.76 146	18	9.84 952	27	10.15 048	9.91 194	9	44	7 18.9 18.2
17	9.76 164	18	9.84 979	27	10.15 021	9.91 185	9	43	8 21.6 20.8
18	9.76 182	18	9.85 006	27	10.14 994	9.91 176	9	42	9 24.3 23.4
19	9.76 200	18	9.85 033	26	10.14 967	9.91 167	9	41	
20	9.76 218	18	9.85 059	27	10.14 941	9.91 158	9	**40**	
21	9.76 236	17	9.85 086	27	10.14 914	9.91 149	8	39	
22	9.76 253	18	9.85 113	27	19.14 887	9.91 141	9	38	
23	9.76 271	18	9.85 140	26	10.14 860	9.91 132	9	37	
24	9.76 289	18	9.85 166	27	10.14 834	9.91 123	9	36	
25	9.76 307	17	9.85 193	27	10.14 807	9.91 114	9	35	
26	9.76 324	18	9.85 220	27	10.14 780	9.91 105	9	34		18	17
27	0.76 342	18	9.85 247	26	10.14 753	0.91 096	9	33	1 1.8 1.7
28	9.76 360	18	9.85 273	27	10.14 727	9.91 087	9	32	2 3.6 3.4
29	9.76 378	17	9.85 300	27	10.14 700	9.91 078	9	31	3 5.4 5.1
30	9.76 395	18	9.85 327	27	10.14 673	9.91 069	9	**30**	4 7.2 6.8
31	9.76 413	18	9.85 354	26	10.14 646	9.91 060	9	29	5 9.0 8.5
32	9.76 431	17	9.85 380	27	10.14 620	9.91 051	9	28	6 10.8 10.2
33	9.76 448	18	9.85 407	27	10.14 593	9.91 042	9	27	7 12.6 11.9
34	9.76 466	18	9.85 434	26	10.14 566	9.91 033	10	26	8 14.4 13.6
35	9.76 484	17	9.85 460	27	10.14 540	9.91 023	9	25	9 16.2 15.3
36	9.76 501	18	9.85 487	27	10.14 513	9.91 014	9	24	
37	9.76 519	18	9.85 514	26	10.14 486	9.91 005	9	23	
38	9.76 537	17	9.85 540	27	10.14 460	9.90 996	9	22	
39	9.76 554	18	9.85 567	27	10.14 433	9.90 987	9	21	
40	9.76 572	18	9.85 594	26	10.14 406	9.90 978	9	**20**	
41	9.76 590	17	9.85 620	27	10.14 380	9.90 969	9	19	
42	9.76 607	18	9.85 647	27	10.14 353	9.90 960	9	18	
43	9.76 625	17	9.85 674	26	10.14 326	9.90 951	9	17	
44	9.76 642	18	9.85 700	27	10.14 300	9.90 942	9	16		10	9	8
45	9.76 660	17	9.85 727	27	10.14 273	9.90 933	9	15	1 1.0 0.9 0.8
46	9.76 677	18	9.85 754	26	10.14 246	9.90 924	9	14	2 2.0 1.8 1.6
47	9.76 695	17	9.85 780	27	10.14 220	9.90 915	9	13	3 3.0 2.7 2.4
48	9.76 712	18	9.85 807	27	10.14 193	9.90 906	10	12	4 4.0 3.6 3.2
49	9.76 730	17	9.85 834	26	10.14 166	9.90 896	9	11	5 5.0 4.5 4.0
50	9.76 747	18	9.85 860	27	10.14 140	9.90 887	9	**10**	6 6.0 5.4 4.8
51	9.76 765	17	9.85 887	26	10.14 113	9.90 878	9	9	7 7.0 6.3 5.6
52	9.76 782	18	9.85 913	27	10.14 087	9.90 869	9	8	8 8.0 7.2 6.4
53	9.76 800	17	9.85 940	27	10.14 060	9.90 860	9	7	9 9.0 8.1 7.2
54	9.76 817	18	9.85 967	26	10.14 033	9.90 851	9	6	
55	9.76 835	17	9.85 993	27	10.14 007	9.90 842	10	5	
56	9.76 852	18	9.86 020	26	10.13 980	9.90 832	9	4	
57	9.76 870	17	9.86 046	27	10.13 954	9.90 823	9	3	
58	9.76 887	17	9.86 073	27	10.13 927	9.90 814	9	2	
59	9.76 904	18	9.86 100	26	10.13 900	9.90 805	9	1	
60	9.76 922		9.86 126		10.13 874	9.90 796		**0**	
	L Cos	d	L Cot	c d	L Tan	L Sin	d	′	Prop. Pts.

TABLE III   36°

'	L Sin	d	L Tan	c d	L Cot	L Cos	d	'
0	9.76 922	17	9.86 126	27	10.13 874	9.90 796	9	60
1	9.76 939	18	9.86 153	26	10.13 847	9.90 787	10	59
2	9.76 957	17	9.86 179	27	10.13 821	9.90 777	9	58
3	9.76 974	17	9.86 206	26	10.13 794	9.90 768	9	57
4	9.76 991	18	9.86 232	27	10.13 768	9.90 759	9	56
5	9.77 009	17	9.86 259	26	10.13 741	9.90 750	9	55
6	9.77 026	17	9.86 285	27	10.13 715	9.90 741	10	54
7	9.77 043	18	9.86 312	26	10.13 688	9.90 731	9	53
8	9.77 061	17	9.86 338	27	10.13 662	9.90 722	9	52
9	9.77 078	17	9.86 365	27	10.13 635	9.90 713	9	51
10	9.77 095	17	9.86 392	26	10.13 608	9.90 704	10	50
11	9.77 112	18	9.86 418	27	10.13 582	9.90 694	9	49
12	9.77 130	17	9.86 445	26	10.13 555	9.90 685	9	48
13	9.77 147	17	9.86 471	27	10.13 529	9.90 676	9	47
14	9.77 164	17	9.86 498	26	10.13 502	9.90 667	10	46
15	9.77 181	18	9.86 524	27	10.13 476	9.90 657	9	45
16	9.77 199	17	9.86 551	26	10.13 449	9.90 648	9	44
17	9.77 216	17	9.86 577	26	10.13 423	9.90 639	9	43
18	9.77 233	17	9.86 603	27	10.13 397	9.90 630	10	42
19	9.77 250	18	9.86 630	26	10.13 370	9.90 620	9	41
20	9.77 268	17	9.86 656	27	10.13 344	9.90 611	9	40
21	9.77 285	17	9.86 683	26	10.13 317	9.90 602	10	39
22	9.77 302	17	9.86 709	27	10.13 291	9.90 592	9	38
23	9.77 319	17	9.86 736	26	10.13 264	9.90 583	9	37
24	9.77 336	17	9.86 762	27	10.13 238	9.90 574	9	36
25	9.77 353	17	9.86 789	26	10.13 211	9.90 565	10	35
26	9.77 370	17	9.86 815	27	10.13 185	9.90 555	9	34
27	9.77 387	18	9.86 842	26	10.13 158	9.90 546	9	33
28	9.77 405	17	9.86 868	26	10.13 132	9.90 537	10	32
29	9.77 422	17	9.86 894	27	10.13 106	9.90 527	9	31
30	9.77 439	17	9.86 921	26	10.13 079	9.90 518	9	30
31	9.77 456	17	9.86 947	27	10.13 053	9.90 509	10	29
32	9.77 473	17	9.86 974	26	10.13 026	9.90 499	9	28
33	9.77 490	17	9.87 000	27	10.13 000	9.90 490	10	27
34	9.77 507	17	9.87 027	26	10.12 973	9.90 480	9	26
35	9.77 524	17	9.87 053	26	10.12 947	9.90 471	9	25
36	9.77 541	17	9.87 079	27	10.12 921	9.90 462	10	24
37	9.77 558	17	9.87 106	26	10.12 894	9.90 452	9	23
38	9.77 575	17	9.87 132	26	10.12 868	9.90 443	9	22
39	9.77 592	17	9.87 158	27	10.12 842	9.90 434	10	21
40	9.77 609	17	9.87 185	26	10.12 815	9.90 424	9	20
41	9.77 626	17	9.87 211	27	10.12 789	9.90 415	10	19
42	9.77 643	17	9.87 238	26	10.12 762	9.90 405	9	18
43	9.77 660	17	9.87 264	26	10.12 736	9.90 396	10	17
44	9.77 677	17	9.87 290	27	10.12 710	9.90 386	9	16
45	9.77 694	17	9.87 317	26	10.12 683	9.90 377	9	15
46	9.77 711	17	9.87 343	26	10.12 657	9.90 368	10	14
47	9.77 728	16	9.87 369	27	10.12 631	9.90 358	9	13
48	9.77 744	17	9.87 396	26	10.12 604	9.90 349	10	12
49	9.77 761	17	9.87 422	26	10.12 578	9.90 339	9	11
50	9.77 778	17	9.87 448	27	10.12 552	9.90 330	10	10
51	9.77 795	17	9.87 475	26	10.12 525	9.90 320	9	9
52	9.77 812	17	9.87 501	26	10.12 499	9.90 311	10	8
53	9.77 829	17	9.87 527	27	10.12 473	9.90 301	9	7
54	9.77 846	16	9.87 554	26	10.12 446	9.90 292	10	6
55	9.77 862	17	9.87 580	26	10.12 420	9.90 282	9	5
56	9.77 879	17	9.87 606	27	10.12 394	9.90 273	10	4
57	9.77 896	17	9.87 633	26	10.12 367	9.90 263	10	3
58	9.77 913	17	9.87 659	26	10.12 341	9.90 254	10	2
59	9.77 930	16	9.87 685	26	10.12 315	9.90 244	9	1
60	9.77 946		9.87 711		10.12 289	9.90 235		0
	L Cos	d	L Cot	c d	L Tan	L Sin	d	'

Prop. Pts.

	27	26
1	2.7	2.6
2	5.4	5.2
3	8.1	7.8
4	10.8	10.4
5	13.5	13.0
6	16.2	15.6
7	18.9	18.2
8	21.6	20.8
9	24.3	23.4

	18	17	16
1	1.8	1.7	1.6
2	3.6	3.4	3.2
3	5.4	5.1	4.8
4	7.2	6.8	6.4
5	9.0	8.5	8.0
6	10.8	10.2	9.6
7	12.6	11.9	11.2
8	14.4	13.6	12.8
9	16.2	15.3	14.4

	10	9
1	1.0	0.9
2	2.0	1.8
3	3.0	2.7
4	4.0	3.6
5	5.0	4.5
6	6.0	5.4
7	7.0	6.3
8	8.0	7.2
9	9.0	8.1

'	L Sin	d	L Tan	c d	L Cot	L Cos	d		Prop. Pts.
0	9.77 946	17	9.87 711	27	10.12 289	9.90 235	10	60	
1	9.77 963	17	9.87 738	26	10.12 262	9.90 225	9	59	
2	9.77 980	17	9.87 764	26	10.12 236	9.90 216	10	58	
3	9.77 997	16	9.87 790	27	10.12 210	9.90 206	9	57	
4	9.78 013	17	9.87 817	26	10.12 183	9.90 197	9	56	
5	9.78 030	17	9.87 843	26	10.12 157	9.90 187	9	55	
6	9.78 047	16	9.87 869	26	10.12 131	9.90 178	10	54	
7	9.78 063	17	9.87 895	27	10.12 105	9.90 168	9	53	
8	9.78 080	17	9.87 922	26	10.12 078	9.90 159	10	52	27 26
9	9.78 097	16	9.87 948	26	10.12 052	9.90 149	10	51	1 2.7 2.6
10	9.78 113	17	9.87 974	26	10.12 026	9.90 139	9	50	2 5.4 5.2
11	9.78 130	17	9.88 000	27	10.12 000	9.90 130	10	49	3 8.1 7.8
12	9.78 147	16	9.88 027	26	10.11 973	9.90 120	9	48	4 10.8 10.4
13	9.78 163	17	9.88 053	26	10.11 947	9.90 111	10	47	5 13.5 13.0
14	9.78 180	17	9.88 079	26	10.11 921	9.90 101	10	46	6 16.2 15.6
15	9.78 197	16	9.88 105	26	10.11 895	9.90 091	9	45	7 18.9 18.2
16	9.78 213	17	9.88 131	27	10.11 869	9.90 082	10	44	8 21.6 20.8
17	9.78 230	16	9.88 158	26	10.11 842	9.90 072	9	43	9 24.3 23.4
18	9.78 246	17	9.88 184	26	10.11 816	9.90 063	10	42	
19	9.78 263	17	9.88 210	26	10.11 790	9.90 053	10	41	
20	9.78 280	16	9.88 236	26	10.11 764	9.90 043	9	40	
21	9.78 296	17	9.88 262	27	10.11 738	9.90 034	10	39	
22	9.78 313	16	9.88 289	26	10.11 711	9.90 024	10	38	
23	9.78 329	17	9.88 315	26	10.11 685	9.90 014	9	37	
24	9.78 346	16	9.88 341	26	10.11 659	9.90 005	10	36	
25	9.78 362	17	9.88 367	26	10.11 633	9.89 995	10	35	17 16
26	9.78 379	16	9.88 393	27	10.11 607	9.89 985	9	34	1 1.7 1.6
27	9.78 395	17	9.88 420	26	10.11 580	9.89 976	10	33	2 3.4 3.2
28	9.78 412	16	9.88 446	26	10.11 554	9.89 966	10	32	3 5.1 4.8
29	9.78 428	17	9.88 472	26	10.11 528	9.89 956	9	31	4 6.8 6.4
30	9.78 445	16	9.88 498	26	10.11 502	9.89 947	10	30	5 8.5 8.0
31	9.78 461	17	9.88 524	26	10.11 476	9.89 937	10	29	6 10.2 9.6
32	9.78 478	16	9.88 550	27	10.11 450	9.89 927	9	28	7 11.9 11.2
33	9.78 494	16	9.88 577	26	10.11 423	9.89 918	10	27	8 13.6 12.8
34	9.78 510	17	9.88 603	26	10.11 397	9.89 908	10	26	9 15.3 14.4
35	9.78 527	16	9.88 629	26	10.11 371	9.89 898	10	25	
36	9.78 543	17	9.88 655	26	10.11 345	9.89 888	9	24	
37	9.78 560	16	9.88 681	26	10.11 319	9.89 879	10	23	
38	9.78 576	16	9.88 707	26	10.11 293	9.89 869	10	22	
39	9.78 592	17	9.88 733	26	10.11 267	9.89 859	10	21	
40	9.78 609	16	9.88 759	27	10.11 241	9.89 849	9	20	
41	9.78 625	17	9.88 786	26	10.11 214	9.89 840	10	19	
42	9.78 642	16	9.88 812	26	10.11 188	9.89 830	10	18	
43	9.78 658	16	9.88 838	26	10.11 162	9.89 820	10	17	
44	9.78 674	17	9.88 864	26	10.11 136	9.89 810	9	16	10 9
45	9.78 691	16	9.88 890	26	10.11 110	9.89 801	10	15	1 1.0 0.9
46	9.78 707	16	9.88 916	26	10.11 084	9.89 791	10	14	2 2.0 1.8
47	9.78 723	16	9.88 942	26	10.11 058	9.89 781	10	13	3 3.0 2.7
48	9.78 739	17	9.88 968	26	10.11 032	9.89 771	10	12	4 4.0 3.6
49	9.78 756	16	9.88 994	26	10.11 006	9.89 761	9	11	5 5.0 4.5
50	9.78 772	16	9.89 020	26	10.10 980	9.89 752	10	10	6 6.0 5.4
51	9.78 788	17	9.89 046	27	10.10 954	9.89 742	10	9	7 7.0 6.3
52	9.78 805	16	9.89 073	26	10.10 927	9.89 732	10	8	8 8.0 7.2
53	9.78 821	16	9.89 099	26	10.10 901	9.89 722	10	7	9 9.0 8.1
54	9.78 837	16	9.89 125	26	10.10 875	9.89 712	10	6	
55	9.78 853	16	9.89 151	26	10.10 849	9.89 702	9	5	
56	9.78 869	17	9.89 177	26	10.10 823	9.89 693	10	4	
57	9.78 886	16	9.89 203	26	10.10 797	9.89 683	10	3	
58	9.78 902	16	9.89 229	26	10.10 771	9.89 673	10	2	
59	9.78 918	16	9.89 255	26	10.10 745	9.89 663	10	1	
60	9.78 934		9.89 281		10.10 719	9.89 653		0	
	L Cos	d	L Cot	c d	L Tan	L Sin	d	'	Prop. Pts.

TABLE III   38°

'	L Sin	d	L Tan	c d	L Cot	L Cos	d		Prop. Pts.
0	9.78 934		9.89 281		10.10 719	9.89 653		60	
1	9.78 950	16	9.89 307	26	10.10 693	9.89 643	10	59	
2	9.78 967	17	9.89 333	26	10.10 667	9.89 633	10	58	
3	9.78 983	16	9.89 359	26	10.10 641	9.89 624	9	57	
4	9.78 999	16	9.89 385	26	10.10 615	9.89 614	10	56	
5	9.79 015	16	9.89 411	26	10.10 589	9.89 604	10	55	
6	9.79 031	16	9.89 437	26	10.10 563	9.89 594	10	54	
7	9.79 047	16	9.89 463	26	10.10 537	9.89 584	10	53	
8	9.79 063	16	9.89 489	26	10.10 511	9.89 574	10	52	
9	9.79 079	16	9.89 515	26	10.10 485	9.89 564	10	51	
10	9.79 095	16	9.89 541	26	10.10 459	9.89 554	10	50	
11	9.79 111	16	9.89 567	26	10.10 433	9.89 544	10	49	
12	9.79 128	17	9.89 593	26	10.10 407	9.89 534	10	48	
13	9.79 144	16	9.89 619	26	10.10 381	9.89 524	10	47	
14	9.79 160	16	9.89 645	26	10.10 355	9.89 514	10	46	
15	9.79 176	16	9.89 671	26	10.10 329	9.89 504	9	45	
16	9.79 192	16	9.89 697	26	10.10 303	9.89 495	10	44	
17	9.79 208	16	9.89 723	26	10.10 277	9.89 485	10	43	
18	9.79 224	16	9.89 749	26	10.10 251	9.89 475	10	42	
19	9.79 240	16	9.89 775	26	10.10 225	9.89 465	10	41	
20	9.79 256	16	9.89 801	26	10.10 199	9.89 455	10	40	
21	9.79 272	16	9.89 827	26	10.10 173	9.89 445	10	39	
22	9.79 288	16	9.89 853	26	10.10 147	9.89 435	10	38	
23	9.79 304	16	9.89 879	26	10.10 121	9.89 425	10	37	
24	9.79 319	15	9.89 905	26	10.10 095	9.89 415	10	36	
25	9.79 335	16	9.89 931	26	10.10 069	9.89 405	10	35	
26	9.79 351	16	9.89 957	26	10.10 043	9.89 395	10	34	
27	9.79 367	16	9.89 983	26	10.10 017	9.89 385	10	33	
28	9.79 383	16	9.90 009	26	10.09 991	9.89 375	11	32	
29	9.79 399	16	9.90 035	26	10.09 965	9.89 364	10	31	
30	9.79 415	16	9.90 061	25	10.09 939	9.89 354	10	30	
31	9.79 431	16	9.90 086	26	10.09 914	9.89 344	10	29	
32	9.79 447	16	9.90 112	26	10.09 888	9.89 334	10	28	
33	9.79 463	15	9.90 138	26	10.09 862	9.89 324	10	27	
34	9.79 478	16	9.90 164	26	10.09 836	9.89 314	10	26	
35	9.79 494	16	9.90 190	26	10.09 810	9.89 304	10	25	
36	9.79 510	16	9.90 216	26	10.09 784	9.89 294	10	24	
37	9.79 526	16	9.90 242	26	10.09 758	9.89 284	10	23	
38	9.79 542	16	9.90 268	26	10.09 732	9.89 274	10	22	
39	9.79 558	15	9.90 294	26	10.09 706	9.89 264	10	21	
40	9.79 573	16	9.90 320	26	10.09 680	9.89 254	10	20	
41	9.79 589	16	9.90 346	25	10.09 654	9.89 244	11	19	
42	9.79 605	16	9.90 371	26	10.09 629	9.89 233	10	18	
43	9.79 621	15	9.90 397	26	10.09 603	9.89 223	10	17	
44	9.79 636	16	9.90 423	26	10.09 577	9.89 213	10	16	
45	9.79 652	16	9.90 449	26	10.09 551	9.89 203	10	15	
46	9.79 668	16	9.90 475	26	10.09 525	9.89 193	10	14	
47	9.79 684	15	9.90 501	26	10.09 499	9.89 183	10	13	
48	9.79 699	16	9.90 527	26	10.09 473	9.89 173	11	12	
49	9.79 715	16	9.90 553	25	10.09 447	9.89 162	10	11	
50	9.79 731	15	9.90 578	26	10.09 422	9.89 152	10	10	
51	9.79 746	16	9.90 604	26	10.09 396	9.89 142	10	9	
52	9.79 762	16	9.90 630	26	10.09 370	9.89 132	10	8	
53	9.79 778	15	9.90 656	26	10.09 344	9.89 122	10	7	
54	9.79 793	16	9.90 682	26	10.09 318	9.89 112	11	6	
55	9.79 809	16	9.90 708	26	10.09 292	9.89 101	10	5	
56	9.79 825	15	9.90 734	25	10.09 266	9.89 091	10	4	
57	9.79 840	16	9.90 759	26	10.09 241	9.89 081	10	3	
58	9.79 856	16	9.90 785	26	10.09 215	9.89 071	11	2	
59	9.79 872	15	9.90 811	26	10.09 189	9.89 060	10	1	
60	9.79 887		9.90 837		10.09 163	9.89 050		0	
	L Cos	d	L Cot	c d	L Tan	L Sin	d	'	Prop. Pts.

Prop. Pts.

	26	25
1	2.6	2.5
2	5.2	5.0
3	7.8	7.5
4	10.4	10.0
5	13.0	12.5
6	15.6	15.0
7	18.2	17.5
8	20.8	20.0
9	23.4	22.5

	17	16	15
1	1.7	1.6	1.5
2	3.4	3.2	3.0
3	5.1	4.8	4.5
4	6.8	6.4	6.0
5	8.5	8.0	7.5
6	10.2	9.6	9.0
7	11.9	11.2	10.5
8	13.6	12.8	12.0
9	15.3	14.4	13.5

	11	10	9
1	1.1	1.0	0.9
2	2.2	2.0	1.8
3	3.3	3.0	2.7
4	4.4	4.0	3.6
5	5.5	5.0	4.5
6	6.6	6.0	5.4
7	7.7	7.0	6.3
8	8.8	8.0	7.2
9	9.9	9.0	8.1

′	L Sin	d	L Tan	c d	L Cot	L Cos	d		Prop. Pts.
0	9.79 887	16	9.90 837	26	10.09 163	9.89 050	10	**60**	
1	9.79 903	15	9.90 863	26	10.09 137	9.89 040	10	59	
2	9.79 918	16	9.90 889	25	10.09 111	9.89 030	10	58	
3	9.79 934	16	9.90 914	26	10.09 086	9.89 020	11	57	
4	9.79 950	15	9.90 940	26	10.09 060	9.89 009	10	56	
5	9.79 965	16	9.90 966	26	10.09 034	8.88 999	10	55	
6	9.79 981	15	9.90 992	26	10.09 008	9.88 989	11	54	
7	9.79 996	16	9.91 018	25	10.08 982	9.88 978	10	53	
8	9.80 012	15	9.91 043	26	10.08 957	9.88 968	10	52			**26**	**25**
9	9.80 027	16	9.91 069	26	10.08 931	9.88 958	10	51	1	2.6	2.5
10	9.80 043	15	9.91 095	26	10.08 905	9.88 948	11	**50**	2	5.2	5.0
11	9.80 058	16	9.91 121	26	10.08 879	9.88 937	10	49	3	7.8	7.5
12	9.80 074	15	9.91 147	25	10.08 853	9.88 927	10	48	4	10.4	10.0
13	9.80 089	16	9.91 172	26	10.08 828	9.88 917	11	47	5	13.0	12.5
14	9.80 105	15	9.91 198	26	10.08 802	9.88 906	10	46	6	15.6	15.0
15	9.80 120	16	9.91 224	26	10.08 776	9.88 896	10	45	7	18.2	17.5
16	9.80 136	15	9.91 250	26	10.08 750	9.88 886	11	44	8	20.8	20.0
17	9.80 151	15	9.91 276	25	10.08 724	9.88 875	10	43	9	23.4	22.5
18	9.80 166	16	9.91 301	26	10.08 699	9.88 865	10	42	
19	9.80 182	15	9.91 327	26	10.08 673	9.88 855	11	41	
20	9.80 197	16	9.91 353	26	10.08 647	9.88 844	10	**40**	
21	9.80 213	15	9.91 379	25	10.08 621	9.88 834	10	39	
22	9.80 228	16	9.91 404	26	10.08 596	9.88 824	11	38	
23	9.80 244	15	9.91 430	26	10.08 570	9.88 813	10	37	
24	9.80 259	15	9.91 456	26	10.08 544	9.88 803	10	36	
25	9.80 274	16	9.91 482	25	10.08 518	9.88 793	11	35	
26	9.80 290	15	9.91 507	26	10.08 493	9.88 782	10	34			**16**	**15**
27	9.80 305	15	9.91 533	26	10.08 467	9.88 772	11	33	1	1.6	1.5
28	9.80 320	16	9.91 559	26	10.08 441	9.88 761	10	32	2	3.2	3.0
29	9.80 336	15	9.91 585	25	10.08 415	9.88 751	10	31	3	4.8	4.5
30	9.80 351	15	9.91 610	26	10.08 390	9.88 741	11	**30**	4	6.4	6.0
31	9.80 366	16	9.91 636	26	10.08 364	9.88 730	10	29	5	8.0	7.5
32	9.80 382	15	9.91 662	26	10.08 338	9.88 720	11	28	6	9.6	9.0
33	9.80 397	15	9.91 688	25	10.08 312	9.88 709	10	27	7	11.2	10.5
34	9.80 412	16	9.91 713	26	10.08 287	9.88 699	11	26	8	12.8	12.0
35	9.80 428	15	9.91 739	26	10.08 261	9.88 688	10	25	9	14.4	13.5
36	9.80 443	15	9.91 765	26	10.08 235	9.88 678	10	24	
37	9.80 458	15	9.91 791	25	10.08 209	9.88 668	11	23	
38	9.80 473	16	9.91 816	26	10.08 184	9.88 657	10	22	
39	9.80 489	15	9.91 842	26	10.08 158	9.88 647	11	21	
40	9.80 504	15	9.91 868	25	10.08 132	9.88 636	10	**20**	
41	9.80 519	15	9.91 893	26	10.08 107	9.88 626	11	19	
42	9.80 534	16	9.91 919	26	10.08 081	9.88 615	10	18	
43	9.80 550	15	9.91 945	26	10.08 055	9.88 605	11	17	
44	9.80 565	15	9.91 971	25	10.08 029	9.88 594	10	16			**11**	**10**
45	9.80 580	15	9.91 996	26	10.08 004	9.88 584	11	15	1	1.1	1.0
46	9.80 595	15	9.92 022	26	10.07 978	9.88 573	10	14	2	2.2	2.0
47	9.80 610	15	9.92 048	25	10.07 952	9.88 563	11	13	3	3.3	3.0
48	9.80 625	16	9.92 073	26	10.07 927	9.88 552	10	12	4	4.4	4.0
49	9.80 641	15	9.92 099	26	10.07 901	9.88 542	11	11	5	5.5	5.0
50	9.80 656	15	9.92 125	25	10.07 875	9.88 531	10	**10**	6	6.6	6.0
51	9.80 671	15	9.92 150	26	10.07 850	9.88 521	11	9	7	7.7	7.0
52	9.80 686	15	9.92 176	26	10.07 824	9.88 510	11	8	8	8.8	8.0
53	9.80 701	15	9.92 202	25	10.07 798	9.88 499	10	7	9	9.9	9.0
54	9.80 716	15	9.92 227	26	10.07 773	9.88 489	11	6	
55	9.80 731	15	9.92 253	26	10.07 747	9.88 478	10	5	
56	9.80 746	16	9.92 279	25	10.07 721	9.88 468	11	4	
57	9.80 762	15	9.92 304	26	10.07 696	9.88 457	10	3	
58	9.80 777	15	9.92 330	26	10.07 670	9.88 447	11	2	
59	9.80 792	15	9.92 356	25	10.07 644	9.88 436	11	1	
60	9.80 807		9.92 381		10.07 619	9.88 425		**0**	
	L Cos	d	L Cot	c d	L Tan	L Sin	d	′	Prop. Pts.

∠ A = 50° 40′

TABLE III   40°

'	L Sin	d	L Tan	c d	L Cot	L Cos	d	
0	9.80 807	15	9.92 381	26	10.07 619	9.88 425	10	60
1	9.80 822	15	9.92 407	26	10.07 593	9.88 415	11	59
2	9.80 837	15	9.92 433	25	10.07 567	9.88 404	10	58
3	9.80 852	15	9.92 458	26	10.07 542	9.88 394	11	57
4	9.80 867	15	9.92 484	26	10.07 516	9.88 383	11	56
5	9.80 882	15	9.92 510	25	10.07 490	9.88 372	10	55
6	9.80 897	15	9.92 535	26	10.07 465	9.88 362	11	54
7	9.80 912	15	9.92 561	26	10.07 439	9.88 351	11	53
8	9.80 927	15	9.92 587	25	10.07 413	9.88 340	10	52
9	9.80 942	15	9.92 612	26	10.07 388	9.88 330	11	51
10	9.80 957	15	9.92 638	25	10.07 362	9.88 319	11	50
11	9.80 972	15	9.92 663	26	10.07 337	9.88 308	10	49
12	9.80 987	15	9.92 689	26	10.07 311	9.88 298	11	48
13	9.81 002	15	9.92 715	25	10.07 285	9.88 287	11	47
14	9.81 017	15	9.92 740	26	10.07 260	9.88 276	10	46
15	9.81 032	15	9.92 766	26	10.07 234	9.88 266	11	45
16	9.81 047	14	9.92 792	25	10.07 208	9.88 255	11	44
17	9.81 061	15	9.92 817	26	10.07 183	9.88 244	10	43
18	9.81 076	15	9.92 843	25	10.07 157	9.88 234	11	42
19	9.81 091	15	9.92 868	26	10.07 132	9.88 223	11	41
20	9.81 106	15	9.92 894	26	10.07 106	9.88 212	11	40
21	9.81 121	15	9.92 920	25	10.07 080	9.88 201	10	39
22	9.81 136	15	9.92 945	26	10.07 055	9.88 191	11	38
23	9.81 151	15	9.92 971	25	10.07 029	9.88 180	11	37
24	9.81 166	14	9.92 996	26	10.07 004	9.88 169	11	36
25	9.81 180	15	9.93 022	26	10.06 978	9.88 158	10	35
26	9.81 195	15	9.93 048	25	10.06 952	9.88 148	11	34
27	9.81 210	15	9.93 073	26	10.06 927	9.88 137	11	33
28	9.81 225	15	9.93 099	25	10.06 901	9.88 126	11	32
29	9.81 240	14	9.93 124	26	10.06 876	9.88 115	10	31
30	9.81 254	15	9.93 150	25	10.06 850	9.88 105	11	30
31	9.81 269	15	9.93 175	26	10.06 825	9.88 094	11	29
32	9.81 284	15	9.93 201	26	10.06 799	9.88 083	11	28
33	9.81 299	15	9.93 227	25	10.06 773	9.88 072	11	27
34	9.81 314	14	9.93 252	26	10.06 748	9.88 061	10	26
35	9.81 328	15	9.93 278	25	10.06 722	9.88 051	11	25
36	9.81 343	15	9.93 303	26	10.06 697	9.88 040	11	24
37	9.81 358	14	9.93 329	25	10.06 671	9.88 029	11	23
38	9.81 372	15	9.93 354	26	10.06 646	9.88 018	11	22
39	9.81 387	15	9.93 380	26	10.06 620	9.88 007	11	21
40	9.81 402	15	9.93 406	25	10.06 594	9.87 996	11	20
41	9.81 417	14	9.93 431	26	10.06 569	9.87 985	10	19
42	9.81 431	15	9.93 457	25	10.06 543	9.87 975	11	18
43	9.81 446	15	9.93 482	26	10.06 518	9.87 964	11	17
44	9.81 461	14	9.93 508	25	10.06 492	9.87 953	11	16
45	9.81 475	15	9.93 533	26	10.06 467	9.87 942	11	15
46	9.81 490	15	9.93 559	25	10.06 441	9.87 931	11	14
47	9.81 505	14	9.93 584	26	10.06 416	9.87 920	11	13
48	9.81 519	15	9.93 610	26	10.06 390	9.87 909	11	12
49	9.81 534	15	9.93 636	25	10.06 364	9.87 898	11	11
50	9.81 549	14	9.93 661	26	10.06 339	9.87 887	10	10
51	9.81 563	15	9.93 687	25	10.06 313	9.87 877	11	9
52	9.81 578	14	9.93 712	26	10.06 288	9.87 866	11	8
53	9.81 592	15	9.93 738	25	10.06 262	9.87 855	11	7
54	9.81 607	15	9.93 763	26	10.06 237	9.87 844	11	6
55	9.81 622	14	9.93 789	25	10.06 211	9.87 833	11	5
56	9.81 636	15	9.93 814	26	10.06 186	9.87 822	11	4
57	9.81 651	14	9.93 840	25	10.06 160	9.87 811	11	3
58	9.81 665	15	9.93 865	26	10.06 135	9.87 800	11	2
59	9.81 680	14	9.93 891	25	10.06 109	9.87 789	11	1
60	9.81 694		9.93 916		10.06 084	9.87 778		0
	L Cos	d	L Cot	c d	L Tan	L Sin	d	'

Prop. Pts.

	26	25
1	2.6	2.5
2	5.2	5.0
3	7.8	7.5
4	10.4	10.0
5	13.0	12.5
6	15.6	15.0
7	18.2	17.5
8	20.8	20.0
9	23.4	22.5

	15	14
1	1.5	1.4
2	3.0	2.8
3	4.5	4.2
4	6.0	5.6
5	7.5	7.0
6	9.0	8.4
7	10.5	9.8
8	12.0	11.2
9	13.5	12.6

	11	10
1	1.1	1.0
2	2.2	2.0
3	3.3	3.0
4	4.4	4.0
5	5.5	5.0
6	6.6	6.0
7	7.7	7.0
8	8.8	8.0
9	9.9	9.0

′	L Sin	d	L Tan	c d	L Cot	L Cos	d		Prop. Pts.
0	9.81 694		9.93 916		10.06 084	9.87 778		**60**	
1	9.81 709	15	9.93 942	26	10.06 058	9.87 767	11	59	
2	9.81 723	14	9.93 967	25	10.06 033	9.87 756	11	58	
3	9.81 738	15	9.93 993	26	10.06 007	9.87 745	11	57	
4	9.81 752	14	9.94 018	25	10.05 982	9.87 734	11	56	
5	9.81 767	15	9.94 044	26	10.05 956	9.87 723	11	55	
6	9.81 781	14	9.94 069	25	10.05 931	9.87 712	11	54	
7	9.81 796	15	9.94 095	26	10.05 905	9.87 701	11	53	
8	9.81 810	14	9.94 120	25	10.05 880	9.87 690	11	52	
9	9.81 825	15	9.94 146	26	10.05 854	9.87 679	11	51	
10	9.81 839	14	9.94 171	25	10.05 829	9.87 668	11	**50**	
11	9.81 854	15	9.94 197	26	10.05 803	9.87 657	11	49	
12	9.81 868	14	9.94 222	25	10.05 778	9.87 646	11	48	
13	9.81 882	14	9.94 248	26	10.05 752	9.87 635	11	47	
14	9.81 897	15	9.94 273	25	10.05 727	9.87 624	11	46	
15	9.81 911	14	9.94 299	26	10.05 701	9.87 613	12	45	
16	9.81 926	15	9.94 324	25	10.05 676	9.87 601	11	44	
17	9.81 940	14	9.94 350	26	10.05 650	9.87 590	11	43	
18	9.81 955	15	9.94 375	25	10.05 625	9.87 579	11	42	
19	9.81 969	14	9.94 401	26	10.05 599	9.87 568	11	41	
20	9.81 983	14	9.94 426	25	10.05 574	9.87 557	11	**40**	
21	9.81 998	15	9.94 452	26	10.05 548	9.87 546	11	39	
22	9.82 012	14	9.94 477	25	10.05 523	9.87 535	11	38	
23	9.82 026	14	9.94 503	26	10.05 497	9.87 524	11	37	
24	9.82 041	15	9.94 528	25	10.05 472	9.87 513	12	36	
25	9.82 055	14	9.94 554	26	10.05 446	9.87 501	11	35	
26	9.82 069	14	9.94 579	25	10.05 421	9.87 490	11	34	
27	9.82 084	15	9.94 604	26	10.05 396	9.87 479	11	33	
28	9.82 098	14	9.94 630	25	10.05 370	9.87 468	11	32	
29	9.82 112	14	9.94 655	26	10.05 345	9.87 457	11	31	
30	9.82 126	15	9.94 681	25	10.05 319	9.87 446	12	**30**	
31	9.82 141	14	9.94 706	26	10.05 294	9.87 434	11	29	
32	9.82 155	14	9.94 732	25	10.05 268	9.87 423	11	28	
33	9.82 169	15	9.94 757	26	10.05 243	9.87 412	11	27	
34	9.82 184	14	9.94 783	25	10.05 217	9.87 401	11	26	
35	9.82 198	14	9.94 808	26	10.05 192	9.87 390	12	25	
36	9.82 212	14	9.94 834	25	10.05 166	9.87 378	11	24	
37	9.82 226	14	9.94 859	25	10.05 141	9.87 367	11	23	
38	9.82 240	15	9.94 884	26	10.05 116	9.87 356	11	22	
39	9.82 255	14	9.94 910	25	10.05 090	9.87 345	11	21	
40	9.82 269	14	9.94 935	26	10.05 065	9.87 334	12	**20**	
41	9.82 283	14	9.94 961	25	10.05 039	9.87 322	11	19	
42	9.82 297	14	9.94 986	26	10.05 014	9.87 311	11	18	
43	9.82 311	15	9.95 012	25	10.04 988	9.87 300	12	17	
44	9.82 326	14	9.95 037	25	10.04 963	9.87 288	11	16	
45	9.82 340	14	9.95 062	26	10.04 938	9.87 277	11	15	
46	9.82 354	14	9.95 088	25	10.04 912	9.87 266	11	14	
47	9.82 368	14	9.95 113	26	10.04 887	9.87 255	12	13	
48	9.82 382	14	9.95 139	25	10.04 861	9.87 243	11	12	
49	9.82 396	14	9.95 164	26	10.04 836	9.87 232	11	11	
50	9.82 410	14	9.95 190	25	10.04 810	9.87 221	12	**10**	
51	9.82 424	15	9.95 215	25	10.04 785	9.87 209	11	9	
52	9.82 439	14	9.95 240	26	10.04 760	9.87 198	11	8	
53	9.82 453	14	9.95 266	25	10.04 734	9.87 187	12	7	
54	9.82 467	14	9.95 291	26	10.04 709	9.87 175	11	6	
55	9.82 481	14	9.95 317	25	10.04 683	9.87 164	11	5	
56	9.82 495	14	9.95 342	26	10.04 658	9.87 153	12	4	
57	9.82 509	14	9.95 368	25	10.04 632	9.87 141	11	3	
58	9.82 523	14	9.95 393	25	10.04 607	9.87 130	11	2	
59	9.82 537	14	9.95 418	26	10.04 582	9.87 119	12	1	
60	9.82 551		9.95 444		10.04 556	9.87 107		**0**	
	L Cos	d	L Cot	c d	L Tan	L Sin	d	′	Prop. Pts.

Prop. Pts.

	26	25
1	2.6	2.5
2	5.2	5.0
3	7.8	7.5
4	10.4	10.0
5	13.0	12.5
6	15.6	15.0
7	18.2	17.5
8	20.8	20.0
9	23.4	22.5

	15	14
1	1.5	1.4
2	3.0	2.8
3	4.5	4.2
4	6.0	5.6
5	7.5	7.0
6	9.0	8.4
7	10.5	9.8
8	12.0	11.2
9	13.5	12.6

	12	11
1	1.2	1.1
2	2.4	2.2
3	3.6	3.3
4	4.8	4.4
5	6.0	5.5
6	7.2	6.6
7	8.4	7.7
8	9.6	8.8
9	10.8	9.9

TABLE III   42°

′	L Sin	d	L Tan	c d	L Cot	L Cos	d		Prop. Pts.
0	9.82 551		9.95 444		10.04 556	9.87 107		**60**	
1	9.82 565	14	9.95 469	25	10.04 531	9.87 096	11	59	
2	9.82 579	14	9.95 495	26	10.04 505	9.87 085	11	58	
3	9.82 593	14	9.95 520	25	10.04 480	9.87 073	12	57	
4	9.82 607	14	9.95 545	25	10.04 455	9.87 062	11	56	
5	9.82 621	14	9.95 571	26	10.04 429	9.87 050	12	55	
6	9.82 635	14	9.95 596	25	10.04 404	9.87 039	11	54	
7	9.82 649	14	9.95 622	26	10.04 378	9.87 028	11	53	
8	9.82 663	14	9.95 647	25	10.04 353	9.87 016	12	52	
9	9.82 677	14	9.95 672	25	10.04 328	9.87 005	11	51	
10	9.82 691	14	9.95 698	26	10.04 302	9.86 993	12	**50**	
11	9.82 705	14	9.95 723	25	10.04 277	9.86 982	11	49	
12	9.82 719	14	9.95 748	25	10.04 252	9.86 970	12	48	
13	9.82 733	14	9.95 774	26	10.04 226	9.86 959	11	47	
14	9.82 747	14	9.95 799	25	10.04 201	9.86 947	12	46	
15	9.82 761	14	9.95 825	26	10.04 175	9.86 936	11	45	
16	9.82 775	14	9.95 850	25	10.04 150	9.86 924	12	44	
17	9.82 788	13	9.95 875	25	10.04 125	9.86 913	11	43	
18	9.82 802	14	9.95 901	26	10.04 099	9.86 902	11	42	
19	9.82 816	14	9.95 926	25	10.04 074	9.86 890	12	41	
20	9.82 830	14	9.95 952	26	10.04 048	9.86 879	11	**40**	
21	9.82 844	14	9.95 977	25	10.04 023	9.86 867	12	39	
22	9.82 858	14	9.96 002	25	10.03 998	9.86 855	12	38	
23	9.82 872	14	9.96 028	26	10.03 972	9.86 844	11	37	
24	9.82 885	13	9.96 053	25	10.03 947	9.86 832	12	36	
25	9.82 899	14	9.96 078	25	10.03 922	9.86 821	11	35	
26	9.82 913	14	9.96 104	26	10.03 896	9.86 809	12	34	
27	9.82 927	14	9.96 129	25	10.03 871	9.86 798	11	33	
28	9.82 941	14	9.96 155	26	10.03 845	9.86 786	12	32	
29	9.82 955	14	9.96 180	25	10.03 820	9.86 775	11	31	
30	9.82 968	13	9.96 205	25	10.03 795	9.86 763	12	**30**	
31	9.82 982	14	9.96 231	26	10.03 769	9.86 752	11	29	
32	9.82 996	14	9.96 256	25	10.03 744	9.86 740	12	28	
33	9.83 010	14	9.96 281	25	10.03 719	9.86 728	12	27	
34	9.83 023	13	9.96 307	26	10.03 693	9.86 717	11	26	
35	9.83 037	14	9.96 332	25	10.03 668	9.86 705	12	25	
36	9.83 051	14	9.96 357	25	10.03 643	9.86 694	11	24	
37	9.83 065	14	9.96 383	26	10.03 617	9.86 682	12	23	
38	9.83 078	13	9.96 408	25	10.03 592	9.86 670	12	22	
39	9.83 092	14	9.96 433	26	10.03 567	9.86 659	11	21	
40	9.83 106	14	9.96 459	25	10.03 541	9.86 647	12	**20**	
41	9.83 120	14	9.96 484	26	10.03 516	9.86 635	12	19	
42	9.83 133	13	9.96 510	25	10.03 490	9.86 624	11	18	
43	9.83 147	14	9.96 535	25	10.03 465	9.86 612	12	17	
44	9.83 161	14	9.96 560	26	10.03 440	9.86 600	12	16	
45	9.83 174	13	9.96 586	25	10.03 414	9.86 589	11	15	
46	9.83 188	14	9.96 611	25	10.03 389	9.86 577	12	14	
47	9.83 202	14	9.96 636	26	10.03 364	9.86 565	12	13	
48	9.83 215	13	9.96 662	25	10.03 338	9.86 554	11	12	
49	9.83 229	14	9.96 687	25	10.03 313	9.86 542	12	11	
50	9.83 242	13	9.96 712	26	10.03 288	9.86 530	12	**10**	
51	9.83 256	14	9.96 738	25	10.03 262	9.86 518	11	9	
52	9.83 270	14	9.96 763	25	10.03 237	9.86 507	12	8	
53	9.83 283	13	9.96 788	26	10.03 212	9.86 495	12	7	
54	9.83 297	14	9.96 814	25	10.03 186	9.86 483	11	6	
55	9.83 310	13	9.96 839	25	10.03 161	9.86 472	12	5	
56	9.83 324	14	9.96 864	26	10.03 136	9.86 460	12	4	
57	9.83 338	14	9.96 890	25	10.03 110	9.86 448	12	3	
58	9.83 351	13	9.96 915	25	10.03 085	9.86 436	11	2	
59	9.83 365	14	9.96 940	26	10.03 060	9.86 425	12	1	
60	9.83 378	13	9.96 966		10.03 034	9.86 413		**0**	
	L Cos	d	L Cot	c d	L Tan	L Sin	d	′	Prop. Pts.

Prop. Pts.

	26	25
1	2.6	2.5
2	5.2	5.0
3	7.8	7.5
4	10.4	10.0
5	13.0	12.5
6	15.6	15.0
7	18.2	17.5
8	20.8	20.0
9	23.4	22.5

	14	13
1	1.4	1.3
2	2.8	2.6
3	4.2	3.9
4	5.6	5.2
5	7.0	6.5
6	8.4	7.8
7	9.8	9.1
8	11.2	10.4
9	12.6	11.7

	12	11
1	1.2	1.1
2	2.4	2.2
3	3.6	3.3
4	4.8	4.4
5	6.0	5.5
6	7.2	6.6
7	8.4	7.7
8	9.6	8.8
9	10.8	9.9

47°

′	L Sin	d	L Tan	c d	L Cot	L Cos	d		Prop. Pts.
0	9.83 378		9.96 966		10.03 034	9.86 413		**60**	
1	9.83 392	14	9.96 991	25	10.03 009	9.86 401	12	59	
2	9.83 405	13	9.97 016	25	10.02 984	9.86 389	12	58	
3	9.83 419	14	9.97 042	26	10.02 958	9.86 377	12	57	
4	9.83 432	13	9.97 067	25	10.02 933	9.86 366	11	56	
5	9.83 446	14	9.97 092	25	10.02 908	9.86 354	12	55	
6	9.83 459	13	9.97 118	26	10.02 882	9.86 342	12	54	
7	9.83 473	14	9.97 143	25	10.02 857	9.86 330	12	53	
8	9.83 486	13	9.97 168	25	10.02 832	9.86 318	12	52	
9	9.83 500	14	9.97 193	25	10.02 807	9.86 306	12	51	
10	9.83 513	13	9.97 219	26	10.02 781	9.86 295	11	**50**	
11	9.83 527	14	9.97 244	25	10.02 756	9.86 283	12	49	
12	9.83 540	13	9.97 269	25	10.02 731	9.86 271	12	48	
13	9.83 554	14	9.97 295	26	10.02 705	9.86 259	12	47	
14	9.83 567	13	9.97 320	25	10.02 680	9.86 247	12	46	
15	9.83 581	14	9.97 345	25	10.02 655	9.86 235	12	45	
16	9.83 594	13	9.97 371	26	10.02 629	9.86 223	12	44	
17	9.83 608	14	9.97 396	25	10.02 604	9.86 211	12	43	
18	9.83 621	13	9.97 421	25	10.02 579	9.86 200	11	42	
19	9.83 634	13	9.97 447	26	10.02 553	9.86 188	12	41	
20	9.83 648	14	9.97 472	25	10.02 528	9.86 176	12	**40**	
21	9.83 661	13	9.97 497	25	10.02 503	9.86 164	12	39	
22	9.83 674	13	9.97 523	26	10.02 477	9.86 152	12	38	
23	9.83 688	14	9.97 548	25	10.02 452	9.86 140	12	37	
24	9.83 701	13	9.97 573	25	10.02 427	9.86 128	12	36	
25	9.83 715	14	9.97 598	25	10.02 402	9.86 116	12	35	
26	9.83 728	13	9.97 624	26	10.02 376	9.86 104	12	34	
27	9.83 741	13	9.97 649	25	10.02 351	9.86 092	12	33	
28	9.83 755	14	9.97 674	25	10.02 326	9.86 080	12	32	
29	9.83 768	13	9.97 700	26	10.02 300	9.86 068	12	31	
30	9.83 781	13	9.97 725	25	10.02 275	9.86 056	12	**30**	
31	9.83 795	14	9.97 750	25	10.02 250	9.86 044	12	29	
32	9.83 808	13	9.97 776	26	10.02 224	9.86 032	12	28	
33	9.83 821	13	9.97 801	25	10.02 199	9.86 020	12	27	
34	9.83 834	13	9.97 826	25	10.02 174	9.86 008	12	26	
35	9.83 848	14	9.97 851	25	10.02 149	9.85 996	12	25	
36	9.83 861	13	9.97 877	26	10.02 123	9.85 984	12	24	
37	9.83 874	13	9.97 902	25	10.02 098	9.85 972	12	23	
38	9.83 887	13	9.97 927	25	10.02 073	9.85 960	12	22	
39	9.83 901	14	9.97 953	26	10.02 047	9.85 948	12	21	
40	9.83 914	13	9.97 978	25	10.02 022	9.85 936	12	**20**	
41	9.83 927	13	9.98 003	25	10.01 997	9.85 924	12	19	
42	9.83 940	13	9.98 029	26	10.01 971	9.85 912	12	18	
43	9.83 954	14	9.98 054	25	10.01 946	9.85 900	12	17	
44	9.83 967	13	9.98 079	25	10.01 921	9.85 888	12	16	
45	9.83 980	13	9.98 104	26	10.01 896	9.85 876	12	15	
46	9.83 993	13	9.98 130	25	10.01 870	9.85 864	13	14	
47	9.84 006	14	9.98 155	25	10.01 845	9.85 851	12	13	
48	9.84 020	13	9.98 180	26	10.01 820	9.85 839	12	12	
49	9.84 033	13	9.98 206	25	10.01 794	9.85 827	12	11	
50	9.84 046	13	9.98 231	25	10.01 769	9.85 815	12	**10**	
51	9.84 059	13	9.98 256	25	10.01 744	9.85 803	12	9	
52	9.84 072	13	9.98 281	26	10.01 719	9.85 791	12	8	
53	9.84 085	13	9.98 307	25	10.01 693	9.85 779	13	7	
54	9.84 098	14	9.98 332	25	10.01 668	9.85 766	12	6	
55	9.84 112	13	9.98 357	26	10.01 643	9.85 754	12	5	
56	9.84 125	13	9.98 383	25	10.01 617	9.85 742	12	4	
57	9.84 138	13	9.98 408	25	10.01 592	9.85 730	12	3	
58	9.84 151	13	9.98 433	25	10.01 567	9.85 718	12	2	
59	9.84 164	13	9.98 458	26	10.01 542	9.85 706	13	1	
60	9.84 177		9.98 484		10.01 516	9.85 693		**0**	
	L Cos	d	L Cot	c d	L Tan	L Sin	d	′	Prop. Pts.

Prop. Pts.

	26	25
1	2.6	2.5
2	5.2	5.0
3	7.8	7.5
4	10.4	10.0
5	13.0	12.5
6	15.6	15.0
7	18.2	17.5
8	20.8	20.0
9	23.4	22.5

	14	13
1	1.4	1.3
2	2.8	2.6
3	4.2	3.9
4	5.6	5.2
5	7.0	6.5
6	8.4	7.8
7	9.8	9.1
8	11.2	10.4
9	12.6	11.7

	12	11
1	1.2	1.1
2	2.4	2.2
3	3.6	3.3
4	4.8	4.4
5	6.0	5.5
6	7.2	6.6
7	8.4	7.7
8	9.6	8.8
9	10.8	9.9

46°

TABLE III   44°

′	L Sin	d	L Tan	c d	L Cot	L Cos	d	′
0	9.84 177		9.98 484		10.01 516	9.85 693		60
1	9.84 190	13	9.98 509	25	10.01 491	9.85 681	12	59
2	9.84 203	13	9.98 534	25	10.01 466	9.85 669	12	58
3	9.84 216	13	9.98 560	26	10.01 440	9.85 657	12	57
4	9.84 229	13	9.98 585	25	10.01 415	9.85 645	12	56
5	9.84 242	13	9.98 610	25	10.01 390	9.85 632	13	55
6	9.84 255	13	9.98 635	25	10.01 365	9.85 620	12	54
7	9.84 269	14	9.98 661	26	10.01 339	9.85 608	12	53
8	9.84 282	13	9.98 686	25	10.01 314	9.85 596	12	52
9	9.84 295	13	9.98 711	25	10.01 289	9.85 583	13	51
10	9.84 308	13	9.98 737	26	10.01 263	9.85 571	12	50
11	9.84 321	13	9.98 762	25	10.01 238	9.85 559	12	49
12	9.84 334	13	9.98 787	25	10.01 213	9.85 547	12	48
13	9.84 347	13	9.98 812	25	10.01 188	9.85 534	13	47
14	9.84 360	13	9.98 838	26	10.01 162	9.85 522	12	46
15	9.84 373	13	9.98 863	25	10.01 137	9.85 510	12	45
16	9.84 385	12	9.98 888	25	10.01 112	9.85 497	13	44
17	9.84 398	13	9.98 913	25	10.01 087	9.85 485	12	43
18	9.84 411	13	9.98 939	26	10.01 061	9.85 473	12	42
19	9.84 424	13	9.98 964	25	10.01 036	9.85 460	13	41
20	9.84 437	13	9.98 989	25	10.01 011	9.85 448	12	40
21	9.84 450	13	9.99 015	26	10.00 985	9.85 436	13	39
22	9.84 463	13	9.99 040	25	10.00 960	9.85 423	12	38
23	9.84 476	13	9.99 065	25	10.00 935	9.85 411	12	37
24	9.84 489	13	9.99 090	26	10.00 910	9.85 399	13	36
25	9.84 502	13	9.99 116	25	10.00 884	9.85 386	12	35
26	9.84 515	13	9.99 141	25	10.00 859	9.85 374	13	34
27	9.84 528	12	9.99 166	25	10.00 834	9.85 361	12	33
28	9.84 540	13	9.99 191	26	10.00 809	9.85 349	12	32
29	9.84 553	13	9.99 217	25	10.00 783	9.85 337	13	31
30	9.84 566	13	9.99 242	25	10.00 758	9.85 324	12	30
31	9.84 579	13	9.99 267	26	10.00 733	9.85 312	13	29
32	9.84 592	13	9.99 293	25	10.00 707	9.85 299	12	28
33	9.84 605	13	9.99 318	25	10.00 682	9.85 287	13	27
34	9.84 618	12	9.99 343	25	10.00 657	9.85 274	12	26
35	9.84 630	13	9.99 368	26	10.00 632	9.85 262	12	25
36	9.84 643	13	9.99 394	25	10.00 606	9.85 250	13	24
37	9.84 656	13	9.99 419	25	10.00 581	9.85 237	12	23
38	9.84 669	13	9.99 444	25	10.00 556	9.85 225	13	22
39	9.84 682	12	9.99 469	26	10.00 531	9.85 212	12	21
40	9.84 694	13	9.99 495	25	10.00 505	9.85 200	13	20
41	9.84 707	13	9.99 520	25	10.00 480	9.85 187	12	19
42	9.84 720	13	9.99 545	25	10.00 455	9.85 175	13	18
43	9.84 733	12	9.99 570	26	10.00 430	9.85 162	12	17
44	9.84 745	13	9.99 596	25	10.00 404	9.85 150	13	16
45	9.84 758	13	9.99 621	25	10.00 379	9.85 137	12	15
46	9.84 771	13	9.99 646	26	10.00 354	9.85 125	13	14
47	9.84 784	12	9.99 672	25	10.00 328	9.85 112	12	13
48	9.84 796	13	9.99 697	25	10.00 303	9.85 100	13	12
49	9.84 809	13	9.99 722	25	10.00 278	9.85 087	13	11
50	9.84 822	13	9.99 747	26	10.00 253	9.85 074	12	10
51	9.84 835	12	9.99 773	25	10.00 227	9.85 062	13	9
52	9.84 847	13	9.99 798	25	10.00 202	9.85 049	12	8
53	9.84 860	13	9.99 823	25	10.00 177	9.85 037	13	7
54	9.84 873	12	9.99 848	26	10.00 152	9.85 024	12	6
55	9.84 885	13	9.99 874	25	10.00 126	9.85 012	13	5
56	9.84 898	13	9.99 899	25	10.00 101	9.84 999	13	4
57	9.84 911	12	9.99 924	25	10.00 076	9.84 986	12	3
58	9.84 923	13	9.99 949	26	10.00 051	9.84 974	13	2
59	9.84 936	13	9.99 975	25	10.00 025	9.84 961	12	1
60	9.84 949		10.00 000		10.00 000	9.84 949		0
	L Cos	d	L Cot	c d	L Tan	L Sin	d	′

Prop. Pts.

	26	25
1	2.6	2.5
2	5.2	5.0
3	7.8	7.5
4	10.4	10.0
5	13.0	12.5
6	15.6	15.0
7	18.2	17.5
8	20.8	20.0
9	23.4	22.5

	14	13	12
1	1.4	1.3	1.2
2	2.8	2.6	2.4
3	4.2	3.9	3.6
4	5.6	5.2	4.8
5	7.0	6.5	6.0
6	8.4	7.8	7.2
7	9.8	9.1	8.4
8	11.2	10.4	9.6
9	12.6	11.7	10.8

TABLE IV

Squares, Cubes, Square and Cube Roots,
and Reciprocals of the Numbers
1 *to* 100

TABLE IV   1-50

No.	Square	Cube	Sq. Root	Cu. Root	Reciprocal
1	1	1	1.0000	1.0000	1.000000000
2	4	8	1.4142	1.2599	.500000000
3	9	27	1.7321	1.4422	.333333333
4	16	64	2.0000	1.5874	.250000000
5	25	125	2.2361	1.7100	.200000000
6	36	216	2.4495	1.8171	.166666667
7	49	343	2.6458	1.9129	.142857143
8	64	512	2.8284	2.0000	.125000000
9	81	729	3.0000	2.0801	.111111111
10	100	1,000	3.1623	2.1544	.100000000
11	121	1,331	3.3166	2.2240	.090909091
12	144	1,728	3.4641	2.2894	.083333333
13	169	2,197	3.6056	2.3513	.076923077
14	196	2,744	3.7417	2.4101	.071428571
15	225	3,375	3.8730	2.4662	.066666667
16	256	4,096	4.0000	2.5198	.062500000
17	289	4,913	4.1231	2.5713	.058823529
18	324	5,832	4.2426	2.6207	.055555556
19	361	6,859	4.3589	2.6684	.052631579
20	400	8,000	4.4721	2.7144	.050000000
21	441	9,261	4.5826	2.7589	.047619048
22	484	10,648	4.6904	2.8020	.045454545
23	529	12,167	4.7958	2.8439	.043478261
24	576	13,824	4.8990	2.8845	.041666667
25	625	15,625	5.0000	2.9240	.040000000
26	676	17,576	5.0990	2.9625	.038461538
27	729	19,683	5.1962	3.0000	.037037037
28	784	21,952	5.2915	3.0366	.035714286
29	841	24,389	5.3852	3.0723	.034482759
30	900	27,000	5.4772	3.1072	.033333333
31	961	29,791	5.5678	3.1414	.032258065
32	1,024	32,768	5.6569	3.1748	.031250000
33	1,089	35,937	5.7446	3.2075	.030303030
34	1,156	39,304	5.8310	3.2396	.029411765
35	1,225	42,875	5.9161	3.2711	.028571429
36	1,296	46,656	6.0000	3.3019	.027777778
37	1,369	50,653	6.0828	3.3322	.027027027
38	1,444	54,872	6.1644	3.3620	.026315789
39	1,521	59,319	6.2450	3.3912	.025641026
40	1,600	64,000	6.3246	3.4200	.025000000
41	1,681	68,921	6.4031	3.4482	.024390244
42	1,764	74,088	6.4807	3.4760	.023809524
43	1,849	79,507	6.5574	3.5034	.023255814
44	1,936	85,184	6.6332	3.5303	.022727273
45	2,025	91,125	6.7082	3.5569	.022222222
46	2,116	97,336	6.7823	3.5830	.021739130
47	2,209	103,823	6.8557	3.6088	.021276596
48	2,304	110,592	6.9282	3.6342	.020833333
49	2,401	117,649	7.0000	3.6593	.020408163
50	2,500	125,000	7.0711	3.6840	.020000000

No.	Square	Cube	Sq. Root	Cu. Root	Reciprocal
50	2,500	125,000	7.0711	3.6840	.020000000
51	2,601	132,651	7.1414	3.7084	.019607843
52	2,704	140,608	7.2111	3.7325	.019230769
53	2,809	148,877	7.2801	3.7563	.018867925
54	2,916	157,464	7.3485	3.7798	.018518519
55	3,025	166,375	7.4162	3.8030	.018181818
56	3,136	175,616	7.4833	3.8259	.017857143
57	3,249	185,193	7.5498	3.8485	.017543860
58	3,364	195,112	7.6158	3.8709	.017241379
59	3,481	205,379	7.6811	3.8930	.016949153
60	3,600	216,000	7.7460	3.9149	.016666667
61	3,721	226,981	7.8102	3.9365	.016393443
62	3,844	238,328	7.8740	3.9579	.016120032
63	3,969	250,047	7.9373	3.9791	.015873016
64	4,096	262,144	8.0000	4.0000	.015625000
65	4,225	274,625	8.0623	4.0207	.015384615
66	4,356	287,496	8.1240	4.0412	.015151515
67	4,489	300,763	8.1854	4.0615	.014925373
68	4,624	314,432	8.2462	4.0817	.014705882
69	4,761	328,509	8.3066	4.1016	.014492754
70	4,900	343,000	8.3666	4.1213	.014285714
71	5,041	357,911	8.4261	4.1408	.014084507
72	5,184	373,248	8.4853	4.1602	.013888889
73	5,329	389,017	8.5440	4.1793	.013698630
74	5,476	405,224	8.6023	4.1983	.013513514
75	5,625	421,875	8.6603	4.2172	.013333333
76	5,776	438,976	8.7178	4.2358	.013157895
77	5,929	456,533	8.7750	4.2543	.012987013
78	6,084	474,552	8.8318	4.2727	.012820513
79	6,241	493,039	8.8882	4.2908	.012658228
80	6,400	512,000	8.9443	4.3089	.012500000
81	6,561	531,441	9.0000	4.3267	.012345679
82	6,724	551,368	9.0554	4.3445	.012195122
83	6,889	571,787	9.1104	4.3621	.012048193
84	7,056	592,704	9.1652	4.3795	.011904762
85	7,225	614,125	9.2195	4.3968	.011764706
86	7,396	636,056	9.2736	4.4140	.011627907
87	7,569	658,503	9.3274	4.4310	.011494253
88	7,744	681,472	9.3808	4.4480	.011363636
89	7,921	704,969	9.4340	4.4647	.011235955
90	8,100	729,000	9.4868	4.4814	.011111111
91	8,281	753,571	9.5394	4.4979	.010989011
92	8,464	778,688	9.5917	4.5144	.010869565
93	8,649	804,357	9.6437	4.5307	.010752688
94	8,836	830,584	9.6954	4.5468	.010638298
95	9,025	857,375	9.7468	4.5629	.010526316
96	9,216	884,736	9.7980	4.5789	.010416667
97	9,409	912,673	9.8489	4.5947	.010309278
98	9,604	941,192	9.8995	4.6104	.010204082
99	9,801	970,299	9.9499	4.6261	.010101010
100	10,000	1,000,000	10.0000	4.6416	.010000000